Y0-CCG-640

Spring Flora of Wisconsin

Other books by Norman C. Fassett published by
The University of Wisconsin Press

THE LEGUMINOUS PLANTS OF WISCONSIN: The Taxonomy, Ecology, and Distribution of the Leguminosae Growing in the State without Cultivation. 1939.

GRASSES OF WISCONSIN: The Taxonomy, Ecology, and Distribution of the Gramineae Growing in the State without Cultivation. 1951.

THE FERNS AND FERN ALLIES OF WISCONSIN. Second edition, 1953. With R. M. Tryon, Jr., D. W. Dunlop, and M. E. Diemer.

A MANUAL OF AQUATIC PLANTS. Revised edition, 1957.

SPRING FLORA OF WISCONSIN

A manual of plants growing without cultivation and flowering before June 15

---

by NORMAN C. FASSETT

Third Edition

with revisions by MARGARET S. BERGSENG

THE UNIVERSITY OF WISCONSIN PRESS

Madison, Milwaukee, and London, 1967

Published by the University of Wisconsin Press
Madison, Milwaukee, and London
U.S.A.: Box 1379, Madison, Wisconsin 53701
U.K.: 26–28 Hallam Street, London W.1

First edition, 1931, and second edition, 1947, published under the auspices of the University of Wisconsin Botany Department; the third edition, 1957, by the University of Wisconsin Press

Third edition, second printing, 1959; third printing, 1963; fourth printing, 1967

Printed in the United States of America
Library of Congress Catalog Card Number 57-5043

Preface

Among the tasks on which Norman Fassett was engaged at the time of his death in 1954 was the revision of *Spring Flora*. This little book, originally published in 1931, reprinted in 1938, and in a second edition in 1947, has been in steady demand by botanists, amateur and professional, for nearly twenty-five years. The latest edition of *Gray's Manual* and the general increase in botanical knowledge had made revision for this new edition seem desirable, and Fassett devoted time during his final, tragic illness to the task.

The University of Wisconsin Press is pleased to be the publisher of this book, because in so many ways it fulfills the purposes for which the Press was established. First, this is a work of real scholarship. Small though it is, there is compressed here a rich accumulation of knowledge derived from a lifetime of study and patient, energetic field work. It is also a work of interpretation, written not for specialists as such, though they may find much of value. The author has presented here his own wide knowledge in a form which can be understood and put to use by anyone with a real interest in botany who is willing to spend a few minutes learning how to use this book. Not only is the information here; so also are all the instructions for finding it efficiently. And, finally, this is a book about Wisconsin, the region which Fassett made his own and which it has been our good fortune to share with him.

Most of all, however, the Press is pleased to serve as publisher of this book because in so many ways it reflects the spirit of Norman Fassett, the scholar, the field investigator, the teacher, the man who would not compromise with the careless or the insincere but whose genius was the presentation of the complex with a simple clarity that made botany fascinating to his students and even, to their surprise, to Rotarians, who issued him many invitations to speak. That same simplicity of presentation, which yet does not obscure the complexities of fact, is the principal quality of this little book.

Working against time, Fassett was unable to complete the revision. At the time of his death, he had reached only to about page 57 of the present edition. His colleagues have completed the task. Margaret S. Bergseng spent long hours on both manuscript and proof; James H. Zimmerman assisted with revisions in manuscript, as did G. N. Jones (of the University of Illinois) with his knowledge of knotty problems in nomenclature and of some recent generic revisions; Richard I. Evans made necessary alterations and revisions in the drawings; John W. Thomson read both manuscript and proof critically and offered welcome suggestions for improvement —all contributing their time and talents toward making this a book of which Fassett would have been proud.

THE PUBLISHER

Contents

Spring Flora of Wisconsin

Introduction

THE CLASSIFICATION OF PLANTS

Plants are grouped into species. A species is composed of all the individuals in existence which resemble each other closely enough to be considered of one kind. Species are grouped into genera, and the name of a plant is composed of the generic name followed by the specific name. Thus we have grouped under the genus *Cypripedium* the various species, or kinds, of Lady's Slipper: *Cypripedium arietinum*, the Ram's Head Lady's Slipper; *Cypripedium candidum*, the White Lady's Slipper; *Cypripedium acaule*, the Stemless Lady's Slipper. Genera are grouped into families; *Cypripedium*, *Habenaria*, *Orchis*, and various others are included in the *Orchidaceae*, or Orchid Family. Family names, with a few exceptions, end in *-aceae*.

The plants with true flowers, or Angiospermae, are divided into two groups, the Monocotyledoneae and the Dicotyledoneae. The Monocotyledoneae are characterized by having the vascular bundles scattered in the stem, no cambium, parallel-veined leaves, parts of the flowers in 3's or 6's, and one seed-leaf (cotyledon). The Dicotyledoneae have the bundles in a ring in the stem, cambium, the veins of the leaves branching, parts of the flowers in 4's and 5's, and two cotyledons. To all these characters there are exceptions in some species. In this book the Monocotyledoneae include the families through the *Orchidaceae;* the Dicotyledoneae include the families from the *Salicaceae* through the *Compositae.*

An understanding of certain characters used in classification should be gained. It is necessary to observe whether the petals are separate (as in Figs. 395 and 396), or united into a tube (as in Fig. 397). If they are separate, the petals may be all alike, so that the flower is symmetrical on three or more radii, or they may be of different shapes, so that the flower is bilaterally symmetrical, like a violet or a sweet pea. Likewise a corolla of united petals may be symmetrical on several radii, or it may be more or less two-lipped, like that of a Snapdragon. Another important character is found in the position of the sepals, petals, and stamens, in relation to the ovary. In many flowers they are borne at the base of the ovary, as is shown in Fig. 395. The usually somewhat enlarged tip of the stem on which all the floral organs are borne is called the receptacle. The receptacle is indicated in Fig. 395 by vertical shading. In many flowers the sepals, petals, and stamens apparently arise at the summit of the ovary, as in Fig. 396. Of course they are not really borne *on* the ovary. The ovary is made up of one carpel, or of two or more united carpels, which are morphologically leaves (sporophylls), and the sepals, etc., are also really modified leaves. One leaf is not borne on another leaf. Actually, the receptacle is continued up and around the ovary, and it is from this continuation of the receptacle that the other organs arise. The receptacle is indicated in Fig. 396 by vertical shading. It is well illustrated in an apple, in which the inner part of the core is formed from the ovary, while the fleshy outer part is the enlarged receptacle, with the small sepals persisting at the end opposite the pedicel ("stem"). The same condition obtains in a currant, gooseberry, or blueberry, except that in these fruits the ovary is in comparison much more enlarged and fleshy.

Besides the fusion of the petals with one another, we sometimes find a union of the stamens with one another and with other parts of the flower. In many families with separate petals (the *Rosaceae*, for example) they are "borne on the calyx" (again, really on an extension of the receptacle), while in a number of families with united petals they are fused at the base with the corolla-tube.

The highest development of the flower is found in the *Compositae*. Here the petals form a tube or flat body; the anthers are united into a tube, while the filaments are joined at the base with the corolla; the calyx is modified and often split into hair-like or awl-shaped processes; and all these organs are borne (on the receptacle) at the summit of the ovary. Besides this, many flowers are aggregated into a head, which is surrounded by a characteristic involucre of many bracts. A single head, as exemplified by a Dandelion, Daisy, or Sunflower, simulates a flower.

THE USE OF KEYS

The first step in the identification of a plant is the determination of the family to which it belongs. Unfortunately this is often the hardest step, because there are so many families, and because a family may contain plants of diverse aspect.

The key to families follows approximately the classification outlined above, diverging, however, at a number of points. A series of alternatives is presented. The unknown plant is compared with these contrasting descriptions. The first question comes (p. 11) in whether it has "*A*. Both stamens and pistils on the same plant" or (p. 19) "*AA*. Staminate and pistillate flowers on different plants." If it answers the first description, we pass to alternative *B*. Here we find a choice of "*B*. Leaves with 3 or more parallel veins; leaves never compound" or (p. 11) "*BB*. Leaves with branching veins, or all but the midvein inconspicuous; leaves simple or compound." Suppose we find that our plant has branching veins in the leaves; we pass, as directed, to *C*, on p. 12. Here we find: "*C*. Flowers not in dense heads, etc.," and (p. 19) "*CC*. Flowers in a dense head, with an involucre; the head simulating a single flower." *CC* refers to the *Compositae*, which family will, after only a little experience, be easily recognized and distinguished from plants like the clover, which have flowers in a head without an involucre. This procedure of choosing between two contrasting descriptions, and passing on to the next alternative as directed, eliminates group after group until the search narrows down to one family. It is then necessary to turn to this family and in the key there presented to determine the genus, then the species, to which the plant belongs. After some experience has been gained, it will be found that the family may often be recognized at sight, and the most difficult part is eliminated.

Under each family heading is given a description that applies to all the genera in that family. Again, under the genus heading is presented a description applicable to all the species in that genus. When the species is determined, it may be compared with the description following the specific name. Here the more important characters, particularly those by which it may be distinguished from closely related species, are given in italics. But characters mentioned in the keys are not repeated in the generic and specific descriptions; it must therefore be borne in mind that much of the description of each species, and often an enumeration of the most conspicuous and important characters lies in the keys.

Names of Plants

The order of families, genera, and species is for the most part that of *Gray's Manual*, ed. 8. The names are the same as those used in that work, except in cases where those names have for one reason or another been shown to be incorrect. When the name used differs from that in *Gray's Manual*, the *Manual* name will be found in parentheses, after the specific description.

To aid in the pronunciation of names, two kinds of accents are used: the acute indicates a short vowel, as in *Lílium;* the grave indicates a long vowel, as in *Clintonia.*

Illustrations

An illustrated book on plants always tempts the user to make an identification by simply looking at the pictures. Use of the keys, while more difficult at first, will pay dividends in the increasing ease with which plants may be named. These drawings are made not always to show the appearance of the whole plant, but to illustrate certain diagnostic characters.

Whenever they will be of real help, the drawings are referred to in the keys and text.

These illustrations are the product of many hands. They were made by the following: Dr. G. O. Cooper, Mr. W. E. Dickinson, Dr. R. I. Evans, Miss Jane M. Gilbert, Mr. S. Kliman, Miss Florence B. Livergood, Mr. W. T. McLaughlin, Miss Ruth P. Morgan, and Miss Katharine P. Smith. Most of the plates were worked on by at least two persons, some by three or four. The original lettering was done by Mr. McLaughlin, additional lettering in the 1947 edition by Mr. Wilson N. Stewart, and some redrawing in the 1957 edition by Dr. R. I. Evans.

How to Press Plants

The usual method of preserving flowering plants and ferns for study is by pressing. The plant is laid in a single page of newspaper folded once, and dried under pressure. For this the botanist uses sheets of heavy blotting paper (the "deadening felt" sold by most hardware stores and lumber dealers is excellent) cut to 12 × 18 inches. One of these blotters, usually termed "driers," is placed on a table, and on it the open sheet of newspaper. The plant specimen is laid on one half of the paper; the other half is folded over it, and another drier put on top. Another plant in a newspaper follows, then another drier, etc. When all the plants are put in press, a board, a latticework frame, or beaverboard, is placed above and another below, and the whole is strapped or tied tightly, or placed under a heavy weight.

After an interval of from 6 to 24 hours the driers should be changed for fresh crisp dry ones, and the old damp driers baked in the sun or over artificial heat. After that a careful worker will change driers every 24 hours until the plants are stiff and dry. When done they will usually not feel cold to the touch, and will not droop limply when picked up.

The amateur will find several thicknesses of newspaper nearly as satisfactory as the felt driers. These may be used folded in half, and if they are laid down with the fold on the right-hand side, and the single folded sheets holding the plants have the fold on the left-hand side, there will be little danger of taking out plants by mistake when the driers are changed. The diagram shows this arrangement.

If the press is small, it may, of course, be placed on the floor and a weight placed on it. If a very few plants are being pressed, or if one wishes to press an occasional plant when traveling and a press is inconvenient to carry, a *Saturday Evening Post* placed under a few books, or under a suitcase in an automobile, will be found to be a good emergency press.

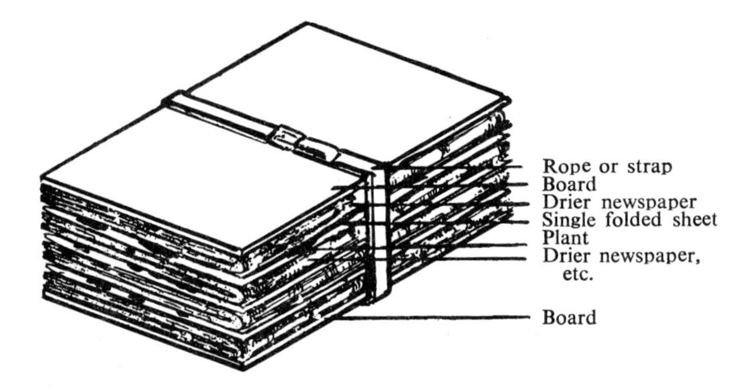

When it is put in press each plant should be accompanied by certain data. The locality, habitat, and date should be included, and the size of the plant if it is a tree, shrub, or herb too large to be pressed in its entirety. The best place for these data is one corner of the folded paper in which the plant is pressed, for then the information will be with the plant. Or the data may be written on a slip of paper which is put in with the plant. Some collectors prefer to put only a number with the plant, and keep the data in a notebook with corresponding numbers, but this necessitates keeping the notebook with the collections. Then, too, a notebook is sometimes lost; many good collections have thus been made valueless.

Special Points in Collecting and Pressing

Plants should be collected carefully. In the case of small herbs, the underground parts should be dug up and washed free of adhering dirt. (But plants should be dug up only if they are to be pressed and kept for study in a herbarium.) Shrubs and trees should be accompanied by a piece of bark. Both flowers and fruit should be secured whenever possible.

Small plants should be laid out so that they will not touch each other, or they will stick together as they dry. Plants longer than the longest dimension of the pressing paper may be folded. Choose the place on the stem where it is to be folded and at this point crush it with the fingers or with the back of a jackknife; this will minimize the danger of its breaking.

Most plants have too many leaves to make good specimens. About two-thirds of these should be removed, the bases of the petioles being left to show where the leaves were.

The first time the driers are changed the plant parts should be rearranged or "fixed." Crumpled leaves are straightened, and flowers laid out smoothly. Stems should be laid *over* leaves, as should flowers. Leaves which persistently curl or remain folded may be "tamed" by placing over them a piece of wet paper to hold them in place. This paper will scale off when the plant is dry. Leaves should be turned so that some of them show the under side.

Plants will be less apt to blacken if dried quickly. The driers should be bone dry. Drying of plants is hastened by putting the press in the sunlight or near a stove or open fire. But the first set of driers in which the plants are put need not be very dry, nor should the press be put in a hot place until after the first change of driers.

If the press is put in the sunlight, or the driers are dried out-of-doors, they should not be left out after 3:30 P.M., as then the air grows damp and the driers absorb moisture.

Mounting Pressed Plants

Pressed plants are mounted on sheets of cardboard; the

usual size is $11\frac{1}{2} \times 16\frac{3}{4}$ inches. This is sometimes done by fastening the plant to the cardboard with strips of mending tissue. A much better method is pasting. A sheet of glass is given a light coating of paste; the plant is laid on this, then carefully lifted and placed on the cardboard. To do this skillfully requires a little practice. The sheet of cardboard is placed under pressure for a few hours, until the paste is dry. Then, if desired, strips of mending tissue may be used as reinforcement over stems, etc.

When it is mounted, the plant should be labeled, usually in the lower right-hand corner of the sheet. A good form of label is as follows:

ONEIDA CO., WISCONSIN
Sarracenia purpurea L.
Sphagnum bog, shore of Hill Lake.
J. L. Greene — Minocqua
No. 5172 — August 10, 1916

If the collections are numbered, each number should cover all plants of the same species, collected at one time from one patch, or from one shrub or tree.

Points concerning Certain Groups

Ferns. Both spore-bearing and sterile fronds should be represented on each sheet. Rootstocks (underground stems) should be collected. Some species, like the Spinulose Fern, have thick rootstocks which may be split lengthwise to be made less bulky in drying. In this form two fronds are usually enough to leave on the plant; a large number will make it difficult to make out the details of any individual.

Pondweeds, Arrowheads, Umbellifers, Mustards, and Sedges are worthless without mature fruit.

Blackberries. The first year's growth lacks flowers and fruits, and usually has five-parted leaves. The second year flowering canes are produced, usually with three-parted leaves. Both should be collected from the same clump. The tip of the first year's growth should be included. When first put in press the blackberries are "bad actors," snapping out of place like pieces of spring steel, but they are very easy to handle the first time the driers are changed.

VIOLETS have diagnostic characters in the tip of the style and on the inner side of the petals. When first put into press the flowers may be flattened between the fingers in such a way that these parts show.

CACTI and STONECROPS, fleshy plants, are tenacious of life and often live and even grow in press. They may be killed by dipping them in boiling water.

GENTIANS and LADY'S SLIPPERS. The flowers may be stuffed with cotton to give them a little body. The common mistake is to put in too much cotton, so that the flowers break as they get older. Gentians have diagnostic characters in the stamens; some of the tubular flowers may be split down one side and laid open.

BLADDERWORTS, PONDWEEDS, and other aquatics should be floated in a large pan or tub in about an inch of water, a large piece of stiff paper slid under the plant and carefully lifted out. If simply laid on the paper these will make worthless, shapeless masses.

Most COMPOSITES should have mature fruit.

Flowers which are to be dissected after having been pressed may be softened by boiling for about one minute. A few extra flowers should always be collected for this purpose and kept in a folded paper pocket glued to the sheet.

HELP IN IDENTIFICATION

Plants may be sent to the Herbarium of the University of Wisconsin for identification. They should be carefully pressed and accompanied by full data, so that they will be useful additions to the collections there. That is the only pay asked for identification service. If the collections are numbered, and each number (i.e., individual collection of each species) consists of several sheets, one sheet of each collection may be sent to the University; the list of identifications will be sent back with the list of numbers.

Key to Families

A. Both stamens and pistils on the same plant, usually in the same flower (*AA* on p. 19)
B. Leaves with 3 or more parallel veins; leaves never compound
C. Flowers in the axils of dry overlapping scales forming spikelets, without perianth
D. Stem cylindric, usually hollow, with hard nodes; anthers attached near their middle . GRAMINEAE p. 21
DD. Stem triangular in cross section, with soft nodes; anthers attached at their base . . CYPERACEAE p. 21
CC. Flowers not in the axils of dry overlapping scales, with sepals and petals (except in the *Araceae*)
D. Flowers on a fleshy common axis several mm. thick *Figs. 4, 5* . . . . ARACEAE p. 21
DD. Flowers not on a fleshy axis
E. Flowers in a head with an involucre *Figs. 388, 393* . . . . COMPOSITAE p. 165
EE. Flowers not in an involucrate head
F. Petals all alike
G. Filaments with long hairs. . . . . COMMELINACEAE p. 22
GG. Filaments without long hairs
H. Perianth borne (on the receptacle) at the base of the ovary
I. Sepals and petals papery, or stiff and scale-like
J. Sepals and petals each 3, stiff and sharp . . . . JUNCACEAE p. 23
JJ. Sepals and petals each 4, papery . . . . PLANTAGINACEAE p. 155
II. At least the petals soft, and white or colored
J. Petals 2 or 3 . . . . . . LILIACEAE p. 23
JJ. Petals 5 . . . . LINACEAE p. 103
HH. Perianth borne (on the receptacle) at the summit of the ovary
I. Stamens 6 . . AMARYLLIDACEAE p. 31
II. Stamens 3 . . . . IRIDACEAE p. 31
FF. One petal different from the others, and modified to form a lip *Figs. 36–53* . ORCHIDACEAE p. 33
BB. Leaves with branching veins, or with all but the midvein inconspicuous; leaves simple or compound

C. Flowers not in dense heads, or if in heads, then without an involucre (*CC* on p. 19)
D. Plants parasitic and growing on the twigs of needle-bearing trees. . . . . LORANTHACEAE p. 48
DD. Plants not parasitic on twigs
E. Flowers on a fleshy common axis at least several mm. thick *Figs. 1–4* . . . . ARACEAE p. 21
EE. Flowers not on a fleshy common axis
F. At least the staminate flowers in catkins *Figs. 60–74*
G. Leaves simple
H. Foliage and bruised buds not fragrant
I. Pistillate flowers in catkins, or, if not in catkins then each with a leaf-like bract . . . . BETULACEAE p. 43
II. Pistillate flowers 1–3 together, with an involucre of small overlapping scales below. . . . . FAGACEAE p. 45
HH. Foliage and bruised buds fragrant . . . . MYRICACEAE p. 40
GG. Leaves pinnately compound. JUGLANDACEAE p. 41
FF. None of the flowers in catkins
G. Corolla, or calyx, or both absent (*GG* on p. 13)
H. Calyx and stamens borne at summit of the ovary
I. Low matted herbs *Fig. 165* . . . . SAXIFRAGACEAE p. 78
II. Stems or leaves upright
J. Woody plants
K. Trees; leaves lobed PLATANACEAE p. 83
KK. Shrubs; leaves simple . . . . CORNACEAE p. 127
JJ. Herbs
L. Leaves compound . . . . UMBELLIFERAE p. 121
LL. Leaves simple
M. Leaves narrowly oblong . . . . SANTALACEAE p. 48
MM. Leaves heart-shaped. . . . . ARISTOLOCHIACEAE p. 48
HH. Calyx and stamens borne at base of the ovary
I. Pistil one in each flower
J. Plants herbaceous
K. Juice milky, white or colored
L. Juice red . . . PAPAVERACEAE p. 67
LL. Juice white EUPHORBIACEAE p. 107
KK. Juice not milky
L. Styles or stigmas 2–several
M. Anthers not conspicuous
N. Styles 2–5-branched . . . . . . CARYOPHYLLACEAE p. 49
NN. Styles 3, the stigmas each with a tuft of hairs at tip. . . . . . . POLYGONACEAE p. 48

MM. Anthers conspicuous, yellow or red *Fig. 165*. . . . . SAXIFRAGACEAE p. 78
LL. Style and stigma one, unbranched or slightly lobed
M. Leaves divided into 2 half-ovate leaflets *Fig. 132* . . . . .BERBERIDACEAE p. 65
MM. Leaves otherwise
N. Calyx about 1 cm. in diameter, corolla-like *Fig. 81* . . . . . . NYCTAGINACEAE p. 49
NN. Calyx much smaller
O. Flowers in terminal racemes . . . . .CRUCIFERAE p. 68
OO. Flowers in axillary clusters . . . . .URTICACEAE p. 48
JJ. Plants woody
K. Trees
L. Leaves compound . . . . OLEACEAE p. 136
LL. Leaves simple
M. Sap not milky; leaves asymetric at base; fruit a winged samara or a nut. . . .ULMACEAE p. 45
MM. Sap milky; leaves symetric at base, lobed; fruit fleshy . . . . MORACEAE p. 47
KK. Shrubs
L. Leaves not toothed, coming after the flowers . . . . THYMELAEACEAE p. 120
LL. Leaves toothed, coming with the flowers . . . .RHAMNACEAE p. 111
II. Pistils several or many in each flower, or, if pistil only one, then leaves several times compounded. . RANUNCULACEAE p. 56
GG. Both calyx and corolla present, the latter sometimes represented by mere scales (*G* on p. 12)
H. Petals not joined to each other (*HH* on p. 17)
I. Calyx and corolla borne at the base of the ovary (*II* on p. 16)
J. Stamens 10 or fewer (*JJ* on p. 15)
K. Corolla symmetrical on several radii (*KK* on p. 15)
L. Petals 3
M. Leaves simple . . . LILIACEAE p. 23
MM. Leaves pinnately compound . . . . LIMNANTHACEAE p . 108
LL. Petals 4 or more
M. Stigmas 2–5, or each flower with several separate pistils

N. Leaves 3–foliolate
O. Herbs . . OXALIDACEAE p. 104
OO. Trees or shrubs . . . . . . STAPHYLEACEAE p. 109
NN. Leaves simple
O. Woody plants
P. Leaves 3–5-lobed
Q. Ovary 2–lobed . . . . . . ACERACEAE p. 109
QQ. Ovary not lobed. . . SAXIFRAGACEAE p. 78
PP. Leaves not lobed. . . . . . RHAMNACEAE p. 111
OO. Herbs
P. Leaves lobed . . . . GERANIACEAE p. 104
PP. Leaves not lobed
Q. Sepals 2; leaves on stem opposite, unlobed, fleshy. . . . . . . PORTULACACEAE p. 54
QQ. Sepals or calyx-lobes 4 or 5
R. Leaves opposite or whorled at several nodes on the stem CARYOPHYLLACEAE p. 49
RR. Leaves alternate, or clustered at base of plant (in which case the stem may bear one pair of opposite leaves)
S. Leaves fleshy, much thickened . . . CRASSULACEAE p. 78
SS. Leaves flat, or thread-like
T. Most or all of the leaves in a basal rosette SAXIFRAGACEAE p. 78
TT. Leaves all on the stem . . LINACEAE p. 103
MM. Style and stigma 1, the stigma rarely 2–3-lobed
N. Herbaceous plants, or low, woody perennials (not vines or tall shrubs)
O. Petals 5–8
P. Leaves compound, with 2 or more leaflets . . . BERBERIDACEAE p. 65

PP. Leaves simple (or none in *Monotropa*) . . . . PYROLACEAE p. 129
OO. Petals 4 CRUCIFERAE p. 68
NN. Woody plants, climbing vines, or tall shrubs
O. Leaves compound
P. Climbing or trailing vines
Q. Leaflets 5 or more . . . . . VITACEAE p. 112
QQ. Leaflets 3. . . . . . ANACARDIACEAE p. 108
PP. Plants erect
Q. Shrub . . . . ANACARDIACEAE p. 108
QQ. Tree . . OLEACEAE p. 136
OO. Leaves simple
P. Leaves not lobed
Q. Stems with spines . . . BERBERIDACEAE p. 65
QQ. Stems without spines
R. Leaves with an abrupt short point *Fig. 251* AQUIFOLIACEAE p. 108
RR. Leaves long-pointed *Figs. 252–253* . . CELASTRACEAE p. 108
PP. Leaves palmately lobed and veined
Q. Flowers in a raceme . . SAXIFRAGACEAE p. 78
QQ. Flowers in a panicle . . . . VITACEAE p. 112
KK. Corolla irregular (*K* on p. 13)
L. Leaves compound
M. Sepals 2, small and scale-like. . . . . . .FUMARIACEAE p. 67
MM. Sepals 5, sometimes united, occasionally making a 2–lipped calyx
N. Stamens 10; leaves alternate . . . . .LEGUMINOSAE p. 96
NN. Stamens 7; leaves opposite . HIPPOCASTANACEAE p. 111
LL. Leaves simple, sometimes deeply cleft
M. Flowers in heads or spikes, or solitary and erect. . . . . POLYGALACEAE p. 107
MM. Flowers solitary and nodding . . . . VIOLACEAE p. 115
JJ. Stamens more than 10, sometimes partly sterile (*J* on p. 13)
K. Filaments not united

L. Leaves flat or thread-like
M. Sepals 2
N. Juice red-orange or yellow . . .
. . . PAPAVERACEAE p. 67
NN. **Juice not colored** . . . . . .
. . PORTULACACEAE p. 54
MM. Sepals 3 or more
N. Sepals 5 or more, in one row
O. Stamens free from the calyx
. RANUNCULACEAE p. 56
OO. Stamens apparently attached to the calyx (when a sepal is pulled off stamens come with it)
P. Leaves opposite . . . . .
SAXIFRAGACEAE p. 78
PP. Leaves alternate . . . .
. . . . ROSACEAE p. 83
NN. Sepals in 2 rows, or if in 1 row then only 3 sepals present
O. Plants terrestrial
P. Petals 6–9
Q. Climbing vines . . . .
MENISPERMACEAE p. 65
QQ. Shrubs or herbs . . .
BERBERIDACEAE p. 65
PP. Petals 5 . . CISTACEAE p. 115
OO. Plants aquatic, or at least in muddy places . . . .
. . NYMPHAEACEAE p. 55
LL. Leaves inflated and hollow *Fig. 160*
. . . . SARRACENIACEAE p. 78
KK. Filaments united in one or several groups
L. Herbs . . . . . . MALVACEAE p. 113
LL. Trees. . . . . . . TILIACEAE p. 113
II. Calyx and corolla borne at the summit of the ovary (*I* on p. 13)
J. Corolla irregular with one petal different from the others ORCHIDACEAE p. 33
JJ. Corolla regular, all the petals alike
K. Sepals 2 . . . PORTULACACEAE p. 54
KK. Sepals 4 or 5
L. Stamens more than 10
M. Leaves alternate . ROSACEAE p. 83
MM. Leaves opposite . . . . . .
. . . SAXIFRAGACEAE p. 78
LL. Stamens 4–10
M. Woody plants
N. Leaves 3–5-lobed . . . . . .
. . SAXIFRAGACEAE p. 78
NN. Leaves not lobed
O. Leaves toothed . . . . . .
. . . RHAMNACEAE p. 111

OO. Leaves not toothed . . . . CORNACEAE p. 127

MM. Herbs

N. Leaves simple, not deeply cleft

O. Flowers in a close cluster surrounded by 4 or more white petal-like bracts *Fig. 293* CORNACEAE p. 127

OO. Flowers without petal-like bracts

P. Petals narrow or fringed, dull or whitish . . . . SAXIFRAGACEAE p. 78

PP. Petals inverted-heart-shaped, bright yellow . . ONAGRACEAE p. 120

NN. Leaves compound, or palmately deeply cleft

O. Petioles not winged at base *Figs. 278–280* . . . . ARALIACEAE p. 120

OO. Petioles winged at base, clasping the stem *Figs. 290–292*. . . . . UMBELLIFERAE p. 121

HH. Petals united with each other (*H* on p. 13)

I. Calyx and corolla borne at the base of the ovary (*II* on p. 19)

J. Corolla symmetrical on several radii (*JJ* on p. 18)

K. Stamens 5–10

L. Stigma entire; leaves simple (except in one vine)

M. Ovary not lobed

N. Corolla funnel-shaped, 12 mm. or more long; leaves with large triangular basal lobes (*Figs. 328–329*). . . . . . CONVOLVULACEAE p. 141

NN. Corolla shorter; leaves without triangular basal lobes

O. Filaments united; juice often milky ASCLEPIADACEAE p. 137

OO. Filaments separate; juice not milky

P. Stems woody (or else creeping and bearing tough evergreen leaves) . . . ERICACEAE p. 130

PP. Stems herbaceous (except in *Lycium*) and erect; leaves not evergreen (except possibly in a rosette at ground level)

Q. Stamens opposite the corolla-lobes. . . . . PRIMULACEAE p. 135
QQ. Stamens alternate with the corolla-lobes
R. Leaf-bases forming wings down the stem . . . . . . SCROPHULARIACEAE p. 149
RR. Stems at most ridged, not winged. . SOLANACEAE p. 149
MM. Ovary deeply 4–lobed . . . . BORAGINACEAE p. 143
LL. Stigma 2–5 cleft; leaves simple or compound
M. Leaves or leaflets toothed . . . HYDROPHYLLACEAE p. 142
MM. Leaves or leaflets not toothed
N. Leaves simple or pinnately compound POLEMONIACEAE p. 141
NN. Leaves 3–foliolate
O. Petals with copious wavy hairs GENTIANACEAE p. 137
OO. Petals without hairs . . . . . . OXALIDACEAE p. 104
KK. Stamens 2 or 4
L. Woody plants. . . . OLEACEAE p. 136
LL. Herbs
M. Leaves all at the base of the scapes PLANTAGINACEAE p. 155
MM. Leaves on the stems
N. Ovary 4–lobed LABIATAE p. 147
NN. Ovary not lobed, or shallowly 2–lobed . . . . SCROPHULARIACEAE p. 149
JJ. Corolla irregular, without all lobes alike
K. Plants green
L. Plants terrestrial, sometimes in damp places
M. Stamens united in 1 or 2 groups . . . . . POLYGALACEAE p. 107
MM. Stamens separate
N. Sepals usually 5, united
O. Ovary with 4 lobes . . . . LABIATAE p. 147
OO. Ovary not lobed, or shallowly lobed . . . . SCROPHULARIACEAE p. 149
NN. Sepals 2, separate . . . . .FUMARIACEAE p. 67
LL. Plants submerged, with finely divided leaves . . . . .LENTIBULARIACEAE p. 154

KK. Plants not green, parasitic . . . . OROBANCHACEAE p. 155

II. Calyx and corolla apparently borne at the summit of the ovary (*I* on p. 17)

J. Stamens free from the corolla-tube

K. Corolla not blue, sometimes purple . . . . ERICACEAE p. 130

KK. Corolla blue CAMPANULACEAE p. 163

JJ. Stamens borne on the corolla-tube

K. Leaves without stipules (except sometimes in the shrub *Viburnum*) and not whorled

L. Leaves simple, or if pinnately compound, shrubs . . . . CAPRIFOLIACEAE p. 159

LL. Leaves much divided; delicate herbs . . . . . ADOXACEAE p. 163

KK. Leaves with stipules, or whorled . . . . RUBIACEAE p. 156

CC. Flowers in a dense head, with an involucre, the head simulating a single flower *Figs. 388–394* (*C* on p. 12) . . . . COMPOSITAE p. 165

AA. Staminate and pistillate flowers on different plants (*A* on p. 11)

B. Flowers in an umbel, the rays uniform in length and longer than the flowers . . . . *Smilax* p. 31

BB. Flowers not in an umbel, or rarely in an umbel with rays not uniform in length

C. Trailing or climbing vines

D. Leaves compound . . . . *Clematis* p. 63

DD. Leaves simple

E. Leaves palmately veined

F. Leaf-blades not toothed or lobed *Fig. 29 Dioscorea* p. 31

FF. Leaf-blades with 3–7 coarse teeth or shallow lobes

G. Petiole attached to the blade a few mm. from its edge . . . . *Menispermum* p. 65

GG. Petiole attached at the edge of the blade *Vitis* p. 112

EE. Leaves pinnately veined . . . . *Celastrus* p. 109

CC. Erect plants

D. Stems woody

E. Flowers not pediceled, in heads or catkins

F. Catkins and leaves fragrant when crushed *Myrica* p. 40

FF. Catkins and leaves not fragrant when crushed

G. Veins of the leaves curved, not quite reaching the margin . . . . SALICACEAE p. 39

GG. Veins straight, reaching the margin . . . . BETULACEAE p. 43

EE. Flowers pediceled or in spherical heads, not in catkins

F. Leaves compound

G. Stems prickly . . . . *Xanthoxylum* p. 105

GG. Stems not prickly

H. Leaves alternate . . . . *Rhus* p. 108

HH. Leaves opposite

I. Petiole with a pad of hairs on the inner side at base . . . . *Acer* p. 109
II. Petiole without a pad of hairs at base. . . . . *Fraxinus* p. 136

FF. Leaves simple
G. Leaves toothed
H. Leaves palmately veined
I. Flowers pediceled or in hemispherical heads . . . . *Acer* p. 109
II. Flowers in dense spherical heads . . . . *Platanus* p. 83
HH. Leaves pinnately veined
I. Leaf-blades tapered at base evenly on both sides *Figs. 260, 261* . . . . . *Rhamnus* p. 111
II. Leaf-blades asymmetrical at base *Fig. 75* . . . . URTICACEAE p. 48
GG. Leaves not toothed or lobed
H. Leaves with a close silvery or brownish scurf . . . . *Shepherdia* p. 120
HH. Leaves not scurfy
I. Tree . . . . *Nyssa* p. 129
II. Shrub . . . . *Nemopanthus* p. 108

DD. Stems not woody
E. Leaves compound, with 3 or more leaflets
F. Leaflets 3–11, 1 dm. or more long . . . *Arisaema* p. 22
FF. Leaflets very many, not over 3 cm. long. . . . . *Thalictrum* p. 60
EE. Leaves simple, sometimes deeply lobed, but without stalked leaflets
F. Stems without cobwebby hairs
G. Leaf-margins not fringed with hairs
H. Leaf-blades entire or with 2 lobes at base
I. Petals absent; sepals 3, green . . . *Rumex* p. 49
II. Petals 3, white like the 3 sepals *Asparagus* p. 27
HH. Leaf-blades deeply lobed *Fig. 266* *Napaea* p. 115
GG. Leaf-margins fringed with fine hairs
H. Flowers 5 mm. or less long, in a pyramidal panicle . . . . *Valeriana* p. 163
HH. Flowers 1 cm. or more long, the inflorescense leafy-bracted . . . . . *Lychnis* p. 53
FF. Stems whitened with cobwebby hairs
G. Basal leaves not toothed or lobed, present at flowering time . . . . *Antennaria* p. 166
GG. Basal leaves toothed or lobed, usually absent at flowering time . . . . *Petasites* p. 168

Descriptive Spring Flora

GRAMÍNEAE Grass Family

Tall slender plants with *hollow stems;* leaves consisting of two parts, the lower (sheath) rolled around the stem but with the *edges usually not joined*, the upper part (blade) ribbon-like and ascending or spreading; flowers minute, without sepals or petals, mostly hidden by *overlapping chaff-like scales*, only the yellow or purple stamens and feathery usually 2-branched styles extending beyond these scales for a few days.

A large and difficult family. See Norman C. Fassett, *Grasses of Wisconsin* (Madison, Wis.: University of Wisconsin Press, 1951).

CYPERÀCEAE Sedge Family

Grass-like plants, with the stems usually triangular in cross section; the edges of the leaf-sheath joined to make a short tube surrounding the stem; leaves usually arranged in 3 rows when the stem or rosette is viewed from above. A large family, many of whose members (204 in Wisconsin) can be found in flower, if not in fruit, in spring. Because considerable experience is required to identify them, they are omitted here, except for one of the common sedges whose yellow stamens are especially conspicuous in early spring.

Càrex pensylvánica Lam. Forms tufts of leaves 1–3 mm. broad, from elongate slender rootstocks covered with red-brown fibers; culms 1–3 dm. tall, the staminate spike 8–25 mm. long at the top, and below it 1–3 very small pistillate spikes; scales of spikes dark reddish or purplish brown. Forms colonies in woods and on open banks; absent from wet ground.

ARÀCEAE Arum Family

Flowers minute, closely crowded on a spadix, which has a *spathe* around or below it; juice acrid.

a. Leaves not grass-like, the veins netted or at least curved *b.*

b. Leaves palmately compound. . . . . 1. *Arisaema*.
b. Leaves simple, the blades more or less heart-shaped *c*.
c. Spathe white, open, not rolled around the spadix 2. *Calla*.
c. Spathe brownish, marked with purple and green, strongly rolled and enclosing the spadix 3. *Symplocarpus*.
a. Leaves grass-like, the parallel veins all essentially straight. . . . . 4. *Acorus*.

1. Arisaèma

Spathe rolled into a tube below, arched above; *spadix long-cylindric*, covered with flowers below, *the upper part sterile and smooth;* stem somewhat fleshy, arising from a corm.

1. **A. atrórubens** (Ait.) Blume. INDIAN TURNIP; JACK-IN-THE-PULPIT. *Leaves 3-foliolate*, with elliptic-ovate pointed leaflets; *spadix entirely included* in the spathe, the upper sterile part club-shaped (Fig. 1); the whole plant, especially the bright red berries, which appear in late summer, pervaded by strongly acrid crystals. —Common in damp woods.

2. **A. Dracóntium** (L.) Schott. GREEN DRAGON. Leaves divided into *7–11* oblong-lanceolate pointed leaflets; sterile part of the spadix prolonged into a *tapering point extending far beyond the spathe* (Fig. 2).—Less common, in low rich woods.

2. Cálla WATER ARUM

C. palústris L. Plants with long creeping stems, from which the leaves and scapes arise; leaves 1–4 dm. long, the blade usually shorter than the petiole; *spadix short-cylindric; spathe ovate, white abruptly contracted into a point* 4–10 mm. long (Fig. 3).—Quaking bogs, rather common northward, rare southward to La Crosse, Waukesha, and Milwaukee Counties.

3. Symplocárpus SKUNK CABBAGE

S. foètidus (L.) Nutt. Whole plant ill-smelling when bruised; flowers appearing before the leaves, which are rolled into a cigar-shaped mass at flowering time; *spadix globose*, completely hidden by the spathe (Fig. 4); leaves all arising near the ground, large and flat, with thick midribs.—Wet open ground.

4. Ácorus SWEET FLAG

A. Cálamus L. *Leaves sword-shaped and stiff*, erect from a tough rootstock; *spadix cylindric*, closely covered with small yellow flowers; *spathe appearing like a continuation of the scape* (Fig. 5). —Shallow muddy bogs.

COMMELINÀCEAE SPIDERWORT FAMILY

Leaves grass-like, with a *short tubular inflated sheath;* sepals 3, green, rather boat-shaped; petals 3. Chiefly a tropical family, including the Inch Plant or Wandering Jew.

Tradescántia SPIDERWORT

Flowers in an umbel terminating the stem or its branches (Fig. 6); petals blue (rarely white or pink), soon withering.

1. **T. ohiénsis** Raf. (Fig. 6) Sepals without hairs except occasionally at tips.—Sandy soil and along railroads, mostly southward.

2. **T. virginiàna** L. Sepals with glandless hairs.—Reported from Fountain City.

3. **T. bracteàta** Small. Sepals with glandless and gland-tipped hairs intermixed.—Lake St. Croix and rarely along railroads elsewhere.

4. **T. occidentàlis** (Britton) Smyth. Sepals with gland-tipped hairs. —Sand terraces from Burnett to Pepin Counties.

JUNCÀCEAE RUSH FAMILY

Floral structure similar to that of the Lily Family (*q. v.*) but the perianth-lobes *scale-like*, seldom exceeding 5 mm. in length; fruit a capsule of 3 carpels; *plants with grass-like aspect.*

a. Leaves without hairs . . . . 1. *Juncus.*
a. Leaves with scattered long soft hairs . . . . 2. *Luzula.*

1. **Júncus** RUSH

Flowers in close or loose clusters; *leaves* usually *thick* or *tubular;* capsule many-seeded. A large genus, with species hardly distinguishable in the spring.

2. **Lúzula** WOOD RUSH

Leaves flat and grass-like, mostly at the base of the plant, a few on the stem; capsule 3-seeded.

1. **L. carolìnae** S. Wats., var. **saltuénsis** Fern. Flowers 3–4.5 mm. long, in an umbel (Fig. 7) with rays about 2 cm. long (*L. acuminata*). —Cool woods, mostly northward.

2. **L. multiflòra** (Ehrh.) Lejeune. Flowers about 2 mm. long, in *dense clusters* at the ends of unequal rays (Fig. 8).—In fields or open woods, more common in the southern half of the state.

LILIÀCEAE LILY FAMILY

Flowers regular, with ordinarily 3 colored or white petals, 3 similar or green sepals, 6 stamens, and an ovary of 3 carpels which develops into a capsule or berry.

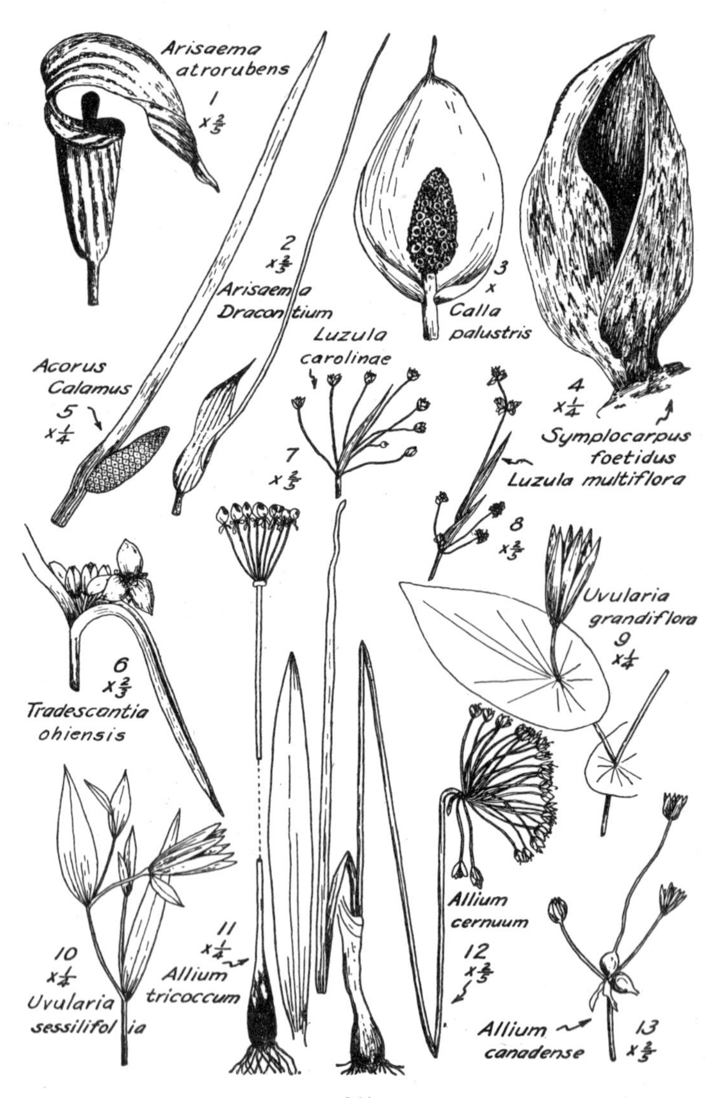
Arisaema
atrorubens
1
x 2/3
2
x 2/3
Arisaema
Dracontium
3
x
Calla
palustris
4
x 1/4
Symplocarpus
foetidus
Acorus
Calamus
5
x 1/4
Luzula
carolinae
7
x 2/3
Luzula multiflora
8
x 2/3
6
x 2/3
Tradescantia
ohiensis
Uvularia
grandiflora
9
x 1/4
Allium
cernuum
10
x 1/4
Uvularia
sessilifolia
11
x 1/4
Allium
tricoccum
12
x 2/3
Allium
canadense
13
x 2/3

a. Leaves growing only from the base of the plant *b.*
- *b.* Flowers 8 mm. or less long, in an umbel . . . . . 4. *Allium.*
- *b.* Flowers 1 cm. or more long, or, if shorter, in a raceme *c.*
  - *c.* Leaves not more than 10 times longer than broad *d.*
    - *d.* Flower solitary, nodding; leaves 1–2.5 cm. broad, obscurely veined. . . . . . . 6. *Erythronium.*
    - *d.* Flowers usually 2 or more; leaves 3–8 cm. broad, strongly veined . . . . 9. *Clintonia.*
  - *c.* Leaves grass-like, many times longer than broad *e.*
    - *e.* Flowers pale blue . . . . 7. *Camassia.*
    - *e.* Flowers greenish or whitish *f.*
      - *f.* One flower in the axil of each bract; pedicels longer than the flower 2. *Zigadenus.*
      - *f.* Several flowers from each axil; pedicel at flowering time shorter than the flower . . . . 1. *Tofieldia.*

a. Leaves elevated on the stem *g.*
- *g.* Leaves scattered or in many whorls *h.*
  - *h.* Flowers solitary, or 2 in the axil of a leaf *i.*
    - *i.* Flowers 1.5 cm. or more long, and at least half as wide *j.*
      - *j.* Leaves 2, opposite . . . . 6. *Erythronium.*
      - *j.* Leaves many, alternate or whorled *k.*
        - *k.* Flowers 6 cm. or more long. . . . . 5. *Lilium.*
        - *k.* Flowers 1.5–4.5 cm. long . . . . . . 3. *Uvularia.*
    - *i.* Flowers 1 cm. or less long, or if longer about a fourth as wide *l.*
      - *l.* Leaves reduced to brownish scales . . . 8. *Asparagus.*
      - *l.* Leaves broad and flat *m.*
        - *m.* Each peduncle appearing just under a leaf . . . . 12. *Streptopus.*
        - *m.* Each peduncle just above a leaf. . . 13. *Polygonatum.*
  - *h.* Flowers in an umbel or raceme, or 2—several on a peduncle *n.*
    - *n.* Flowers 5 cm. or more long . . . . . . 5. *Lilium.*
    - *n.* Flowers 2 cm. or less long *o.*
      - *o.* Flowers in umbels, the staminate and pistillate on different plants. . . . 16. *Smilax.*
      - *o.* Flowers not in umbels, each with stamens and pistil *p.*
        - *p.* Flowers in terminal racemes *q.*
          - *q.* Stamens 4 . . . . 11. *Maianthemum.*
          - *q.* Stamens 6 . . . . 10. *Smilacina.*
        - *p.* Flowers 1–6 in each leaf-axil. . . . 13. *Polygonatum.*
- *g.* Leaves in 1 or 2 whorls *r.*
  - *r.* Flowers 1 cm. or less long . . . . 14. *Medeola.*
  - *r.* Flowers 1.5 cm. or more long. . . . . 15. *Trillium.*

1. Tofièldia

T. glutinòsa (Michx.) Pers. Plant grass-like, with 2–ranked leaves from a small rootstock. Scape 2–5 dm. tall, covered with sticky dark glands just below the inflorescence, which is 1–5 cm. long. Flowers about 5 mm. long.—Springy meadows, eastern Wisconsin; rare.

2. Zigádenus

Scape 3–9 dm. high, from a papery bulb; flowers about 1 cm. long, in an inflorescence 5–20 cm. long.

1. **Z. élegans** Pursh. Leaves thin, sharp-pointed; flowers usually in a raceme with simple branches; upper bracts with papery margins and summits; capsule twice as long as the sepals.—Swamps, hillsides, etc., locally northward to Door and Buffalo Counties; adventive at Superior. Grades into the next.

2. **Z. glaùcus** Nutt. Leaves firm, blunt; upper bracts with green margins and awl-shaped tips; inflorescence usually with compound branches; capsule barely longer than the sepals.—Door County and perhaps elsewhere.

3. **Uvulària** BELLWORT

Stems erect from rootstocks, somewhat branched; flowers yellowish.

1. **U. grandiflòra** Sm. *Stem apparently passing through the leaves* (Fig. 9); leaves finely hairy beneath; flowers 2.5–4.5 cm. long; fruit a 3-lobed capsule.—Common in woods, especially southward.

2. **U. sessilifòlia** L. (Fig. 10) Leaves rather narrow, whitened beneath; flowers 1.2–2 cm. long; fruit 3-winged.—Woods, south to Brown, Dane, and rarely Grant Counties.

4. **Allium** WILD ONION

Foliage strong-scented; umbel subtended by an involucre which envelopes all the buds.

a. Inflorescence without bulbets, but with 8 or more flowers *b.*
b. Flowers greenish-white; umbel erect . . . . 1. *A. tricoccum.*
b. Flowers pink; umbel nodding. . . . . 2. *A. cernuum.*
a. Inflorescence with bulbets, and 3 or fewer flowers . . 3. *A. canadense*

1. **A. tricóccum** Ait. WILD LEEK. Bulb smooth; *leaves flat*, 1–2.3 dm. long and 1–6 cm. broad, appearing in the early spring and *dying before the flowers mature* (Fig. 11); pedicels 1–1.5 cm. long. —Rich woods.

2. **A. cérnuum** Roth. Bulb with papery scales; *leaves flattened, keeled, ribbon-like* (Fig. 12).—Prairies and along railroads, southeastern counties.

3. **A. canadénse** L. WILD GARLIC. Bulb with fibrous coat; *leaves ribbon-like, thick and fleshy;* umbel erect, the pedicels reaching 5 cm. in length (Fig. 13).—Woods and meadows, north to Polk, Waupaca, and Brown Counties.

5. **Lílium** LILY

Erect plants 4–20 dm. high; *leaves narrow*, without petioles; *flowers large*, in our species reddish or orange.

1. **L. philadélphicum** L. WOOD LILY. Flowers 1–5, *erect;* perianth-segments dark-spotted at the base of the broader part, *much narrowed at the lower end, not recurved* (Fig. 14); leaves whorled.—Door County and perhaps elsewhere, rare.—Var. **andìnum** (Nutt.) Ker., with the *leaves mostly scattered,* occurs throughout the state.

2. **L. michiganénse** Farw. WESTERN TURK'S-CAP LILY. *Flowers nodding;* perianth-segments finely dotted with dark purple, *not narrowed at the lower end, strongly recurved* (Fig. 15); leaves whorled (*L. canadense* and *L. superbum* are eastern species with which this has been confused).—Meadowland.

6. Erythrònium FAWN-LILY; ADDER'S-TONGUE

Plants with a deep-seated white bulb shaped like a canine tooth; leaves 2, flat and shining; *flower usually solitary,* nodding.

1. **E. americànum** Ker. YELLOW ADDER'S-TONGUE. Leaves mottled with purplish and whitish; flowers light yellow; anthers yellow or reddish brown; style club-shaped, with *united stigmas* (Fig. 16).—Rich woods.

2. **E. álbidum** Nutt. WHITE ADDER'S-TONGUE. Leaves less mottled or not at all; flowers pinkish-white; anthers yellow; style slender except at tip, with *3 spreading stigmas* (Fig. 17).—Rich woods.

7. Camássia WILD HYACINTH

C. scilloìdes (Raf.) Cory. Scape 1.5–7 dm. high, from a dark papery bulb; flowers 10–14 mm. long, in a raceme 1–3 dm. long.—Lafayette to Rock Counties, rare.

8. Aspáragus GARDEN ASPARAGUS

A. officínalis L. Plants tall, from matted rootstocks; leaves represented by small brown scales, with green branchlets from their axis; flowers 3–5 mm. long, developing into red berries.—Occasionally escaping from cultivation and found in open ground or sunny woods.

9. Clintònia

C. boreàlis (Ait.) Raf. Leaves flat, oval, 1.5–2 dm. long; flowers 3–6 in an umbel or short raceme, straw-colored (Fig. 18); berries blue.—In cool woods and swamps, south to the Baraboo Hills, Madison (where probably extinct), and along the Lake Michigan shore to Kenosha County.

10. Smilacìna FALSE SOLOMON'S SEAL

Plants from rootstocks; leaves alternate, many-nerved, without petioles; flowers white; fruit a berry.

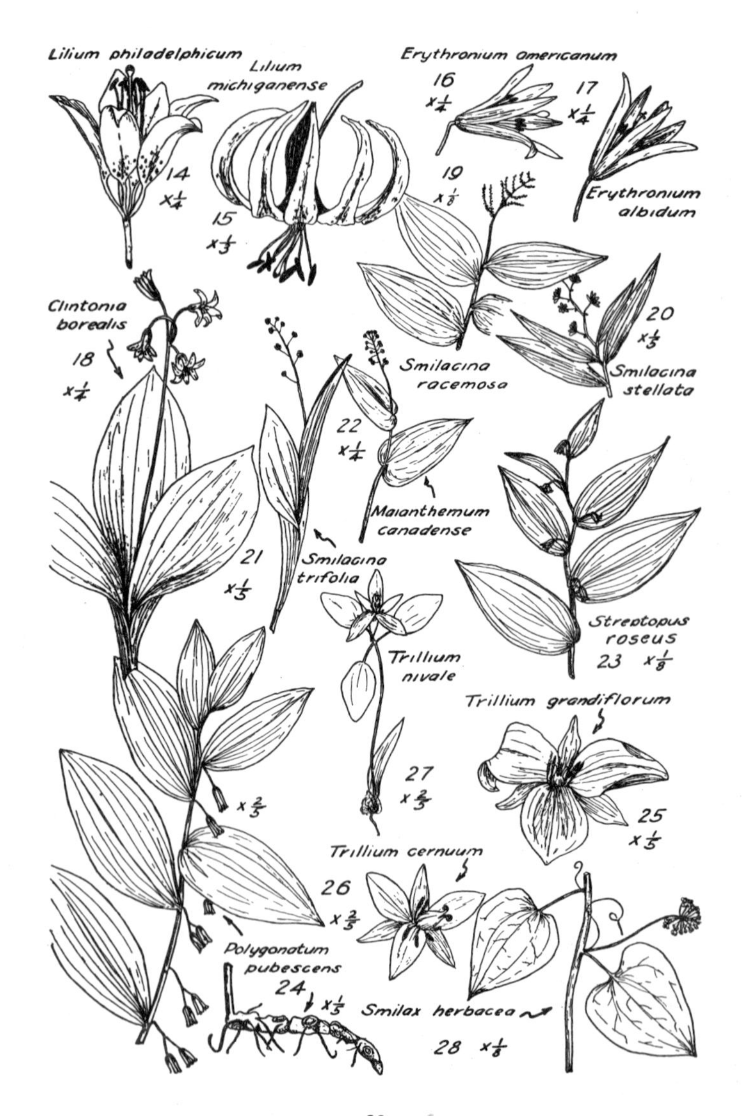
Lilium philadelphicum
Lilium michiganense
Erythronium americanum
16 x¼
17 x¼
14 x¼
19 x⅛
Erythronium albidum
15 x⅓
Clintonia borealis
18 x¼
20 x⅕
Smilacina racemosa
Smilacina stellata
22 x¼
Maianthemum canadense
21 x⅕
Smilacina trifolia
Streptopus roseus
23 x⅛
Trillium nivale
Trillium grandiflorum
x ⅖
27 x ⅖
25 x⅕
Trillium cernuum
26 x⅖
Polygonatum pubescens
24 x⅕
Smilax herbacea
28 x⅛

a. Flowers 2 mm. long; stamens longer than the petals. 1. *S. racemosa.*
a. Flowers 4–5 mm. long; stamens shorter than the petals *b.*
b. Leaves 7–12, clasping the stem with their bases. . 2. *S. stellata.*
b. Leaves 2–4, sheathing at base . . . . 3. *S. trifolia.*

1. **S. racemòsa** (L.) Desf. *Flowers very numerous*, on pedicels about 2 mm. long; leaves taper-pointed, *minutely downy* (Fig. 19). Individuals with more slender panicles or racemes are treated as var. **cylindràta** in *Gray's Manual*, 8th ed.—Common in woods.

2. **S. stellàta** (L.) Desf. Plants 2–5 dm. high; *flowers 3–14*, on longer pedicels; leaves pointed but not tapered, *smooth* (Fig. 20). —Open ground.

3. **S. trifòlia** (L.) Desf. *Plants 1.3–2 dm. high;* flowers 8–11; leaves smooth (Fig. 21).—Peat bogs, south to Jackson and Brown Counties, and along the Lake Michigan shore to Milwaukee.

11. **Maiánthemum** CANADA MAYFLOWER; DWARF SOLOMON'S SEAL

M. canadénse Desf. Plants 6–22 cm. high, smooth; leaves usually 2, flat, *heart-shaped at base* (Fig. 22); petioles short or none; flowers 2 mm. long, with *2 sepals and 2 petals.*—Throughout the state, but more common northward.—Var. **intèrius** Fernald, with the stem and usually the leaves covered with short hairs, is common southward, but occurs also in the north.

12. **Stréptopus** TWISTED-STALK

Plants 2–9 dm. high; leaves 5–11 cm. long, sharply pointed; flowers solitary in the leaf-axils, each on a *bent peduncle;* fruit a red berry.

1. **S. amplexifòlius** (L.) DC., var. **denticulàtus** Fassett. Leaves strongly clasping the stem, whitened beneath, the *margin not fringed with hairs*, minutely toothed; flowers greenish-white.—Cool moist woods in counties bordering on Lake Superior; Door County.

2. **S. ròseus** Michx., var. **lóngipes** (Fernald) Fassett. Leaves slightly clasping or merely sessile, not whitened beneath, *copiously fringed with fine hairs;* flowers light pink, spotted with deep pink (Fig. 23).— Common in woods northward, and occurring locally southward to the Baraboo Hills, to Racine and Walworth Counties, and occasionally in tamarack bogs southwestward.

13. **Polygónatum** SOLOMON'S SEAL

Stems simple, from rootstocks which bear the scars of attachment of previous stems (the "seals"); leaves alternate, elliptic, not petioled; flowers 1–4 on axillary peduncles.

1. **P. pubéscens** (Willd.) Pursh. SMALL SOLOMON'S SEAL. Plant 3–9 dm. high (Fig. 24); leaves whitened and *finely hairy beneath;* flowers 10–12 mm. long (*P. biflorum*).—Low rich woods; common northward, rare southward.

2. **P. canaliculàtum** (Muhl.) Pursh. GREAT SOLOMON'S SEAL. Plant 0.6–2 m. high; *leaves smooth*, green on both sides; flowers 1.2–2 cm. long (*P. commutatum*).—Rich woods, north to Washburn, Marathon. and Oconto Counties.

14. **Medèola** INDIAN CUCUMBER-ROOT

M. virginiàna L. Plant 3–9 dm. high, from a white horizontal fleshy tuber; leaves in 2 whorls; flowers borne just above the upper whorl, yellowish, about 1 cm. broad, with *small recurved petals shorter than the styles;* fruit a purple berry.—Damp woods, eastern Wisconsin.

15. **Tríllium**

Stem simple, from a short tuber-like rootstock; leaves 3 (rarely more), whorled, diamond-shaped, usually about as broad as long; flower solitary, terminating the stem.

a. Flower sessile . . . . 1. *T. recurvatum.*
a. Flower peduncled *b.*
  b. Leaves without definite petioles *c.*
    c. Stigmas exceeded by the stamens, usually not coiled or only slightly recurved at tip . . . 2. *T. grandiflorum.*
    c. Stigmas equaling or exceeding the stamens, coiled at tip *d.*
      d. Peduncles 1.2–4 cm. long; curved or bent downward; anthers 2.5–6.5 mm. long . 3. *T. cernuum.*
      d. Peduncles 3–12 cm. long; straight; anthers 6–15 mm. long . . . . 4. *T. Gleasoni.*
  b. Leaves short-petioled . . . . 5. *T. nivale.*

1. **T. recurvàtum** Beck. Leaves often short-petioled; sepals recurved; petals 1.3–3 cm. long, *dark red*, narrowed into a claw at base.—Moist woods, north to Green and Milwaukee Counties.

2. **T. grandiflòrum** (Michx.) Salisb. Leaves without petioles; *peduncle erect or nearly so; petals 4–6 cm. long*, white turning rose-color, sometimes marked with green (Fig. 25).—Rich woods.

3. **T. cérnuum** L. *Peduncle recurved or reflexed;* filaments nearly or quite equaling anthers; petals 5–9 mm. broad, white; anthers 2.5–4.5 mm. long.—Rare in northern Wisconsin.—Var. **macránthum** Eames & Wiegand. Petals 10–17 mm. broad; anthers 4–6.5 mm. long (Fig. 26).—Rich woods.

4. **T. Glèasoni** Fern. *Peduncle usually horizontal;* filaments less than half as long as the anthers; petals 2–3.5 cm. long, white (*T. flexipes* Raf.).—Rich woods, north to Vernon and Fond du Lac Counties.

5. **T. nivàle** Riddell. *Plants 5–10 cm. high; leaf-blades rounded at base* (Fig. 27); peduncle short, erect or recurved; petals 1.2–3 cm. long, white.—Rich woods and fields, Manitowoc, Milwaukee, Ozaukee, and Pierce Counties, and doubtless elsewhere in limestone areas.

16. **Smìlax**

Leaves netted-veined, the blades more or less heart-shaped.

a. Stem herbaceous, without prickles or bristles *b.*
b. Stem vine-like, climbing, with tendrils; umbels with 25 or more flowers *c.*
c. Leaves glabrous beneath; berries blue . . . . . 1. *S. herbacea.*
c. Leaves minutely white-hairy beneath; berries black . . . . 2. *S. lasioneura.*
b. Stem erect, without tendrils or with tendrils from a few upper leaves; umbels with 25 or fewer flowers . . . . 3. *S. ecirrhata.*
a. Stem woody, with black bristles . . . . 4. *S. tamnoides.*

1. **S. herbàcea** L. Carrion-flower. Stem extensively climbing; flowers ill-smelling, the umbels long-peduncled from the axils of leaves (Fig. 28).—Scattered and rare in Wisconsin.

2. **S. lasioneùra** Hook. Similar; widespread in open woods and on fences, etc.

3. **S. ecirrhàta** (Engelm.) S. Wats. Umbels from the axils of bladeless bracts on the lower part of the stem.—Low woods, mostly in the southern half of Wisconsin.

4. **S. tamnoìdes** L., var. **híspida** (Muhl.) Fernald.—In woods.

DIOSCOREÀCEAE Yam Family

Herbaceous trailing vines, from thick tuberous rootstocks; leaves petioled, netted-veined; fruit a 3–winged capsule.—A large tropical family.

Dioscorèa villòsa L. Wild Yam Root. Leaf-blades heart-shaped, downy beneath; flowers very small, at intervals of about 4 mm. on drooping slender branches (Fig. 29).—Rich woods, north to Polk, Lincoln, and Oconto Counties.

AMARYLLIDÀCEAE Amaryllis Family

Grass-like plants, from bulbs; fruit a capsule.

Hypóxis hirsùta (L.) Coville. Star Grass. Flowers yellow, 1–4 on a scape, 1–1.5 cm. broad (Fig. 30).—Sunny woods, bluffs, and meadows, north to Pierce, Chippewa, and Oconto Counties.

IRIDÀCEAE Iris Family

Leaves sword-shaped or grass-like; flowers from a spathe; sepals 3; petals 3; fruit a capsule formed of 3 carpels.

a. Stigmas petal-like; flowers several cm. long . . . . . 1. *Iris.*
a. Stigmas thread-like; flowers about 1 cm. long . . . . 2. *Sisyrinchium.*

1. Ìris FLEUR-DE-LIS

Plants from creeping rootstocks; leaves 1–2 cm. broad; flowers showy, mostly blue; sepals and petals united below into a tube; sepals much larger than the petals.

a. Perianth-tube 5 mm. or less in length *b.*
  b. Petals shorter than the styles; ovary less than 2 cm. in length (Fig. 31) . . . . 1. *I. versicolor.*
  b. Petals slightly longer than the styles; ovary 2 cm. or more in length (Fig. 32) . . . . 2. *I. virginica.*
a. Perianth-tube 1 cm. or more in length . . . . 3. *I. lacustris.*

1. **I. versícolor** L. (Fig. 31) Stems 1.5–5 dm. high, stout; flowers 5–8 cm. long; sepals blue, *sometimes with a greenish or yellowish spot* at the base of the blade; *lining of capsule shining.*—Wet places from Washburn, Oneida, and Forest Counties northward.

2. **I. virgínica** L., var. **Shrevèi** (Small) Anderson. (Fig. 32) Similar; *sepals with a bright yellow spot* at the base of the blade; *lining of capsule dull.*—Wet places, north to Barron, Marathon, and Door Counties.

3. **I. lacústris** Nutt. Stem 0.5–1.5 dm. high; free part of sepals about 2 cm. long.—Lake Michigan region; rare.

2. Sisyrínchium BLUE-EYED GRASS

Plants grass-like, *tufted;* stems 2-winged, longer than the leaves; flowers blue or white, clustered, each cluster enclosed by 2 bracts which make up the spathe; spathe or spathes sometimes enclosed by a larger bract.—The species are separated on technical points, and are difficult of determination.

a. Spathes 2, with a single outer leaf-like bract . . . 1. *S. albidum.*
a. Spathes solitary, enclosed by 2 green bracts *b.*
  b. Outer, longer bract with margins free to the base 2. *S. campestre.*
  b. Outer bract with margins united for a short distance above the base *c.*
    c. Spathe terminating the culm (rarely a peduncled spathe present) . . . . 3. *S. montanum.*
    c. Spathes peduncled from the axils of a leaf-like bract . . . . 4. *S. angustifolium.*

1. **S. álbidum** Raf. Outer bract 3–5 cm. long; the two inner subequal; capsules 2–4 mm. high.—Sunny fields from Dane and Milwaukee Counties southward.

2. **S. campéstre** Bicknell. Outer bract 2.5–4.5 cm. long; the inner about half as long (Fig. 33); *capsule 2–4 mm. high.*—Sunny fields, common from Sawyer, Shawano, and Walworth Counties southward.

3. **S. montànum** Greene. *Capsule 4–6 mm. high;* plant light green; capsule light brown at maturity.—Northern Wisconsin, not very common.—Var. **crèbrum** Fernald. Plant darker green; capsule

dark brown to black at maturity.—Northern Wisconsin, not very common.

4. **S. angustifòlium** Mill. *Stem flexuous, 2–6 mm. wide;* spathes on long peduncles, usually two present (Fig. 34); *flowering bracts subequal.*—South to Polk, Lincoln, and Milwaukee Counties.

ORCHIDÀCEAE Orchid Family

Herbs, with thick whitish roots (or sometimes none); perianth borne at the summit of the ovary; sepals 3; petals 3, the posterior twisted so that it extends forward and downward and modified into a *lip*, which sometimes has a *spur* extending from near its base; fertile stamen 1 (in *Cypripedium* 2) united with the style to form the *column;* fruit a capsule formed of 3 carpels, with innumerable minute seeds.

a. Lip a large inflated sac . . . . 1. *Cypripedium.*
a. Lip hardly sac-like, not inflated *b.*
  b. Flowers with a spur 2 mm. or more long *c.*
    c. Leaves 1–2, at or near the base of the stem; each flower exceeded by its bract, which is about 1 cm. wide . . . . 2. *Orchis.*
    c. Leaves several, on the stem (except in two species which have narrow bracts shorter than the flowers) . . . . 3. *Habenaria.*
  b. Flowers without conspicuous spur *d.*
    d. Leaves one or more, green *e.*
      e. Flower solitary, terminal (rarely 2) *f.*
        f. Lip tongue-like, with 3 parallel lines of hairs or crests . . . . 4. *Arethusa.*
        f. Lip spoon-shaped, with a tuft of yellow hairs . . . . 8. *Calypso.*
      e. Flowers several or many, in a raceme *g.*
        g. Leaves 2 cm. or less long, a single pair halfway up the stem . . . . . . 5. *Listera.*
        g. Leaves 5 cm. or more long, at the base of the stem *h.*
          h. Leaves 2. . . . . 7. *Liparis.*
          h. Leaf solitary . . . . 9. *Aplectrum.*
    d. Leaves none; plant not green . . . . . . 6. *Corallorhiza.*

1. Cypripèdium Lady's Slipper

Flowers mostly large, the lip 1.5–5 cm. long, delicate and much inflated, moccasin-shaped; other petals long and spreading; the two lowest sepals, in most species, united into one flat structure below the lip.

a. Leaves several, on the stem *b.*
  b. Petals longer than the lip, twisted *c.*
    c. Lip yellow. . . . . 2. *C. Calceolus.*
    c. Lip white . . . . 3. *C. candidum.*
  b. Petals shorter than the lip, usually not twisted *d.*
    d. Lateral petals white. . . . . 4. *C. reginae*
    d. Lateral petals dark purple-brown, edged with green . . . . 1. *C. arietinum.*
a. Leaves 2, or few, close to the ground. . . . . . 5. *C. acaule.*

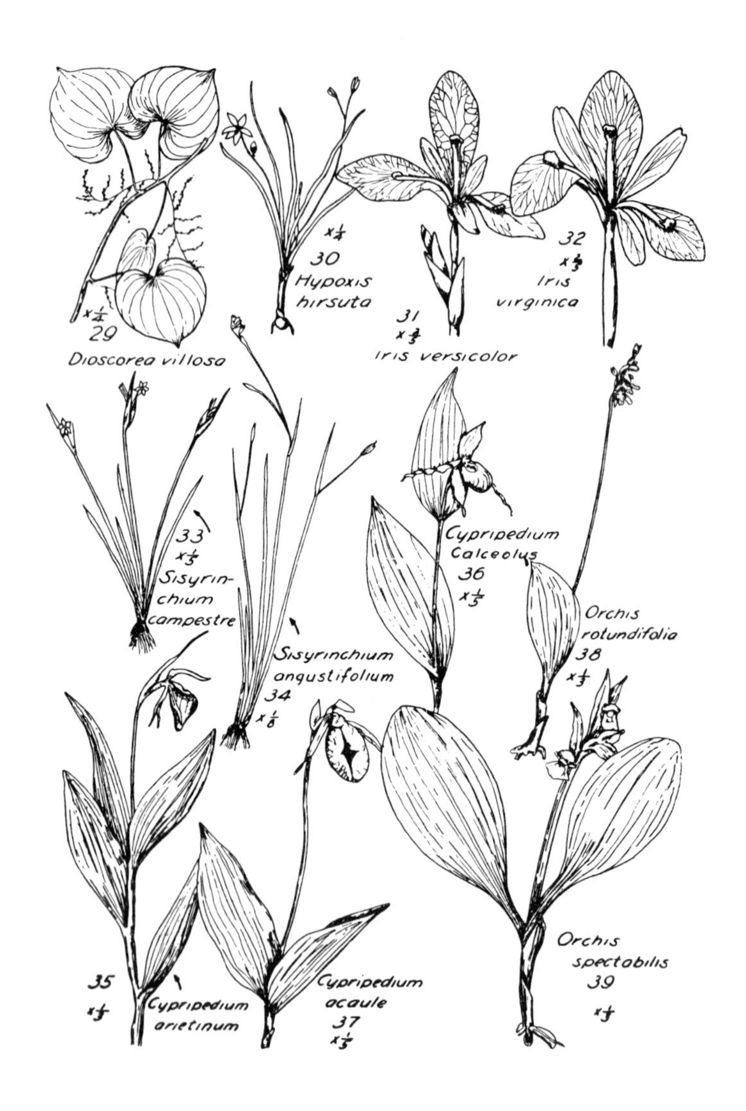

x¼
29
Dioscorea villosa
x¼
30
Hypoxis
hirsuta
31
x⅔
Iris versicolor
32
x⅔
Iris
virginica
33
x⅕
Sisyrinchium
campestre
Sisyrinchium
angustifolium
34
x⅙
Cypripedium
Calceolus
36
x⅕
Orchis
rotundifolia
38
x⅓
35
x⅓
Cypripedium
arietinum
Cypripedium
acaule
37
x⅕
Orchis
spectabilis
39
x⅓

1. **C. arietìnum** R. Br. RAM'S HEAD LADY'S SLIPPER. Stem 15–30 cm. high; leaves 3–4, elliptic-lanceolate, almost without hairs; flower 1.5–2 cm. long; lip whitish with crimson veins, *prolonged at apex into a long blunt spur* (Fig. 35).—Tamarack bogs, very rare, mostly in counties bordering on Lake Michigan.

2. **C. Calcèolus** L., var. **parviflòrum** (Salisb.) Fernald. SMALLER YELLOW LADY'S SLIPPER. Stem 1.9–6 dm. high; leaves oval, acute; lip 2–3 cm. long (Fig. 36).—Swamps.—Var. **pubéscens** (Willd.) Correll. LARGER YELLOW LADY'S SLIPPER. Stem 2.3–7 dm. high; lip 3.5–5 cm. long.—Woodlands, more common. **C. Favilliànum** Curtis and **C. Andrewsii** Fuller are hybrids of *C. candidum* with *C. Calceolus* var. *pubescens* and with var. *parviflorum;* they are intermediate between the parents.

3. **C. cándidum** Muhl. SMALL WHITE LADY'S SLIPPER. Plant 1.6–3 dm. high; leaves oval, folded at the base around the stem; flower usually solitary; *lip about 2 cm. long, white*, purple-striped within. —Meadows and low prairies, southward.

4. **C. regìnae** Walt. SHOWY LADY'S SLIPPER. Plant 4–8 dm. high; stem and leaves covered with short hairs (which on the skin of some persons cause a rash similar to that of poison ivy); leaves ovate, acute, 1.5–2 dm. long, folded at the base around the stem; *lip about 4 cm. long, white, flushed with wine red on face.*—Woods and bogs.

5. **C. acaùle** Ait. STEMLESS LADY'S SLIPPER; PINK MOCCASIN FLOWER. Plant 1.5–4 dm. high; leaves oval, many-nerved; *lip pink* (rarely white), inflated, about 5 cm. long and half as broad (Fig. 37).—Common northward, and coming south in pine woods to the Dells of the Wisconsin, and in tamarack bogs to the southeastern counties.

2. Órchis

Technically separated from the next only by having the discs at the base of the stalk of the pollen masses contained in a special pouch.

1. **O. rotundifòlia** Banks. *Leaf solitary*, 3–8 cm. long; flower pinkish mauve to white (Fig. 38).—Tamarack or white cedar bogs, rare, in counties bordering Lake Michigan.

2. **O. spectábilis** L. SHOWY ORCHIS. *Leaves 2*, 7–17 cm. long, shining; flower white and magenta (Fig. 39).—In rich woods.

3. Habenària REIN ORCHIS

Petals (in our spring-flowering species) greenish, white, or yellowish; flowers in a cylindrical raceme, which is usually much longer than broad.

Lip x2
41
44
x2
Lip
45
Habenaria
Hookeri
x 1/4
46
x 2/5
42 x2
Lip of
Habenaria flava
40
x 1/8
Habenaria
viridis
var bracteata
Arethusa
bulbosa
Habenaria
hyperborea
43
x 1/10
Listera cordata
48 x2
Corallorhiza
trifida
47
x 1/6
49 x2
Corallorhiza
maculata
Corallorhiza
striata
50 x2
54
x 1/4
53
x 2/3
Calypso
bulbosa
Liparis
lilifolia
51
x 1/3
Aplectrum
hyemale
Liparis Loeselii
52 x 1/3

a. Leaves several, raised on the stem *b*.
b. Lip 2–3-toothed at apex (Fig. 41) . . . . 1. *H. viridis.*
b. Lip not toothed at apex *c*.
c. Lip cut square across at the apex, and with 2 tubercles at the base (Fig. 42). . . . . . 2. *H. flava.*
c. Lip tapered at the apex, without tubercles at the base (Fig. 44) *d*.
d. Flowers greenish *e*.
e. Lip tapered at base . . . . 3. *H. hyperborea.*
e. Lip abruptly wider at base . . . . . 4. *H. media.*
d. Flowers white . . . . 5. *H. dilatata.*
a. Leaves 1 or 2, at the base of the stem *f*.
f. Leaf 1 . . . . 6. *H. obtusata.*
f. Leaves 2 *g*.
g. Lip about 1 cm. long . . . . 7. *H. Hookeri.*
g. Lip 1.5–2 cm. long . . . . 8. *H. orbiculata.*

1. **H. víridis** (L.) R. Br., var. **bracteàta** (Muhl.) Gray. Leaves broadly lanceolate, acute or obtuse; raceme loosely flowered; *lowest bracts divergent, 2–4 times as long as the green flowers* (Fig. 40); *lip more than twice as long as the spur.*—Woods.—Var. **interjécta** Fernald. Lowest bracts hardly twice as long as the flowers, the upper shorter.—Driftless Area, rare.

2. **H. flàva** (L.) Spreng., var. **herbìola** (R. Br.) Ames and Correll. Leaves lanceolate, gradually tapering to the acute apex, *the upper very narrow and passing into the lower bracts; spur longer than the lip.*—Wet grassy places, north to Lincoln and Brown Counties.

3. **H. hyperbòrea** (L.) R. Br., var. **huronénsis** (Nutt.) Farw. Leaves linear-lanceolate; *raceme very narrow*, closely flowered; bracts about as long as the flowers (Fig. 43).—Wet ground, northeast of a line drawn from Douglas County to Racine County.

4. **H. mèdia** (Rydb.) Niles. Intermediate between *H. hyperborea* and *H. dilatata* and often more abundant than either.

5. **H. dilatàta** (Pursh) Gray. Similar to No. 3, but flowers more delicate; lip somewhat dilated at base.—Swamps in northern and eastern Wisconsin; rare.

6. **H. obtusàta** (Pursh) Richards. Flowers in a loose raceme, greenish or whitish; lip entire, 6 mm. long, about equaling the slender curving spur.—Wet places, south to Taylor, Oconto, and Manitowoc Counties.

7. **H. Hoòkeri** Torr. Leaves roundish; flat on ground; *scape without bracts;* much like No. 8 (Fig. 45).—Swamps and woods, south to St. Croix, Lincoln, and Waukesha Counties.

8. **H. orbiculàta** (Pursh) Torr. Leaves 6–19 cm. wide, flat on ground, shining above, silvery beneath; *scape with 1–several bracts.*—Swamps and rich damp woods, south to Barron, Lincoln, and Sheboygan Counties.

4. **Arethùsa**

A. bulbòsa L. Stem solitary, 10–25 cm. high, from a bulb; leaves at flowering time hidden by the outer sheaths; flowers pink, 3–5 cm. long (Fig. 46).—Sphagnum bogs, rather rare.

5. **Lístera** TWAYBLADE

Plants slender and delicate, 1–2 dm. high; stems with a pair of leaves near the middle; flowers small, greenish or purplish, in a loose slender raceme.

1. **L. cordàta** (L.) R. Br. Leaves somewhat heart-shaped (Fig. 47); *lip cleft more than half of its length.*—Mossy bogs, south to Burnett, Oneida, and Ozaukee Counties.

2. **L. auriculàta** Wiegand. Leaves rounded at base; *lip cleft a third or less of its length.*—Lake Superior region.

6. **Corallorhìza** CORAL ROOT

Brownish or yellowish saprophytes, living in leaf-mold; rootless, the underground stems much branched, coral-like; capsules turned sharply downward.

a. Sepals about 5 mm. long; lip 3–lobed *b.*
  b. Plant yellowish . . . . 1. *C. trifida.*
  b. Plant purplish . . . . 2. *C. maculata.*
a. Sepals about 1 cm. long; lip not lobed (Fig. 50) . 3. *C. striata.*

1. **C. trífida** Chatelain, var. **verna** (Nutt.) Fern. Plant slender, 4–19 cm. high, 4–12 flowered; lip white, 3–lobed (Fig. 48).—Woods and bogs, northward and eastward.

2. **C. maculàta** Raf. Plant stout, 2–4 dm. high, 10–30-flowered; lip white, usually with crimson spots (Fig. 49).—Dry woodlands.

3. **C. striàta** Lindl. (Fig. 50) Plant 15–40 cm. high, purplish; *sepals and petals conspicuously striped with deep purple.*—South to Washburn and Manitowoc Counties.

7. **Líparis** TWAYBLADE

Plants 1–2 dm. high, from a solid bulb; leaves elliptic, their bases embraced by several bladeless sheaths; flowers few, in a raceme.

1. **L. lilifòlia** (L.) Richard. Pedicels longer than the flowers, spreading; *lip nearly 1 cm. broad, pale purple* (Fig. 51).—Woods, southern and western Wisconsin.

2. **L. Loesèlii** (L.) Richard. Pedicels shorter than the flowers, ascending; *lip about 2 mm. broad, yellowish* (Fig. 52).—Damp places.

8. **Calýpso**

C. bulbòsa (L.) Oakes. Plant 6–18 cm. high, from a solid corm; *leaf solitary*, the blade oval, about as long as the petiole; stem with a few bladeless sheaths; lip whitish, marked with purple and yellow, depressed; the rest of the perianth pink, erect (Fig. 53).—Deep mossy woods northward.

9. **Apléctrum** PUTTY-ROOT; ADAM-AND-EVE

A. hyemàle (Muhl.) Torr. Plant about 4 dm. high, from a solid corm ("Adam") near which is usually the smaller corm of last year ("Eve"); flowers 8–15, in a loose raceme, yellowish or purple (Fig. 54).—Rich woods, north to Dunn and Brown Counties.

SALICÀCEAE WILLOW FAMILY

Trees or shrubs, dioecious; flowers without perianth, in catkins, often covered in bud with silky bracts (as in the "Pussy Willow"); fruit a capsule, the carpels curling back at maturity; seeds many, with a long tuft of silky down.

a. Buds with only one scale; stamens 2–8 in each flower . . . . 1. *Salix.*
a. Buds with several overlapping scales; stamens many in each flower . . . . 2. *Populus.*

1. **Sàlix** WILLOW

Trees or shrubs; *leaves long and pointed*, usually 3 or more times as long as broad; insect-pollinated, each pistillate flower with a honey-bearing gland at its base.—A difficult and complex group, with about 20 species in Wisconsin.

2. **Pópulus** POPLAR

Trees; *leaves ovate-lanceolate to almost round*, less than 3 times as long as broad; wind-pollinated.

a. Leaves densely white-woolly beneath . . . . . . 1. *P. alba.*
a. Leaves not woolly beneath (except on root sprouts in No. 3) *b.*
  b. Petioles not flattened *c.*
    c. Leaves lance-shaped to narrowly heart-shaped, smooth or with very sparse fine hairs on midrib below . . . . 4. *P. balsamifera.*
    c. Leaves broadly heart-shaped, hairy below, especially on midrib and veins . . . . 5. × *P. gileadensis.*
  b. Petioles flattened, at least toward the summit *d.*
    d. Buds and tips of young branches white-woolly . . . . 3. *P. grandidentata.*
    d. Buds and twigs not woolly *e.*
      e. Petiole with 2 small glands on the upper surface at its junction with the blade 6. *P. deltoides.*
      e. Petiole without glands *f.*
        f. Leaf-blades rounded or square across the base . . . . 2. *P. tremuloides.*
        f. Leaf-blades broadly V-shaped at base 7. *P. nigra*, var. *italica.*

1. **P. álba** L. WHITE POPLAR. Leaves somewhat 3–lobed, coarsely and irregularly toothed, *densely white-woolly beneath.*—Cultivated, and frequently spreading by suckers from the roots.

2. **P. tremuloìdes** Michx. QUAKING ASPEN; POPPLE. Usually a small tree, with smooth greenish bark; leaf-blades mostly rounded at base and abruptly short-pointed at tip, with *small regular teeth* (Fig. 55).—Common, especially on cut-over and burned areas. The common var. **tremuloìdes**, with slender twigs 5 mm. or less thick and petioles 1 mm. or less thick, grades into the rare and local var. **magnífica** Vict., with very short internodes 6–12 mm. thick.

3. **P. grandidentàta** Michx. LARGE-TOOTHED ASPEN OR POPPLE. Similar; leaf-blades not abruptly pointed, with *coarse teeth* (Fig. 56).—In somewhat moist places.

4. **P. balsamífera** L. TACCAMAHAC. Tree 6–30 m. high; terminal buds with fragrant gum; leaves lighter green on lower surface with rusty blotches. With glabrous leaves angled or rounded at base (Fig. 57). In low rich soil, mostly northward and eastward, grading into var. **subcordàta** Hylander, with leaves heart-shaped (Fig. 58) and slightly pubescent on the lower surface.

5. × **P. gileadénsis** Rouleau. BALM OF GILEAD. Leaves heart-shaped and pubescent below.—Mostly planted trees.

6. **P. deltoìdes** Marsh. COTTONWOOD. Tree 15–30 m. high; *leaf-blades broadest near the base*, which is as if cut off almost squarely, at tip narrowed to a *tapering point* about 1 cm. long (Fig. 59).—In woods and on the banks of streams. Commonly cultivated.

7. **P. nìgra** L., var. **itálica** Du Roi. LOMBARDY POPLAR. *Branches all ascending;* leaves much like those of the last but more finely toothed.—Sometimes persisting after cultivation.

MYRICÀCEAE SWEET GALE FAMILY

Shrubs; *leaves with fragrant waxy resin;* flowers without perianth, the staminate and pistillate flowers in different catkins; fruit a nutlet.

a. Plants of shores and shallow water . . . . 1. *Myrica.*
a. Plants of dry sand . . . . 2. *Comptonia.*

1. **Myrìca** SWEET GALE

M. Gàle L. *Leaves wedge-shaped at base and toothed toward the rounded tip;* flowers coming after the leaves, in *short cone-like catkins* (Fig. 60).—Wet places, south to Burnett, Lincoln, and Manitowoc Counties.

2. **Comptònia** Sweet-fern

C. peregrìna (L.) Coult. Leaves cut almost to the midrib at intervals of 1 cm. or less, fern-like, rather sticky; flowers coming before the leaves, the staminate in long cylindrical catkins, the *pistillate in globular bur-like heads* (Fig. 61).—In dry sand, south to Columbia and Green Lake (rarely to Rock) Counties.

JUGLANDÀCEAE Walnut Family

Trees; leaves pinnate; staminate flowers in catkins, with an irregular calyx; pistillate flowers solitary or in clusters, with a regular 3–5-lobed calyx; fruit a large nut, enclosed in a husk developed from the calyx.

a. Staminate catkins stout, not stalked; stamens 10–40 in each flower; pith of twigs with cross-partitions . . . . 1. *Juglans.*
a. Staminate catkins slender, several at the tip of a common stalk; stamens 3–10 in each flower; pith of twigs continuous . . . . 2. *Carya.*

1. **Jùglans** Walnut

Nuts 5–6 cm. long, the surface of the shell (beneath the husk) very rough.

1. **J. cinèrea** L. Butternut. Bark gray; leaf usually terminated by a single leaflet (Fig. 62), the petiole and lower surface of leaflets covered with dark brown *sticky hairs;* leaf-scar *with a pad of down* at its upper edge; nut oblong, the husk very sticky.—North to Burnett, Ashland, Lincoln, and Door Counties.

2. **J. nìgra** L. Black Walnut. *Bark dark brown;* leaf usually terminated by a pair of leaflets, the petiole and lower surface of leaflets downy but *not sticky;* leaf-scars *without a pad of down;* nut almost spherical, the husk not sticky.—North to Pierce, Winnebago, and Door Counties.

2. **Càrya** Hickory

Nuts 1.5–3 cm. long, the surface of the shell (beneath the husk) smooth.

1. **C. ovàta** (Mill.) K. Koch. Shell-bark Hickory. *Bark of trunk shaggy with long thick deciduous plates;* bud-scales becoming large and petal-like as the stem starts to elongate; leaflets 5–7, with a *fine tuft of hairs on each tooth;* nut sweet.—North to Pierce and Brown Counties.

2. **C. cordifórmis** (Wang.) K. Koch. Bitternut Hickory. Bark not shaggy; *buds yellow;* leaflets 5–11, the teeth without tufts of hairs (Fig. 63); nut bitter.—Rich woods, north to Burnett, Lincoln, and Door Counties.

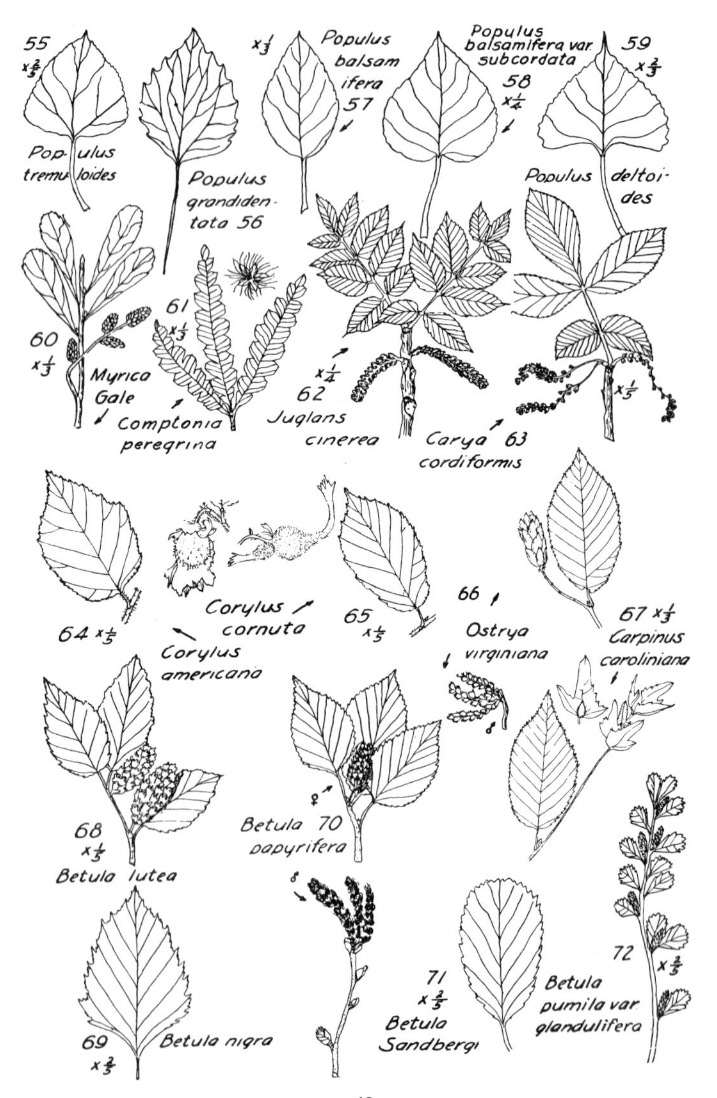
55
x 2/5
Populus tremuloides
Populus grandidentata 56
x 1/3
Populus balsamifera 57
Populus balsamifera var. subcordata
58
x 1/4
59
x 2/3
Populus deltoides
60
x 1/3
Myrica Gale
61
x 1/3
Comptonia peregrina
x 1/4
62
Juglans cinerea
Carya 63 cordiformis
x 1/5
64 x 1/5
Corylus cornuta
Corylus americana
65
x 1/5
66
Ostrya virginiana
67 x 1/3
Carpinus caroliniana
68
x 1/5
Betula lutea
Betula 70 papyrifera
69
x 2/5
Betula nigra
71
x 2/5
Betula Sandbergi
Betula pumila var. glandulifera
72
x 2/5

BETULÀCEAE BIRCH FAMILY

Trees or shrubs; staminate and pistillate flowers separate, at least the former in catkins; fruit a nut, often small.

a. Pistillate flowers solitary, or a few in a cluster . . 1. *Corylus.*
a. Pistillate flowers in catkins *b.*
  b. Each bract of the staminate catkin with but one flower, which lacks a calyx *c.*
    c. Staminate catkins usually in groups of 3 (Fig. 66); bud-scales with lengthwise ridges . 2. *Ostrya.*
    c. Staminate catkins solitary; bud-scales without ridges . . . . 3. *Carpinus.*
  b. Each bract of the staminate catkin with 3–6 flowers, each with a calyx *d.*
    d. Stamens 2; pistillate bracts 3-lobed . . . . 4. *Betula.*
    d. Stamens 4; pistillate bracts 5-lobed . . . . 5. *Alnus.*

Since floral characters are somewhat difficult to see in this group, and last year's fruit can frequently be found, a key is also given using fruit and habit.

a. Each nut with a somewhat leafy involucre *b.*
  b. Shrubs; nut 1 cm. or more long. . . . . . . 1. *Corylus.*
  b. Trees; nut 6 mm. or less long *c.*
    c. Bark furrowed and shredding, grayish-brown; involucre sac-like, enclosing the nut . . . . 2. *Ostrya.*
    c. Bark close, smooth, gray; involucre leafy, open, flat, coarsely toothed. . . . . . . 3. *Carpinus.*
a. Nut without involucre, in the axil of a small scaly bract *d.*
    d. Bracts papery, ascending . . . . 4. *Betula.*
    d. Bracts woody, at right angles to the rachis of the cone. . . . . 5. *Alnus.*

1. Córylus HAZEL

1. **C. americàna** Walt. HAZELNUT. *Twigs and petioles glandular-bristly;* involucre of 2 broad, open, leaf-like bracts, not bristly (Fig. 64).—Thickets and pastures.

2. **C. cornùta** Marsh. BEAKED HAZELNUT. *Twigs and petioles not bristly;* involucre enclosing the nut and prolonged into a beak, covered with bristly hairs (Fig. 65).—Common northward, coming south to Devil's Lake, and along the Lake Michigan shore to Milwaukee.

2. Óstrya IRONWOOD; HOP HORNBEAM

O. virginiàna (Mill.) K. Koch. Slender tree with very hard wood; leaves sharply toothed, long-pointed, not velvety, hairy on the veins; involucre bladdery, the *fruiting mass looking like that of hops* (Fig. 66).—Rich woods.

3. Carpìnus IRONWOOD; HORNBEAM

C. caroliniàna Walt. Resembling *Ostrya*, but with smooth bark covering wood which appears *ridged as if muscular;* fruiting bracts leaf-like and toothed (Fig. 67).—Damp woods and along streams.

4. **Bétula** Birch

Trees or shrubs; the trees with *bark which splits into fine sheets.*

a. Scales of the fruiting catkins persistent; leaves with impressed veins *b.*
  b. Leaf-blades obliquely heart-shaped at base, more or less tapering at tip . . . . 1. *B. lutea.*
  b. Leaf-blades at base tapering to the petiole, acute at tip . . . . 2. *B. nigra.*
a. Scales of the fruiting catkins soon falling; veins not impressed *c.*
  c. Trees; leaf-blades 6–10 cm. long . . . . 3. *B. papyrifera.*
  c. Shrubs; leaf-blades 2–6 cm. long *d.*
    d. Leaves oval to somewhat quadrangular; fruiting catkins 2–3 cm. long, with scales 4–5.5 mm. long; wing as wide as or wider than the nutlet . . . . 4. *B. Sandbergi.*
    d. Leaves oval; fruiting catkins 1–2.8 cm. long, with scales 3–3.5 mm. long; wing narrower than the nutlet . . . . 5. *B. pumila,* var. *glandulifera.*

1. **B. lùtea** Michx. f. Yellow Birch. *Bark yellowish or silvery, peeling in fine ragged fringes* (rarely close and dark); twigs flavored like wintergreen; leaf-blades slightly heart-shaped at base, with 5–9 pairs of veins, doubly serrate (Fig. 68).—Mostly northward, rare south of Devil's Lake and Sheboygan.

2. **B. nìgra** L. Red Birch; River Birch. *Bark reddish, peeling in coarse strips; leaf-blades with four almost straight sides,* the two upper the longer and doubly toothed (Fig. 69).—Mostly following rivers; up the Mississippi to Pierce County; up the Chippewa to Chippewa County; up the Wisconsin and its tributaries to Wood and Portage Counties.

3. **B. papyrífera** Marsh. White Birch. *Bark on mature trees white, peeling back in thin curled pieces;* leaf-blades with 6–9 pairs of veins, wedge-shaped or rounded at base (Fig. 70).—Common northward, confined to north-facing hills southwestward, and largely to bogs southeastward.—Var. **cordifòlia** (Regel) Fernald. Leaf-blades heart-shaped at base.—With the common form, but apparently absent from granitic areas.

4. **B. Sandbérgi** Britton. Shrub 4–8 m. high; bark dark brown, not peeling; plant much like the next, but larger throughout (Fig. 71).—A hybrid between the last and next and often more abundant in bogs than either parent.

5. **B. pùmila** L., var. **glandulífera** Regel. Bog Birch. Shrub 1–2 m. high; *bark dark brown, not peeling;* leaf-blades rounded at tip and wedge-shaped at base (Fig. 72).—Bogs, general except in southwestern Wisconsin.

5. **Álnus** ALDER

Shrubs or small trees; leaves about 1 dm. long, oval, toothed; fruiting catkins oval and hard.

1. **A. críspa** (Ait.) Pursh. GREEN ALDER. (Fig. 73) *Leaves sharply and rather regularly finely toothed*, somewhat sticky beneath when young; fruiting catkins on slender peduncles 5 mm. or more long. —Northern Wisconsin, south to Jackson County.—Var. **móllis** Fernald. DOWNY ALDER. Lower leaf-surfaces velvety.—From Polk and Oneida Counties northward.

2. **A. rugòsa** (Du Roi) Spreng. SPECKLED ALDER. (Fig. 74) *Leaves doubly toothed*, not sticky when young; fruiting catkins on short stout peduncles.—Wet places, common except southwestward.

FAGÀCEAE BEECH FAMILY

Trees, with alternate simple leaves; staminate flowers in catkins; pistillate flowers solitary, each with a scaly involucre.

a. Leaves with small sharp teeth . . . . 1. *Fagus.*
a. Leaves lobed or with wavy margins . . . . . . 2. *Quercus.*

1. **Fàgus** BEECH

F. grandifòlia Ehrh. Large trees with *smooth close ashy bark;* leaves about 1 dm. long, oblong-ovate, rounded at base; fruit a 3-cornered nut, enclosed in a husk-like involucre whose scales are somewhat fused with their long tips free.—Counties near Lake Michigan.

2. **Quércus** OAK

Large or small trees with rough bark, or smooth when young; leaves often 2 dm. long, sometimes deeply lobed; fruit an acorn, with a cup-like involucre of small scales enclosing its base.—The White Oak group may be recognized by pale, somewhat scaly bark, lack of bristles on the teeth of the leaves, 6–8 stamens per flower, and rather sweet nut.—The Red and the Black Oaks have dark furrowed bark, veins excurrent as bristles on the teeth of the leaves, 4–6 stamens per flower, and a bitter nut.

ULMÀCEAE ELM FAMILY

Trees or shrubs with leaves which are asymetrical at base. Fruit a samara or a nut.

a. Flowers in little clusters, coming before the leaves 1. *Ulmus.*
a. Flowers solitary in each leaf-axil, coming with the leaves. . . . . 2. *Celtis.*

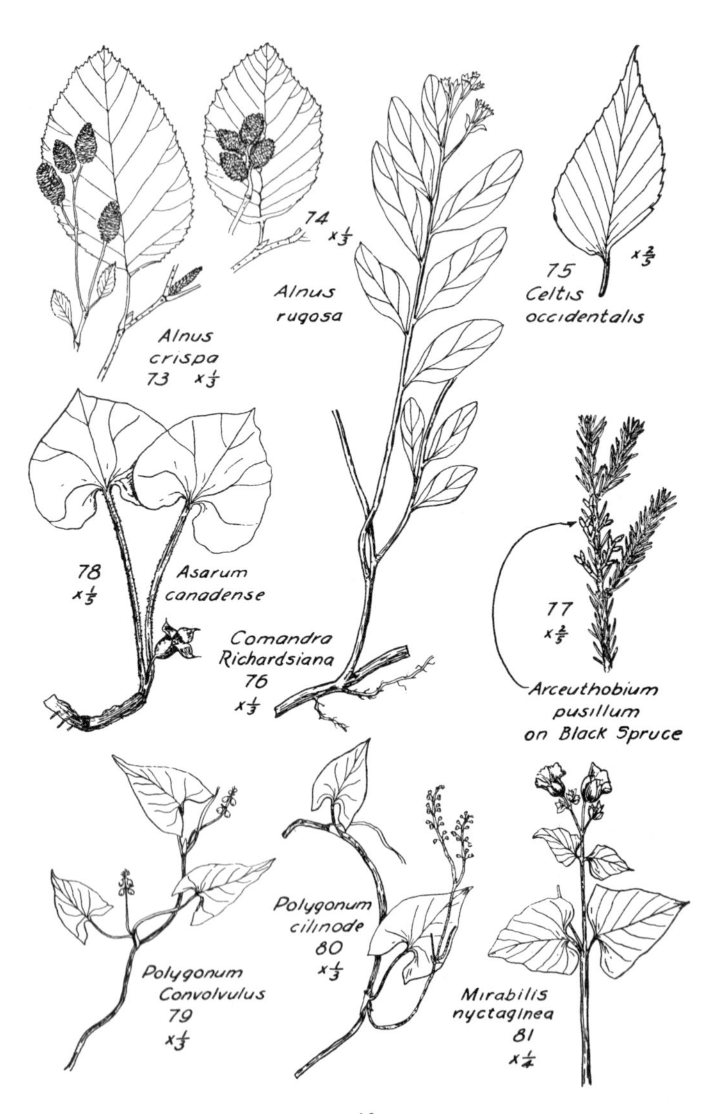
74
x 1/3
Alnus
rugosa
75
x 2/3
Celtis
occidentalis
Alnus
crispa
73 x 1/3
78
x 1/5
Asarum
canadense
Comandra
Richardsiana
76
x 1/3
77
x 2/5
Arceuthobium
pusillum
on Black Spruce
Polygonum
cilinode
80
x 1/3
Polygonum
Convolvulus
79
x 1/3
Mirabilis
nyctaginea
81
x 1/4

1. **Úlmus** Elm

Bark in long ridges and furrows; leaves unlobed, elliptic, doubly-toothed, with many strong, straight, parallel veins branching from the midrib, much like leaves of *Ostrya* and *Carpinus;* fruit small, with broad circular wing.

a. Flowers with hardly any pedicels; leaves very rough above; fruit without a fringe of hairs . . . . 1. *U. rubra.*
a. Flowers with slender pedicels; leaves smooth or slightly rough above; wing of fruit with a fringe of hairs *b.*
  b. Buds with few or no hairs; face of fruit without hairs . . . . 2. *U. americana.*
  b. Buds with fine hairs; face of fruit hairy . . . 3. *U. Thomasi.*

1. **U. rùbra** Muhl. Slippery Elm. *Inner bark mucilaginous when chewed,* fragrant in drying; *buds with copious red shaggy hairs.*—Rich soils, north to Burnett, Lincoln, and Marinette Counties.

2. **U. americàna** L. American Elm. Branches not ridged or mucilaginous; flowers in close bunches, on slender drooping pedicels.—Rich bottom lands or moist hillsides and woods.

3. **U. Thómasi** Sarg. Cork Elm. *Branches often with corky ridges;* flowers in racemes.—Heavy clay soil or rocky slopes, north to Forest and Marinette Counties.

2. **Céltis** Hackberry

C. occidentàlis L. Crown of tree frequently with many "witches' brooms"; *bark of trunk with corky wart-like outgrowths;* leaf-blade tapered to the petiole, the upper two-thirds of the margin toothed (Fig. 75); fruit cherry-like, reddish or yellowish when young, turning dark purple.—Bottom lands and lake shores, north to Polk and Marathon Counties. Leaves variable in shape and texture; several varieties have been described.

MORÀCEAE Mulberry Family

Mòrus Mulberry

Small trees; leaves undivided or deeply 3-lobed or pinnately several-lobed; staminate and pistillate flowers on different trees; each in catkins, the pistillate developing into a white, pink, or red aggregate fruit resembling a blackberry.

1. **M. álba** L. White Mulberry. *Leaves smooth above*, and with hairs only about the axils of the veins below; blades 6–18 cm. long.—Rarely planted.—Var. **tatárica** (L.) Ser. with blades of leaves only 4–8 cm. long. Sometimes escaping from cultivation.

2. **M. rùbra** L. Red Mulberry. *Leaves rough above*, hairy be-

low.—Bottom lands and bluffs in southwestern Wisconsin, up the Mississippi River to Pepin and up the Wisconsin River to Prairie du Sac.

URTICÀCEAE NETTLE FAMILY

Parietària PELLITORY

P. pensylvánica Muhl. Inconspicuous herbs with clusters of green flowers in the axils of nearly all the leaves.—Mostly about the bases of trees, north to St. Croix, Sauk, and Fond du Lac Counties.

SANTALÀCEAE SANDALWOOD FAMILY

1. Comándra BASTARD TOADFLAX

Stems erect from a buried rootstock; leaves alternate, pale smooth; fruit crowned by the 5 calyx-lobes.

C. Richardsiàna Fern. Parasitic on roots of other plants; flowers in dense flat-topped terminal clusters (Fig. 76); fruits dry, greenish. —Dry, sandy ground.

2. Geocaùlon NORTHERN COMANDRA

G. lívidum (Richards.) Fern. Leaves oval; flowers few on an axillary peduncle, only the central one developing the fleshy scarlet fruit.—Rare in bogs and in mossy woods, Door County.

LORANTHÀCEAE MISTLETOE FAMILY

Arceuthòbium pusíllum Peck. DWARF MISTLETOE. Tiny plant, *6–20 mm. tall,* seldom branched, brownish (Fig. 77); leaves scale-like; fruit a small berry, which violently expels its seeds at maturity. —Parasitic on black spruce in northern Wisconsin.

ARISTOLOCHIÀCEAE BIRTHWORT FAMILY

Ásarum canadénse L. WILD GINGER. Stem underground, horizontal, usually with a single scale-like leaf below; *foliage leaves 2, long-petioled, the blades kidney-shaped* (Fig. 78); flowers solitary, between the two leaves; calyx bell-shaped, purple-brown inside, the lobes short-pointed.—In hardwoods.—Var. **acuminàtum** Ashe. Calyx-lobes with long tapering whip-like tips.—Rich woods.

POLYGONÀCEAE BUCKWHEAT FAMILY

Herbs, with usually somewhat swollen nodes and *sheathing stipules.*

a. Sepals 6 . . . . 1. *Rumex.*
a. Sepals 4–5 . . . . 2. *Polygonum.*

1. **Rùmex** DOCK; SORREL

R. Acetosélla L. SHEEP SORREL. Plants 1–3 dm. high, from deep rootstocks; *leaf-blades usually arrow-shaped at base;* sepals yellow on the pistillate plant, red on the staminate.—Poor soils; naturalized from Europe.

The larger Docks, which may be recognized by their green sepals with midrib often grain-like, large leaves with blades several dm. long and not arrow-shaped at base, may be found in late spring, but species are not easily determined until fruits are mature.

2. **Polýgonum**

a. Climbing or trailing vines; sheaths small; flowers in panicled racemes *b.*
  b. Nodes naked . . . . 1. *P. Convolvulus.*
  b. Nodes fringed . . . . 2. *P. cilinode.*
a. Erect or aquatic plants; sheaths 1 cm. or more long; flowers in dense spikes. . . . . 3. *P. amphibium.*

1. **P. Convólvulus** L. BLACK BINDWEED. (Fig. 79) *Stem roughish;* sheath 2–3 mm. long; outer sepals narrowly winged.—Roadsides and cultivated ground; naturalized from Europe.

2. **P. cilinòde** Michx. (Fig. 80) Stem minutely downy, usually reddish; *sheath with a fringe of downward-pointing hairs at its base.* —Fields and cut-over land, south to Jackson and Sheboygan Counties.

3. **P. amphíbium** L., var. **stipulàceum** Coleman. AMPHIBIOUS SMARTWEED. Leaves lanceolate, short-petioled; flowers deep pink, in erect, compact, showy spikes. Plants aquatic, with floating leaves, or terrestrial with spreading green borders on the sheaths.

NYCTAGINÀCEAE FOUR-O'CLOCK FAMILY

Mirábilis nyctagínea (Michx.) MacM. (Fig. 81) Plant 0.3–1.5 m. high; stems repeatedly forked; leaf-blades heart-shaped, on short petioles; calyx pinkish.—Common, especially along railroad tracks.

CARYOPHYLLÀCEAE CHICKWEED AND PINK FAMILY

Herbs, with opposite (or whorled) entire leaves; flowers with 4–5 sepals, and petals equal to them in number or sometimes none; styles 2–5; fruit a pod, with *many seeds attached to a central knob or column.*

a. Sepals separate (CHICKWEED TRIBE) *b.*
  b. Petals entire, not deeply notched *c.*
    c. Leaves whorled . . . . 1. *Spergula.*
    c. Leaves opposite, or some in axillary bunches *d.*
      d. Sepals 4 . . . . 2. *Sagina.*
      d. Sepals 5 . . . . 3. *Arenaria.*

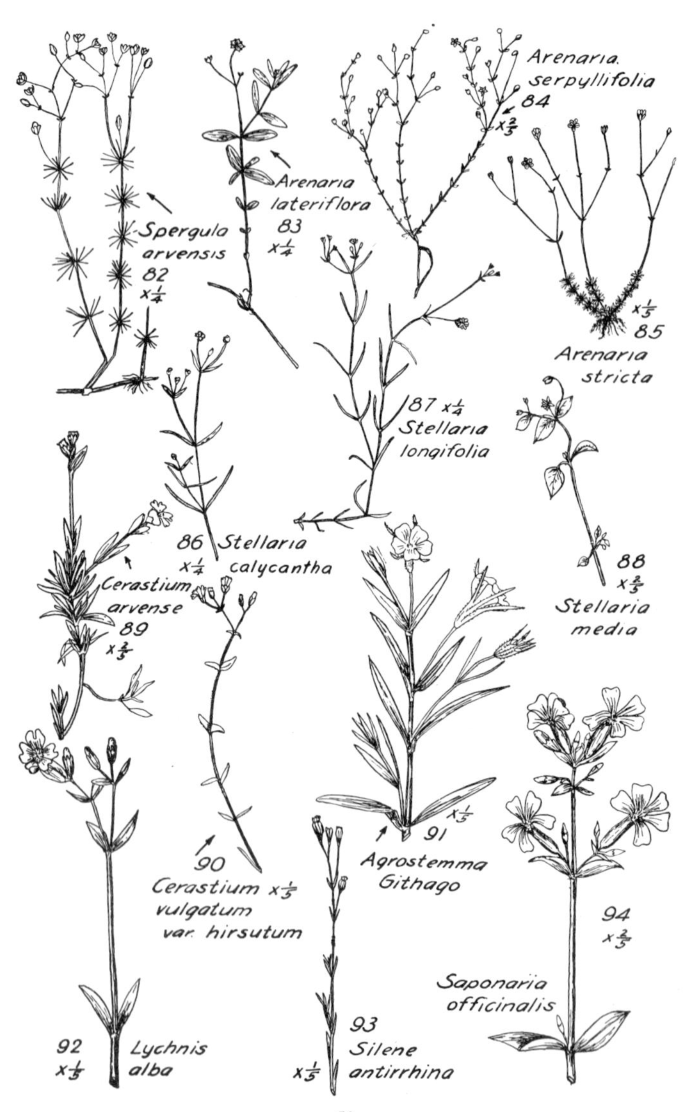
Spergula arvensis
82
x 1/4
Arenaria lateriflora
83
x 1/4
Arenaria serpyllifolia
84
x 2/5
x 1/5
85
Arenaria stricta
86 Stellaria calycantha
x 1/4
87 x 1/4
Stellaria longifolia
88
x 2/5
Stellaria media
Cerastium arvense
89
x 2/5
90
Cerastium vulgatum var. hirsutum
x 1/5
x 1/5
91
Agrostemma Githago
92
x 1/5
Lychnis alba
93
Silene antirrhina
x 1/5
94
x 2/5
Saponaria officinalis

b. Petals 2–cleft or notched at tip *e.*
  e. Styles 3 . . . . 4. *Stellaria.*
  e. Styles 4 or 5 *f.*
    f. Styles opposite sepals; capsule cylindrical 6. *Cerastium.*
    f. Styles alternate with sepals; capsule ovoid 5. *Myosoton.*
a. Sepals united into a tube (PINK TRIBE) *g.*
  g. Lobes of the calyx 2–3 cm. long. . . . . 7. *Agrostemma.*
  g. Lobes of the calyx shorter *h.*
    h. Calyx conspicuously 10–nerved *i.*
      i. Styles 5 . . . . 8. *Lychnis.*
      i. Styles 3 . . . . 9. *Silene.*
    h. Calyx obscurely nerved; styles 2 . . . . . . 10. *Saponaria.*

1. **Spérgula** CORN SPURREY

S. arvénsis L. (Fig. 82) Stems many, *radiating from the summit of a tap-root,* ascending or prostrate; leaves thread-like, *with stipules;* flowers white, in much-branched cymes.—A common weed in northern Wisconsin, occasional southward; naturalized from Europe.

2. **Sagìna** PEARLWORT

S. procúmbens L. *Matted, creeping;* leaves thread-like; petals shorter than the sepals; *styles alternate with the sepals.*—Damp places, Iron County, rare (sometimes found as a weed on golf greens).

3. **Arenària** SANDWORT

Low tufted herbs; leaves without petioles; *each style opposite a sepal;* pod short, splitting into as many sectors as there are styles.

a. Leaves flat *b.*
  b. Leaves 1–2 cm. long *c.*
    c. Leaves soft, blunt . . . . 1. *A. lateriflora.*
    c. Leaves stiff, acute . . . . 2. *A. macrophylla.*
  b. Leaves about 5 mm. long, sharp-pointed . . . 3. *A. serpyllifolia.*
a. Leaves thread-like *d.*
  d. Sepals shorter than the petals, longer than the capsule . . . . 4. *A. stricta.*
  d. Sepals longer than the petals, shorter than the capsule . . . . 5. *A. dawsonensis.*

1. **A. laterifl̀ora** L. (Fig. 83) Stems simple or little branched, from a long slender rootstock; flowers 2–4 to a peduncle, with *obtuse sepals.*—Common in shady woods.

2. **A. macrophýlla** Hook. Similar; *sepals acuminate.*—Rare, on cliffs and rocky ledges in the Gogebic Range.

3. **A. serpyllifòlia** L. (Fig. 84) Stems many, arising from a slender tap-root; flowers many, in compound cymes.—Wet places and gravelly hillsides; naturalized from Europe.

4. **A. strícta** Michx. (Fig. 85) Stems many from a slender rootstock, with a *persistent tuft of many leaves below;* inflorescence much branched, often more than half the height of the entire plant.

—Common and conspicuous on rocky hills and ledges in southern Wisconsin.

5. **A. dawsonénsis** Britton. Similar.—Cliffs along St. Croix River, St. Croix County.

4. **Stellària** CHICKWEED

Styles as in *Arenaria;* pods short.

a. Leaves ribbon-like or narrowly lanceolate, without petioles *b.*
  b. Sepals with curved, usually glabrous, sides, weakly nerved *c.*
    c. Leaves 3–5 times as long as wide; pedicels in axils of green bracts or reduced leaves . 1. *S. calycantha.*
    c. Leaves about 15 times as long as wide; pedicels in axils of dry yellowish bracts 2. *S. longifolia.*
  b. Sepals with straight, usually ciliate, sides, strongly 3-nerved . . . . 3. *S. graminea.*
a. Leaves oval, blades more than ½ as wide as long, at least the lower petioled. . . . . 4. *S. media.*

1. **S. calycántha** (Ledeb.) Bougard. (Fig. 86) *Stems without hairs,* much branched; flowers solitary or a few together; *petals minute or none.*—Northern Wisconsin, south to Marathon County; Dells of the Wisconsin River.

2. **S. longifòlia** Muhl. (Fig. 87) *Stems without hairs,* slender, branched; leaves thin, flat, acute; inflorescence much branched, with spreading pedicels; petals about equaling the sepals.—Open ground.

3. **S. gramínea** L. Leaves long-tapered, 5–10 times as long as wide; inflorescence often longer than leafy portion of plant; pedicels reflexed in fruit.—Damp open ground; naturalized from Europe.

4. **S. mèdia** (L.) Cyrill. COMMON CHICKWEED. (Fig. 88) Stems low, *hairy,* often reclining; leaves somewhat fleshy, the *blades 5–15 mm. long;* flowers few, in the axils of the upper leaves.—A common weed about buildings, etc.; naturalized from Europe.

5. **Myosòton** GIANT CHICKWEED

M. aquáticum (L.) Moench. Similar to *S. media* but much larger and coarser; *leaf-blades 1.5–7 cm. long.*—An occasional weed in moist places; adventive from Europe.

6. **Cerástium** MOUSE-EAR CHICKWEED

Styles opposite the sepals; *pod elongated, often curved,* opening at the summit by twice as many teeth as there were styles.

a. Leaves with axillary bunches of smaller leaves. . 1. *C. arvense.*
a. Leaves without axillary bunches *b.*
  b Petals equaled or exceeded by the sepals *c.*

c. Pedicels longer than the sepals at flowering time . . . . 2. *C. vulgatum.*
c. Pedicels shorter than the sepals at flowering time . . . . 3. *C. viscosum.*
b. Petals longer than the sepals . . . . 4. *C. nutans.*

1. **C. arvénse** L. (Fig. 89) Stems 1–2 dm. high, *perennial, densely tufted,* little branched, with short hairs; leaves stiff, ribbon-like or narrowly lanceolate.—Central Wisconsin; not common.

2. **C. vulgàtum** L. var. **hirsùtum** Fries. (Fig. 90) Plants perennial; inflorescence densely hairy; lower pedicels 4–14 mm. long.—A common weed, naturalized from Europe.

3. **C. viscòsum** L. Plants perennial; stems hairy, 1–2 dm. high; flowers in dense clusters.—Grassy places; naturalized from Europe.

4. **C. nùtans** Raf. Plants with rather woolly *sticky hairs,* 1.5–5 dm. high; fruit often nodding; lower pedicels 1.5–5 cm. long.—Moist places.

7. **Agrostémma** CORN COCKLE

A. Githàgo L. (Fig. 91) Plants stout, 3–5 dm. high; leaves narrowly lanceolate, 1-nerved, 5–10 cm. long, covered with close hairs; *calyx covered with ascending silky hairs;* corolla purplish-red; seeds poisonous.—Roadsides and grain fields; introduced from Europe.

8. **Lýchnis** CAMPION

Plants dioecious, 5–10 dm. high, minutely hairy; leaves ovate, about 1 dm. long, the upper without petioles, the lower sometimes petioled.

1. **L. álba** Mill. (Fig. 92) Flowers white or pink, *fragrant, opening in the evening;* calyx-teeth about 5 mm. long.—Fields and roadsides, adventive from Europe.—Resembles *Silene noctiflora,* from which it differs in having 5 styles and shorter hairs on the stem.

2. **L. dioìca** L. Flowers red, rarely white, *not fragrant, opening during the day;* calyx-teeth about 3 mm. long.—Rare; adventive from Eurasia.

9. **Silène**

Much like *Lychnis,* but with 3 (rarely 4) styles.

a. Corolla pink . . . . 1. *S. antirrhina.*
a. Corolla white *b.*
b. Leaves opposite *c.*
c. Stems hairy and sticky . . . . 2. *S. noctiflora.*
c. Stems without hairs *d.*
d. Uppermost bracts not ciliate . . . . . . 4. *S. Cucubalus.*
d. Uppermost bracts minutely ciliate . . . 5. *S. Cserei.*
b. Leaves in whorls of 4 . . . . 3. *S. stellata.*

1. **S. antirrhìna** L. SLEEPY CATCHFLY. (Fig. 93) Stems usually with a *sticky ring on each internode;* leaves narrow; flowers many in a cyme; calyx-tube 4–6 mm. long.—Dry places, north to Lincoln and Douglas Counties.

2. **S. noctiflòra** L. NIGHT-FLOWERING CATCHFLY. Leaves broader; flowers few, *fragrant, opening in the evening;* calyx-tube 1.5–3 cm. long, cylindrical.—An occasional weed, adventive from Europe. —See *Lychnis alba.*

3. **S. stellàta** (L.) Ait. f. Stems *swollen at the nodes;* leaves long-pointed; flowers many in a cyme; calyx-tube 1–1.5 cm. long, bell-shaped.—Woods, north to Dane and Milwaukee Counties, and in the west to Pierce County.

4. **S. Cucùbalus** Wibel. BLADDER CAMPION. Leaves ovate-lanceolate; *calyx inflated and bladdery,* widest at the summit.—An occasional weed, naturalized from Europe.

5. **S. Csèrei** Baumg. Calyx firmer and *narrowed at the summit.* —Mostly along railroads, naturalized from Europe.

10. **Saponària**

Primary leaves opposite, often with many secondary leaves in their axils; flowers pink; juice mucilaginous, making a lather with water.

1. **S. officinàlis** L. BOUNCING BET; SOAPWORT. (Fig. 94) Leaves oval-lanceolate, 3-nerved; *flowers in 1–several close clusters.*—Roadsides, etc.; introduced from Europe as a garden flower.

2. **S. Vaccària** L. COW-HERB. Leaves broadest near the base, with midrib and sometimes other veins conspicuous; *flowers in open cymes.*—Railroad ballast, etc.; adventive from Europe.

PORTULACÀCEAE PURSLANE FAMILY

Small herbs, with rather fleshy entire leaves; petals 5; sepals 2; stamens 5 to many; fruit a pod, of 3 carpels.

a. Leaves flat, lanceolate; plant from a tuber . . . 1. *Claytonia.*
a. Leaves thread-like; plant from a rootstock . . . 2. *Talinum.*

1. **Claytònia** SPRING BEAUTY

Stems several from a deep-seated globose tuber; leaves usually 2 to each stem, opposite; flowers several, rose-colored, each long-stalked from a central axis.

1. **C. virgínica** L. Leaves linear-lanceolate or ribbon-like, 3–16 cm. long (Fig. 96).—Rich woods, north to Barron and Kewaunee Counties.

2. **C. caroliniàna** Michx. Leaves oval to lanceolate, 2.5–5 cm. long (Fig. 97).—Local in northern Wisconsin.

2. Talìnum

T. rugospérmum Holzinger. (Fig. 98) *Leaves short, much exceeded by the peduncles;* peduncles branched near the summit; flowers light pink, opening but once, between 3:30 and 4 P.M., and closing at 6 P.M., when the petals shrivel; stamens 12–25, their filaments deeper pink than the petals.—Dry sand plains and sandstone ledges, southern Wisconsin, north to St. Croix Falls in the Mississippi Valley, and to Adams County in the Wisconsin Valley.

NYMPHAEÀCEAE WATER LILY FAMILY

Aquatic perennials, with horizontal rootstocks; leaves floating or erect; flowers solitary; sepals 4–6; petals and stamens numerous.

a. Flowers yellow . . . . 1. *Nuphar*.
a. Flowers white or pinkish . . . . 2. *Nymphaea*.

1. Nùphar YELLOW POND LILY; SPATTERDOCK

Rootstock thick and fleshy; leaf-blade rounded, the petiole attached at the base of a deep sinus; *sepals yellow*, marked with green or red, spoon-shaped; petals shorter than the stamens, thick and fleshy; style none; stigma plate-like, marked with conspicuous rays.

a. Anthers at least equaling the filaments *b*.
  b. Lobes of leaf spreading at an angle of 45–80 degrees . . . . 1. *N. advena*.
  b. Lobes overlapping or nearly so . . . . 2. *N. variegatum*.
a. Anthers shorter than the filaments *c*.
  c. Flower about 3 cm. broad . . . . 3. *N. rubrodiscum*.
  c. Flower 2 cm. or less broad . . . . 4. *N. microphyllum*.

1. **N. ádvena** Ait. Leaves erect, petioles oval in cross-section; sepals and fruits rarely marked with red.—Rare in southeastern Wisconsin, and grading into the next.

2. **N. variegàtum** Engelm. (Fig. 99) Leaves mostly floating, 17–28 × 11–22 cm., with petioles flattened on upper side; sepals and fruits marked with red; flowers about 4.5 cm. broad; stigma rays usually 12–14.—Widespread in quiet water.

3. **N. rubrodíscum** Morong. Leaf-blades 7.5–20 × 5.5–14.5 cm., the sinus about $\frac{1}{2}$ as long as the midrib, narrow or closed; stigma rays 8–13, usually 10, 11, or 12; young fruit with a ring of decayed stamens.—In the Lake Superior region.

4. **N. microphýllum** (Pers.) Fernald. Very slender; leaf-blades 3.5–10 × 3.5–7.5 cm., the sinus $\frac{2}{3}$ or more the length of the midrib;

stigma rays 6–10; young fruit without a ring of decaying stamens. —Along our northern borders.

2. Nymphaèa WATER LILY

Rootstock a few cm. thick; leaf-blades round, the petiole attached almost at the center at the base of a deep notch; petals white or pinkish, the outer longer than the sepals, the inner passing gradually into stamens.

1. **N. odoràta** Ait. Sepals and lower surface of leaves often purple; petiole not streaked with purple; flowers fragrant, seldom more than 12 cm. broad.—Throughout the state in quiet shallow water.

2. **N. tuberòsa** Paine. Sepals and leaves not purple; petiole with purple streaks; flowers not fragrant, 12 cm. or more wide.—Throughout the state in quiet shallow water. Perhaps not distinct from *N. odorata.*

RANUNCULÀCEAE BUTTERCUP FAMILY

Mostly herbs; sepals 5–15, often white or colored like petals; petals 0–15; stamens usually many.

a. Leaves simple or once compound *b.*
- *b.* Herbs; not climbing or trailing *c.*
  - *c.* Petals present *d.*
    - *d.* Leaves undivided, or, if compound, with leaflets longer than broad . . . . . 1. *Ranunculus.*
    - *d.* Leaves with 3 leaflets, each as broad as long 9. *Coptis.*
  - *c.* Petals absent; sepals usually petal-like (in *Hepatica* 3 green bracts beneath the petal-like sepals simulate sepals) *e.*
    - *e.* Plants leafy-stemmed *f.*
      - *f.* Flowers yellow . . . . 8. *Caltha.*
      - *f.* Flowers white or greenish *g.*
        - *g.* Lobes of leaves or leaflets acute *h.*
          - *h.* Sepals 5–8, usually silky or downy beneath . . . . . 5. *Anemone.*
          - *h.* Sepals 3, soon falling . . . . 13. *Hydrastis.*
        - *g.* Lobes of leaflets rounded . . . 3. *Anemonella.*
    - *e.* Leaves all at the base of the stem *i.*
      - *i.* Leaves simple with broad 3 lobes . 4. *Hepatica.*
      - *i.* Leaves compound or finely divided into many segments . . . . . 5. *Anemone.*
- *b.* Climbing or trailing vines . . . . 6. *Clematis.*

a. Leaves twice or more compound *j.*
- *j.* Petals large and spurred *k.*
  - *k.* All petals spurred; flowers red and yellow . 10. *Aquilegia.*
  - *k.* One petal spurred; flowers blue or white. . 11. *Delphinium.*
- *j.* Petals when present inconspicuous; sepals often petal-like, but not spurred *l.*
  - *l.* Flowers many in a raceme or panicle *m.*
    - *m.* Leaflets sharply toothed . . . . 12. *Actaea.*
    - *m.* Leaflets bluntly toothed or lobed . . . 2. *Thalictrum.*
  - *l.* Flowers solitary or a few together *n.*
    - *n.* Ultimate leaf-divisions ribbon-like *o.*

o. Plants aquatic. . . . . 1. *Ranunculus.*
o. Plants terrestrial. . . . . 5. *Anemone.*
n. Ultimate leaf-divisions not ribbon-like *p*.
p. Stem with a whorl of simple leaves from the node that gives rise to the flower-stalks. . . . . 3. *Anemonella.*
p. Flowers subtended by compound leaves which are not usually whorled *q*.
q. Leaves with 3 blunt tips . . . . . 7. *Isopyrum.*
q. Leaves with serrate points . . . . 5. *Anemone.*

1. **Ranùnculus** Crowfoot; Buttercup

Leaves mostly palmately lobed or divided; fruit a small nutlet, many making up a head.

a. Plant aquatic; leaves finely dissected *b*.
b. Petals white *c*.
c. Leaves stiff, not collapsing when taken from the water . . . . 1. *R. longirostris.*
c. Leaves soft, collapsing when taken from the water . . . . 2. *R. trichophyllus.*
b. Petals yellow *d*.
d. Petals 6–17 mm. long . . . . 4. *R. flabellaris.*
d. Petals 3.5–5 mm. long. . . . . 5. *R. Gmelini.*
a. Plant terrestrial, often in wet places *e*.
e. Blades of most or all the basal leaves divided less than halfway to the base *f*.
f. Plants hairy . . . . 6. *R. rhomboideus.*
f. Plants not hairy; leaves somewhat shining *g*.
g. Plants with runners at base; flowering stems almost leafless . . . . 3. *R. Cymbalaria.*
g. Plants without runners at base; flowering stems with 3–5 parted leaves . . . . 8. *R. abortivus.*
e. Blades of the basal leaves divided more than halfway to the base, or if lowest leaves are not so deeply divided; plants hairy *h*.
h. Leaves compound, at least the terminal division stalked *i*.
i. Petals bright yellow, much exceeding the sepals *j*.
j. Style 1 mm. or more long, slender, tapering *k*.
k. Lateral leaflets hardly stalked. . . 10. *R. fascicularis.*
k. Lateral leaflets with stalks about 5 mm. long. . . . . 11. *R. septentrionalis.*
j. Style short, stout, recurved *l*.
l. Stems prostrate, rooting at the nodes . . . . 12. *R. repens.*
l. Stems erect . . . . 14. *R. acris.*
i. Petals pale yellow, hardly exceeding the sepals; plant hairy . . . . 13. *R. pensylvanicus.*
h. Leaves simple, usually deeply cleft, the divisions not stalked *m*.
m. Receptacle cylindrical; head of pistils higher than broad . . . . 7. *R. sceleratus.*
m. Receptacle globose; head of pistils about as broad as high *n*.
n. Styles hooked . . . . 9. *R. recurvatus.*
n. Styles straight or curved, not hooked *o*.
o. Stems erect . . . . 14. *R. acris.*
o. Stems prostrate (see *d* above)

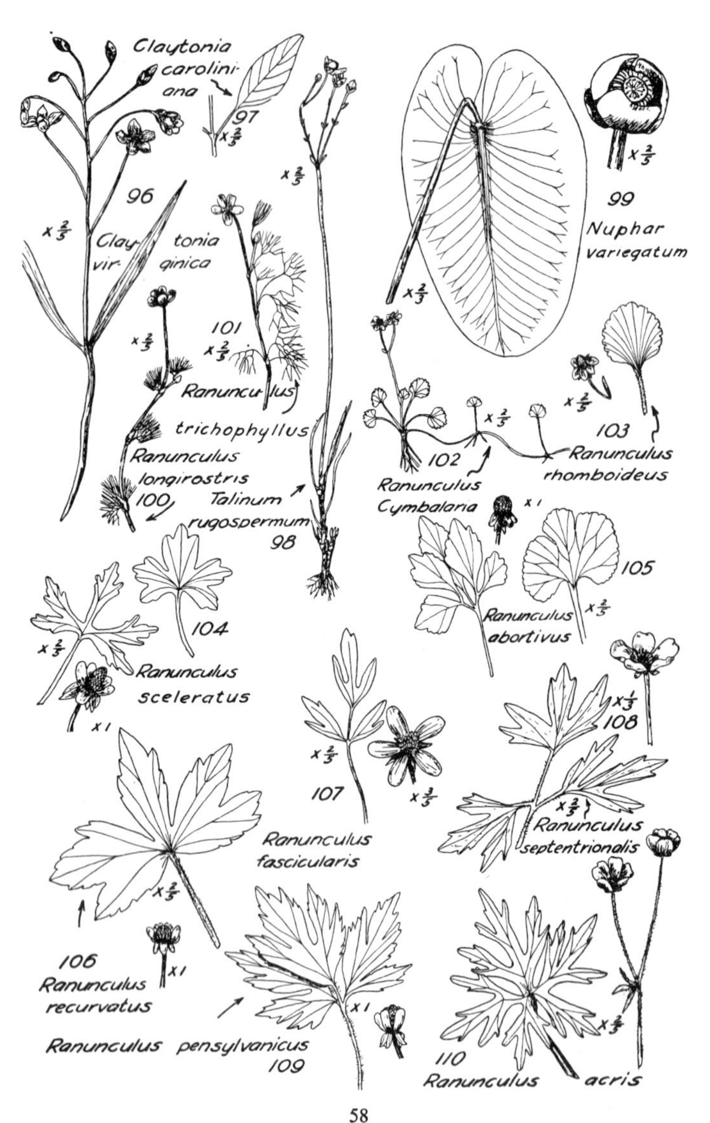
Claytonia caroliniana
97
x 2/5
96
x 2/5
Claytonia virginica
x 2/5
99
Nuphar variegatum
x 2/3
x 2/5
101
x 2/5
Ranunculus trichophyllus
Ranunculus longirostris
100
Talinum rugospermum
98
x 2/5
102
Ranunculus Cymbalaria
x 1
x 2/5
103
Ranunculus rhomboideus
104
x 2/5
Ranunculus sceleratus
x 1
105
x 2/5
Ranunculus abortivus
x 2/5
107
x 3/5
Ranunculus fascicularis
x 1/3
108
x 2/5
Ranunculus septentrionalis
x 2/5
106
Ranunculus recurvatus
x 1
x 1
Ranunculus pensylvanicus
109
110
Ranunculus acris
x 2/5

1. **R. longiróstris** Godron. STIFF WATER CROWFOOT. (Fig. 100) Leaves without petioles, with broad stipules; blades repeatedly forked, *the ultimate divisions thread-like*, peduncles 1-flowered, opposite the leaves, and the only part emerging from the water, raising the flower a cm. or more above the surface.—In quiet shallow water, from Oshkosh southward.

2. **R. trichophýllus** Chaix. WHITE WATER CROWFOOT. (Fig. 101) Similar to No. 1; leaves mostly petioled.—Common in quiet shallow water.

3. **R. Cymbalària** Pursh. SEA-SIDE CROWFOOT. (Fig. 102) Plants 4–22 cm. high; leaves somewhat fleshy, at the base of the flowering stem, long-petioled, with small roundish coarsely toothed blades; petals yellow.—Rare; southeastward and in Douglas County.

4. **R. flabellàris** Raf. YELLOW WATER CROWFOOT. Leaves petioled, dissected, the ultimate divisions mostly flattened; flowers few, mostly terminal.—Shallow water.—Occasionally grows out of water or is left on the mud of drying ponds, when it becomes forma **ripàrius** Fernald, with firmer leaves, with less cut blades and hairy petioles.

5. **R. Gmélini** DC., var. **Hookeri** (D. Don) Benson. Similar to the last but smaller throughout.—Rare, from Lake Superior to Door Co.—Forma **Púrshii** (Richards.) Fassett is a submersed form with the leaves cut into thread-like divisions.

6. **R. rhomboìdeus** Goldie. DWARF BUTTERCUP. (Fig. 103) Plant 1–2 dm. high; *lowest leaves rounded;* upper stem-leaves scarcely petioled, 3–5-parted, the divisions ribbon-like; *petals large*, deep yellow.—Thinly wooded uplands, common from Pierce and Portage Counties southward.

7. **R. sceleràtus** L. CURSED CROWFOOT. (Fig. 104) Plants 1.5–4 dm. high; lowest leaves 3-lobed, rounded; upper leaves 3-parted, the divisions wedge-shaped and usually about 3-lobed; *petals scarcely longer than the calyx.*—Common in wet land from Columbia and Brown Counties eastward.

8. **R. abortìvus** L. SMALL-FLOWERED CROWFOOT. (Fig. 105) Leaf-blades rounded, sometimes deeply palmately cleft, shining, *slightly fleshy; petals pale yellow, shorter than the downwardly bent sepals.*—Everywhere, from dry hillsides to low moist ground.—Var. **acrolàsius** Fernald. Stems with fine hairs.—Mostly northward.

9. **R. recurvàtus** Poir. HOOKED CROWFOOT. (Fig. 106) Plant 3–6 dm. high; stems with stiff spreading hairs; lowest leaves 3-lobed or rarely 3-parted, the divisions elliptic or wedge-shaped; petals pale, shorter than the downwardly bent sepals.—Occasional in woods.

10. **R. fasciculàris** Muhl. EARLY CROWFOOT. (Fig. 107) Plants

1–2.5 dm. high; *roots clustered,* of thickened fibers; *leaflets with ovate or linear divisions,* which are rounded at tip; head of pistils globose; style long and slender, straight or curved.—Common on dry hillsides, north to Dunn and Waupaca Counties.

11. **R. septentrionàlis** Poir. SWAMP BUTTERCUP. (Fig. 108) Stem 3–8 dm. long, sometimes trailing; *leaflets with lanceolate acute divisions;* style stout.—Open ground or wet woods.

12. **R. rèpens** L. CREEPING BUTTERCUP. Leaves 3–parted, the leaflets often white-spotted; flowers about 2 cm. broad; sepals not reflexed; whole plant sometimes hairy.—Damp places, eastern counties; perhaps introduced from Europe.

13. **R. pensylvánicus** L. f. BRISTLY CROWFOOT. (Fig. 109) Plants 4–6 dm. high; stem bristly with many stout spreading hairs; flowers many, axillary and terminal; *pistils in a cylindrical head.*—Common in wet land.

14. **R. ácris** L. BUTTERCUP. (Fig. 110) Plants 6–9 dm. high; stems with fine spreading hairs; leaves deeply cut into 3 divisions, these further cut into deep lobes; inflorescence branched; flowers bright yellow, conspicuous.—Roadsides and pastures, mostly northward and eastward; naturalized from Europe.

2. **Thalíctrum** MEADOW RUE

Leaves 3–parted, the divisions again 3–parted; staminate and pistillate flowers on different plants; sepals petal-like, soon dropping; petals none; *stamens or pistils making up the conspicuous part of the flower.*

a. Plants without rootstocks *b.*
  b. Leaves with petioles . . . . 1. *T. dioicum.*
  b. Leaves without petioles, i.e., the 3 divisions arising close to the stem *c.*
    c. Leaflets with fine hairs beneath . . . . . . 2. *T. dasycarpum.*
    c. Leaflets with waxy glands beneath . . . . 3. *T. revolutum.*
a. Plants with stout rootstocks (rare species of northwestern Wisconsin) *d.*
  d. Stigma 1.5–2 mm. long; anthers with a pointed tip 0.1 mm. long. . . . . 4. *T. venulosum.*
  d. Stigma 2.5–4 mm. long; anthers with a pointed tip 0.4 mm. long. . . . . 5. *T. confine.*

1. **T. dioìcum** L. EARLY MEADOW RUE. Plant 3–6 dm. high, *smooth and pale;* leaflets drooping, *the divisions rounded, 3–7-lobed* (Fig. 111).—Rich woods.

2. **T. dasycárpum** Fisch. & Lall. Plant 6–12 dm. high, usually purplish; *divisions of leaflets oblong, mostly 3-toothed* (Fig. 112). —Wet meadows or open ground.

3. **T. revolùtum** DC. Similar; leaflets thicker, *heavy-scented.*—Not common, mostly southeastward and northwestward.—Oc-

casional plants of southwestern Wisconsin, with perfectly glabrous leaflets, are difficult to place.

4. **T. venulòsum** Trelease. Plants tall and stout; lower leaves short-petioled, the upper sessile.—Along a railroad at Hayward.

5. **T. confìne** Fernald. Similar but larger throughout.—Wisconsin Point, Superior.

3. **Anemonélla** RUE ANEMONE

A. thalictroìdes (L.) Spach. (Fig. 113) Plants very slender and delicate, 1–3 dm. high, from thickened tuberous roots; leaves 3-parted, the leaflets sometimes again 3-parted; flowers several in an umbel, a whorl of leaves sometimes arising with the pedicels; sepals 1.2 cm. long, white or pinkish. Forma **Favillìana** Bergseng, has many sepals.—Open woods, brushy pastures, and borders of cultivated fields. Southward and westward.

4. **Hepática**

Plants covered with spreading white hairs; blades of leaves heart-shaped at base, persisting throughout the winter, the new ones coming after the flowers.

1. **H. americàna** (DC.) Ker. (Fig. 114) Lobes of leaves, and bracts of the involucre, rounded or blunt at tip; flowers bluish, white, or rose.—Woods.

2. **H. acutíloba** DC. (Fig. 115) Similar; lobes of leaves and bracts pointed.—Woods.

5. **Anemòne**

Plants with one or more leaves at the base of the stem, and a whorl of leaves (the involucre) at the base of the peduncle or peduncles.

a. Leaf-segments ribbon-like, not toothed	1. *A. patens*, var. *Wolfgangiana*.
a. Leaf-segments toothed *b*.	
b. Sepals 10–20	2. *A. caroliniana*.
b. Sepals 4–7 *c*.	
c. Sepals hairy on the back *d*.	
d. Involucral leaves petioled *e*.	
e. All the peduncles naked above the involucre	3. *A. cylindrica*.
e. All but the first peduncle with secondary involucral leaves halfway to the flower *f*.	
f. Anthers 0.7–1.2 mm. long	4. *A. riparia*.
f. Anthers 1.2–1.6 mm. long	5. *A. virginiana*.
d. Involucral leaves not petioled	6. *A. canadensis*.
c. Sepals not hairy	7. *A. quinquefolia*.

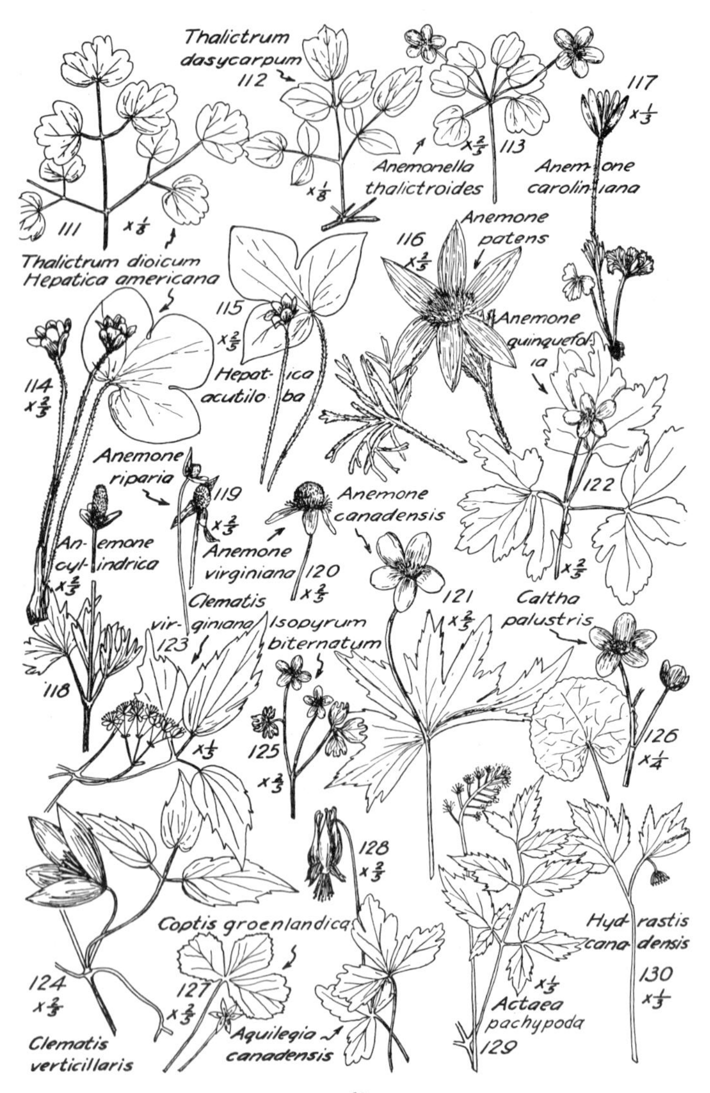

Thalictrum
dasycarpum
112
x 1/8
111
x 1/8
Thalictrum dioicum
Hepatica americana
113
x 2/5
Anemonella
thalictroides
117
x 1/3
Anemone
caroliniana
Anemone
patens
116
x 2/5
115
x 2/5
Hepatica
acutiloba
114
x 2/3
Anemone
quinquefolia
122
x 2/5
Anemone
riparia
119
x 2/3
Anemone
cylindrica
x 2/3
Anemone
virginiana
120
x 2/5
Anemone
canadensis
121
x 2/5
Caltha
palustris
Clematis
virginiana
123
Isopyrum
biternatum
118
x 1/5
125
x 2/3
126
x 1/4
128
x 2/3
Coptis groenlandica
Hydrastis
canadensis
130
x 1/3
124
x 2/3
127
x 2/3
x 1/3
Actaea
pachypoda
129
Clematis
verticillaris
Aquilegia
canadensis

1. **A. pàtens** L., var. **Wolfgangiàna** (Bess.) Koch. PASQUE FLOWER. *Plants covered with long silky hairs;* stems from a woody base; sepals 1.5–3.5 cm. long, purplish or blue to white (Fig. 116).—Dry hillsides, mostly southward, but north to Douglas County in the west.

2. **A. caroliniàna** Walt. (Fig. 117) Plants 7–15 cm. high, *from an ovoid corm;* leaves 3–parted, the leaflets often themselves cleft; involucre 3–parted; sepals about 2 cm. long, *ribbon-like*, purple or whitish.—Rare, on prairies and sand terraces in western Wisconsin.

3. **A. cylíndrica** Gray. THIMBLEWEED. Plants tall, slender, hairy; *pistils densely woolly, so that only the tips of the stigmas are visible;* fruits woolly achenes, in a dense *cylindrical head* (Fig. 118).— Dry hillsides and woodlands.

4. **A. ripària** Fernald. Similar; heads broader, the styles ascending (Fig. 119).—South to Buffalo and Oconto Counties.

5. **A. virginiàna** L. Similar; *pistils less woolly, so that the whole stigmas are plainly visible; heads ovoid*, with spreading styles (Fig. 120).—Woodlands.

6. **A. canadénsis** L. Sepals white, oval, 1.2–1.8 cm. long (Fig. 121).—Thickets, meadows, and roadside ditches.

7. **A. quinquefòlia** L., var. **intèrior** Fernald. WOOD ANEMONE. (Fig. 122) *Plants slender and delicate*, 1–1.5 dm. high; leaves 3–parted, the divisions sometimes deeply cleft; flower solitary, white within; the outer surface of the sepals tinged with red.—Common in woods and brushy pastures.

6. **Clématis** VIRGIN'S BOWER

Stems a little woody; leaves 3–foliolate, the leaflets palmately veined; fruits with feathery tails.

1. **C. virginiàna** L. (Fig. 123) *Flowers in racemes;* sepals 5–8 mm. long, *whitish;* leaflets coarsely toothed.—Shady places.

2. **C. verticillàris** DC. (Fig. 124) *Flowers solitary;* sepals about 4 cm. long, *pinkish-purple;* leaflets slightly or not at all toothed.—Cool rocky woods, not common.

7. **Isopỳrum** FALSE RUE ANEMONE

I. biternàtum (Raf.) T. & G. (Fig. 125) Stems several, from tufted irregularly thickened roots; leaves 3–divided, the leaflets themselves again 3–divided, the ultimate divisions deeply 3–lobed; sepals 5, white.—Moist woods.

8. **Cáltha** MARSH MARIGOLD; COWSLIP

C. palústris L. Plants usually growing in the water or mud; roots thickened; leaf-blades kidney-shaped or round with a deep sinus (Fig. 126); flowers several, bright yellow.—Common in wet places.

9. **Cóptis** GOLDTHREAD

C. groenlándica (Oeder) Fern. Rootstock slender, *yellow;* leaves all borne near the ground; petioles long; blades 3–foliolate, *the leaflets shining, wedge-shaped at base, slightly 3–lobed,* toothed (Fig. 127); sepals white.—In woods northward, southward in tamarack bogs.

10. **Aquilègia** COLUMBINE

A. canadénsis L. (Fig. 128) Stems from a tap-root; leaves chiefly at the base of the stem, 3–divided, the leaflets 3–parted, ultimate divisions 3–lobed, the lobes somewhat cut; upper leaves with branches in their axils; flowers nodding; *petals scarlet, yellow within, each with a hollow straight or curved spur which is enlarged and nectar-containing at its end.*—Rocky bluffs, and in sand.

11. **Delphínium** LARKSPUR

Delphínium viréscens Nutt. PRAIRIE LARKSPUR. Flowers white or bluish; spur once-and-a-half to twice the length of the upper sepal; final lobes of leaves narrowly linear; stems to 1.5 m. high. —Native western perennial; prairies, barrens, and dry, open woods, Jackson and La Crosse Counties northwestward.

12. **Actaèa** BANEBERRY

Stems 3–8 dm. high, from stout rootstocks; leaves pinnately divided, the leaflets themselves pinnately divided, the ultimate divisions sharply and coarsely toothed or deeply cut; flowers small, in a raceme.

1. **A. rùbra** (Ait.) Willd. RED BANEBERRY. Raceme about as broad as long; petals merely bluntly pointed; berries (which come in summer) red or rarely white, *on slender pedicels.*—Rich woods.

2. **A. pachýpoda** Ell. WHITE BANEBERRY. (Fig. 129) Raceme much longer than broad; petals tipped by a brown anther-like body; berries (which come in summer) white or rarely pink, *on thick pedicels.*—Rich woods.

13. **Hydrástis** GOLDEN SEAL

H. canadénsis L. (Fig. 130) *Rootstock yellow;* stems 1.5–4 dm. high, bearing two 5–cleft leaves near the summit; flower solitary, greenish-white.—Rich woods in areas of limestone, now rather rare.

MENISPERMÀCEAE Moonseed Family

Menispérmum canadénse L. Moonseed. *Vine;* dioecious; leaf-blades 0.5–1.5 dm. broad, broadly heart-shaped at base, *3–7-angled;* flowers in dense panicles.—Thickets and river-bottoms, north to Pierce, Marathon, and Manitowoc Counties.

BERBERIDÀCEAE Barberry Family

Sepals in 2 rows (except in *Jeffersonia*); stamens as many as the petals and opposite them (except in *Podophyllum*); anthers opening by valves or lids; style short or none; fruit a pod or berry.

a. Herbs *b.*
  b. Flowers solitary, white *c.*
    c. Leaves deeply palmately cleft (Fig. 131) . . 1. *Podophyllum.*
    c. Leaves divided into 2 half-ovate leaflets (Fig. 132) . . . . 2. *Jeffersonia.*
  b. Flowers in a raceme, green. . . . . 3. *Caulophyllum.*
a. Shrubs . . . . 4. *Berberis.*

1. Podophýllum May Apple; Mandrake

P. peltàtum L. Stems solitary, unbranched, from a creeping rootstock; *leaves 2, 5–9-parted,* the divisions 5–13 cm. long; flower nodding, white, *borne between the 2 leaves* (Fig. 131); stamens many.—Common in rich woods and pastures, north to Wood and Oconto Counties.

2. Jeffersònia Twinleaf

J. diphýlla (L.) Pers. Leaves (Fig. 132) and peduncle all from the ground level; flowers white, 2.5 cm. broad; sepals falling when buds open.—Southern Wisconsin, rare in rich woods.

3. Caulophýllum Blue Cohosh; Papoose Root

C. thalictroìdes (L.) Michx. Plants 3–7.5 dm. high, from matted rootstocks; stems simple below, apparently 3–4-branched above but in reality bearing a single palmately compound leaf without a petiole, the leaflets stalked and themselves twice compound (Fig. 133); inflorescence a raceme, with a leaf at its base.—Rich woods.

4. Bérberis Barberry

Shrubs with yellow wood; branches armed with thorns (which are morphologically leaves); flowers yellow; stamens with their anthers sunk in pockets in the petals, springing toward the pistil when disturbed.

1. **B. vulgàris** L. Common Barberry. Leaves elliptic, on a short jointed petiole, *bristle-toothed along the margins* (Fig. 134); flowers

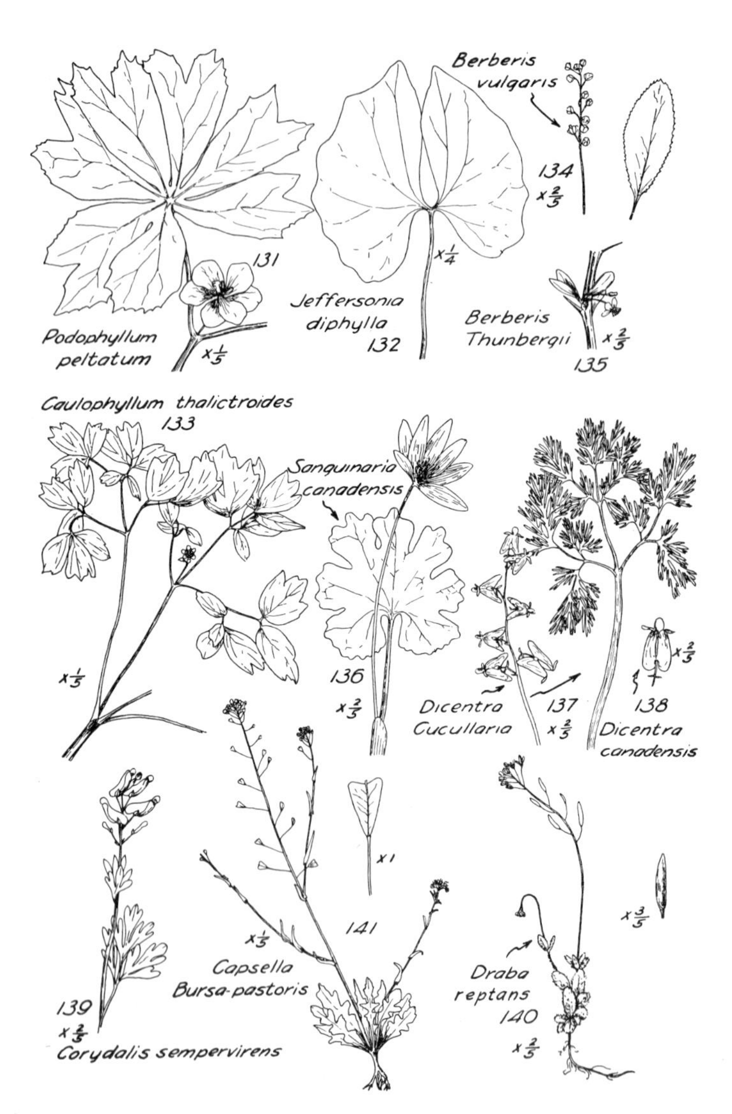
Berberis vulgaris
134
x 2/3
131
x 1/4
Jeffersonia diphylla
132
Berberis Thunbergii
x 2/3
135
Podophyllum peltatum
x 1/5
Caulophyllum thalictroides
133
Sanguinaria canadensis
x 1/5
136
x 2/3
x 2/5
Dicentra Cucullaria
137
x 2/5
138
Dicentra canadensis
x 1
141
x 1/5
Capsella Bursa-pastoris
x 3/5
Draba reptans
140
x 2/5
139
x 2/5
Corydalis sempervirens

in drooping racemes.—Fields, and open woods; escaped from cultivation.—A native of Europe, and the alternate host of the wheat rust.

2. **B. Thunbérgii** DC. JAPANESE BARBERRY. Leaves obovate, *the margins entire* (Fig. 135); flowers 1–3 in a bunch.—Widely cultivated and occasionally escaping.—A native of Japan, and not a host of the wheat rust.

PAPAVERÀCEAE POPPY FAMILY

Rather delicate herbs, with colored juice; sepals 2, falling as the flower expands.

1. Sanguinària BLOODROOT

S. canadénsis L. Rootstock stout; *juice of whole plant red-orange;* leaf solitary, with a stout petiole, the blade palmately 3–9-lobed (Fig. 136); peduncle slender, 1–flowered, a little taller than the leaf; petals 8–12, white, about 2 cm. long.—Rich woods.

2. Chelidònium CELANDINE

C. màjus L. *Juice bright yellow;* leaves pinnate, the leaflets with rounded teeth; flowers yellow.—An uncommon weed.

FUMARIÀCEAE FUMITORY FAMILY

Delicate herbs; leaves 3–divided, the leaflets pinnately divided, these secondary leaflets themselves cut into lanceolate divisions; sepals 2, small and scale-like; petals 4, in 2 pairs; stamens in 2 sets of 3 each; fruit a long pod.

a. Flowers with 2 petals prolonged into spurs (Fig. 137) . . . . 1. *Dicentra.*
a. Flowers with but one spurred petal (Fig. 139) . . 2. *Corydalis.*

1. Dicéntra

Plants about 2 dm. high; flower and leaf-stems arising from a cluster of small white (*yellow* in *D. canadensis*) bulb-like bodies that develop from thickened leaf-bases; flowers 2–many, on short pedicels from a common axis; outer petals rather inflated, prolonged into spurs at base, the apex of each turned back; inner petals hidden except for their jointed tips which appear between the turned-back tips of the outer.

1. **D. Cucullària** (L.) Bernh. DUTCHMAN'S BREECHES. Plants from a cluster of white grain-like bulbs; flowers white or pink, with *long triangular spurs* (Fig. 137).—Woods.

2. **D. canadénsis** (Goldie) Walp. SQUIRREL CORN. Plants from yellow bulb-like bodies resembling grains of corn; flowers greenish-white or rose-tinged, fragrant, *with short rounded spurs* (Fig. 138). —Locally abundant in rich woods.

2. Corýdalis

a. Corolla pink or purplish, with yellow tips . . . . 1. *C. sempervirens.*
a. Corolla yellow throughout *b*.
  b. Corolla 8 mm. long . . . . 2. *C. micrantha.*
  b. Corolla 12 mm. long . . . . 3. *C. aurea.*

1. **C. sempérvirens** (L.) Pers. PALE CORYDALIS. (Fig. 139) Plants 1–6 dm. high, often much branched; stem and leaves bluish-green, with a whitish bloom.—Rocky places and clearings.

2. **C. micrántha** (Engelm.) Gray. Similar to the next, but with smaller flowers; the ascending pods less than 1 cm. long.—Adventive in the stock yards at Blue River, and perhaps elsewhere.

3. **C. aúrea** Willd. GOLDEN CORYDALIS. Plants 1–3.5 dm. high, much branched; pods spreading or pendulous, 1.5–2 cm. long.—Dry soils.

CRUCÍFERAE MUSTARD FAMILY

Herbs; leaves alternate, or in *Dentaria* apparently whorled; flowers mostly in racemes; sepals 4; petals 4 (rarely none), bent outward in the middle so that the *spreading parts make a cross;* stamens 6 (rarely only 2) of *2 long and one short pairs;* fruit a pod of 2 carpels.—A large family, classified chiefly on the form of the fruit. The following key is based on flowering or young fruiting material, and so is purely artificial and not always reliable; specimens with mature fruit may best be identified by use of *Gray's Manual.*

A. Petals white or purplish, sometimes yellow at base, or absent *B*.
  B. Petals 5–15 mm. long *C*.
    C. Leaves or leaflets pointed *D*.
      D. Leaves simple, scattered on the stem; large plants *E*.
        E. Flowers purplish; leaves with regular, short, sharp-pointed teeth; no long, strap-shaped basal leaves . . . . . . 12. *Hesperis.*
        E. Flowers white; leaves with irregular, long, rounded teeth; many long, strap-shaped basal leaves . . . . . 16. *Armoracia.*
      D. Leaves palmately compound, 2 or 3 only . 18. *Dentaria.*
    C. Leaves or leaflets, except the uppermost, rounded *F*.
      F. Stem-leaves tapered or petioled at base . . 19. *Cardamine.*
      F. Stem-leaves sessile and auricled . . . . . . 9. *Conringia*
  B. Petals smaller, or absent (sometimes 8 mm. long in *Arabis*) *G*.
    G. Leaves (at least the basal) pinnate or pinnatifid, cut at least halfway to the midrib *H*.
      H. Leaves on the stem mostly simple, the pinnatifid ones confined to a basal rosette *I*.
        I. Stem-leaves prolonged at base into triangular auricles (Fig. 141). . . . . 5. *Capsella.*
        I. Stem-leaves without auricles *J*.

J. Petioles of basal leaves hairy. . . . 20. *Arabis.*
J. Petioles of basal leaves without hairs 4. *Lepidium.*
H. Stem-leaves pinnate *K.*
K. Leaves in the inflorescence pinnate *L.*
L. Leaflets much longer than broad, often with straight sides (Fig. 156) 19. *Cardamine.*
L. Leaflets about half as broad as long, rounded (Fig. 149) . . . . . . 14. *Nasturtium.*
K. Leaves in the inflorescense simple, sharply toothed. . . . . 15. *Rorippa.*
G. Leaves simple, sometimes toothed, but not cut halfway to the midrib *M.*
M. Leaves small, almost entirely confined to a basal rosette; plant not over 1 dm. high (Fig. 140) . . . . 1. *Draba.*
M. Stems leafy; plants larger *N.*
N. Leaves not toothed *O.*
O. Sepals and rachis of racemes whitened with branched or stellate hairs *P.*
P. Fruits circular, winged; styles about 1 mm. long . . . . . 22. *Alyssum.*
P. Fruits longer than wide, not winged; styles about 2 mm. long . . . . 2. *Berteroa.*
O. Sepals and rachis not whitened, with few spreading hairs or none *Q.*
Q. Young fruit very narrow, the ovary hardly thicker than the stigma . . . . 20. *Arabis.*
Q. Young fruit over half as broad as long, the ovary much thicker than the stigma . . . . . . 6. *Camelina.*
N. Leaves toothed or wavy-margined *R.*
R. Leaves roundish, wavy-margined. . 19. *Cardamine.*
R. Leaves with definite teeth *S.*
S. Basal rosette with branched hairs *T.*
T. Anthers as broad as long . . 1. *Draba.*
T. Anthers much longer than broad . . . . 20. *Arabis.*
S. Basal rosette (if present) with simple hairs or none *U.*
U. Young fruit very narrow, the ovary hardly thicker than the stigma *V.*
V. Leaves much longer than wide. . . . . 20. *Arabis.*
V. Leaves triangular, about as wide as long . . . 21. *Alliaria.*
U. Young fruit over half as broad as long, the ovary much thicker than the stigma *W.*
W. Upper leaves prolonged at base into auricles *X.*
X. Stems without hairs. . 3. *Thlaspi.*
X. Stems with minute spreading hairs . . 4. *Lepidium.*
W. Leaves without auricles *Y.*
Y. Most of the leaves 1 dm. or more long. 15. *Rorippa.*
Y. Leaves less than 1 dm. long . . . . 4. *Lepidium.*

A. Petals yellow *Z*.
- *Z*. Leaves simple, not deeply cleft *a*.
  - *a*. Leaves not prolonged backward into lobes or auricles *b*.
    - *b*. Axis of inflorescence roughened with many short appressed hairs . . . . 13. *Erysimum*.
    - *b*. Axis of inflorescence smooth or with a few soft spreading hairs . . . . 8. *Brassica*
  - *a*. Leaves at base prolonged backward into lobes or auricles *c*.
    - *c*. Lobes rounded . . . . 9. *Conringia*.
    - *c*. Lobes pointed *d*.
      - *d*. Young fruit very narrow, the ovary hardly thicker than the stigma . . . . 20. *Arabis*.
      - *d*. Young fruit over half as broad as long, the ovary much thicker than the stigma *e*.
        - *e*. Sepals 2.5–3.5 mm. long . . . . 6. *Camelina*.
        - *e*. Sepals 1–1.5 mm. long. . . . . 7. *Neslia*.
- *Z*. Leaves pinnately divided, or cleft at least halfway to the midrib *f*.
  - *f*. Lobes of the leaves rounded . . . . 17. *Barbarea*.
  - *f*. Lobes of the leaves pointed *g*.
    - *g*. Fruit about twice as long as broad . . . . . 15. *Rorippa*.
    - *g*. Fruit many times as long as broad *h*.
      - *h*. Stem with stellate hairs or stalked glands . 11. *Descurainia*.
      - *h*. Stem with simple hairs or none *i*.
        - *i*. Leaves cleft to the midrib, the divisions with parallel sides . . . . 10. *Sisymbrium*.
        - *i*. Leaves not cleft to the midrib, the divisions not with parallel sides *j*.
          - *j*. Flowering branches exceeded by the subtending leaves; fruit about 1 mm. thick . . . . 10. *Sisymbrium*.
          - *j*. Flowering branches longer than their subtending leaves; fruit 2–6 mm. thick. . . . . 8. *Brassica*.

1. **Dràba**

Pods narrowly oblong, flat; seeds in 2 rows in each compartment, marginless.

a. Style none *b*.
- *b*. Leaves not toothed . . . . 1. *D. reptans*.
- *b*. Leaves few-toothed . . . . 2. *D. nemorosa*.

a. Style well-developed *c*.
- *c*. Pods without hairs . . . . 3. *D. arabisans*.
- *c*. Pods with minute star-like hairs. . . . . 4. *D. lanceolata*.

1. **D. réptans** (Lam.) Fernald. (Fig. 140) Leaves 1 cm. or less long, not toothed, whitened by close matted hairs; peduncle slender, hairy, bearing a few leaves toward the base; flowers on short pedicels on a short common axis which elongates as the fruits mature.—Rocks and dry sand, north to Columbia and Pepin Counties.—Var. **micrántha** (Nutt.) Fernald, with pods finely hairy, is rare from Dane County southeastward.

2. **D. nemoròsa** L. Stems leafy to the base of the inflorescence; leaves 4–8 mm. long, ovate.—Open sandy soil, Marinette.

3. **D. arábisans** Michx. Stems much branched and prostrate below, with numerous crowded leaves; erect branches mostly simple with scattered toothed leaves; fruit usually twisted.—Rocky woods and cliffs, Door Co., and at Oakfield in Fond du Lac Co.

4. **D. lanceolàta** Royle. Similar.—Limestone cliffs, Fish Creek and perhaps elsewhere in Door Co.

2. Berteròa

B. incàna (L.) DC. Plants 3–6 dm. high, branched or simple; *stem roughened with many short star-like hairs;* leaves not toothed, roughened; petals 2–parted; pod elliptic.—Roadsides and railroad tracks, naturalized from Europe.

3. Thláspi PENNY CRESS

T. arvénse L. Stem smooth; lower leaves without petioles, the upper clasping the stem, sometimes toothed; pod rounded in outline, much flattened at right angles to the partition, notched at summit, winged, 1.2 cm. broad; seeds 2–8 in each cell.—Waste-land, railroads, and cultivated ground, local; naturalized from Europe.

4. Lepídium PEPPERGRASS

Pod round, flat, about 3 mm. broad, each cell 1–seeded.

a. Leaves tapered to the base *b.*
  b. Leaves simple, toothed *c.*
    c. Petals shorter than sepals or absent . . . . . 1. *L. densiflorum.*
    c. Petals longer than sepals . . . . 2. *L. virginicum.*
  b. Leaves twice pinnately divided . . . . 3. *L. ruderale.*
a. Leaves broadest at base *d.*
  d. Leaves embracing the stem . . . . 4. *L. perfoliatum.*
  d. Leaves with a lobe on each side of stem . . . . 5. *L. campestre.*

1. **L. densiflòrum** Schrad. Pods slightly narrower than long; seed with back of one cotyledon against the embryonic root.—A common weed; naturalized from Europe.

2. **L. virgínicum** L. Pods as wide as long; seed with edges of both cotyledons against the embryonic root.—Waste places, southern Wisconsin.

3. **L. ruderàle** L. Upper leaves lobed nearly to midrib.—A weed in Milwaukee County; adventive from Europe.

4. **L. perfoliàtum** L. Upper leaves nearly as broad as long; lower leaves much divided.—A rare weed of southeastern Wisconsin; adventive from Europe.

5. **L. campéstre** (L.) R. Br. Plants minutely downy; fruits slightly cupped.—Abundant in cultivated fields in southern Wisconsin; naturalized from Europe.

5. **Capsélla** SHEPHERD'S PURSE

C. Búrsa-pastòris (L.) Medic. (Fig. 141) Leaves of the basal rosette variable, mostly deeply cleft; those of the stem much smaller, entire; pod 5–8 mm. long, shaped like an isosceles triangle with the pedicel at the apex, and the base somewhat notched; seeds numerous in each cell.—A weed everywhere, naturalized from Europe.

6. **Camélina** FALSE FLAX

1. **C. satìva** (L.) Crantz. Stem and leaves glabrous to sparsely pubescent, the simple hairs not projecting beyond the stellate. Fruits commonly 7–10 mm. long, 5–7 mm. wide, 3 to 4 times as long as the style.

2. **C. microcárpa** Andrz. Stem and leaves rough-pubescent with both simple and branched hairs, the short stellate hairs exceeded by simple hairs 1–2 mm. long. Fruits erect, 5.5–8 mm. long, 4–5 mm. wide, about twice as long as the style.

7. **Néslia** BALL MUSTARD

N. paniculàta (L.) Desv. Stem and leaves covered with stiff usually *star-like hairs;* pod subglobose, the surface marked with net-like ridges; style persistent as a beak; seeds usually but one in each pod.—Uncommon in waste ground; naturalized from Europe.

8. **Brássica**

Pod with a stout beak.—This genus includes Mustard, Turnip, Rape, and Cabbage, which sometimes persist after cultivation, or escape from gardens.—The fruit characters are more reliable for identification of species than the vegetative ones used in the following key.

a. Leaves without petioles or with short winged petioles (Fig. 142) . . . . 1. *B. Kaber.*
a. Leaves petioled, the petiole not winged *b.*
  b. Plants smooth or nearly so . . . . 2. *B. juncea.*
  b. Plants with scattered hairs . . . . 3. *B. nigra.*

1. **B. Kaber** (DC.) L. C. Wheeler, var. **pinnatífida** (Stokes) L. C. Wheeler. WILD MUSTARD; CHARLOCK. Beak as long as the rest of the capsule (Fig. 142).—A common weed; naturalized from Europe.

2. **B. júncea** (L.) Cosson. Pods 3.5 cm. long, on slender spreading pedicels (Fig. 143).—A weed; naturalized from Europe.

3. **B. nìgra** (L.) Koch. BLACK MUSTARD. Capsules 1.5–1.8 cm. long, appressed to the stem, with a short beak (Fig. 144).—Occasional as a weed; naturalized from Europe.

9. **Conríngia** HARE'S-EAR MUSTARD

C. orientàlis (L.) Dumort. Plants reaching 7 dm. in height; leaves smooth and somewhat fleshy, rounded at tip; pod 4–angled, reaching 1 dm. in length; seeds in 1 row in each cell.—Waste places, occasional; adventive from Europe.

10. **Sisýmbrium** HEDGE MUSTARD

Leaves pinnately deeply lobed to compound; pods very long and narrow.

1. **S. officinàle** (L.) Scop. Lower leaves with the terminal segment larger than the *triangular and toothed lateral ones* (Fig. 145); leaves and fruits densely covered with simple hairs; flowers yellow; *pod 1–1.5 cm. long.*—Naturalized from Europe and less common in Wisconsin than var. **leiocárpum** DC., which has few hairs on the leaves and none on the fruit, and is also from Europe.

2. **S. altíssimum** L. TUMBLE MUSTARD. Leaves compound, the segments of the lower ones elliptic or narrowly triangular and coarsely toothed, segments of the upper ones *ribbon-like or thread-like* (Fig. 146); hairs on stem scattered, long and spreading, or lacking; flowers pale yellow; *pod 6–10 cm. long.*—Waste places and roadsides; introduced from Europe.

11. **Descuraìnia**

1. **D. pinnàta** (Walt.) Britton, var. **brachycárpa** (Richards.) Fernald. Plants very leafy; leaves much divided, the ultimate leaflets 2–5 mm. long and often lobed (Fig. 147); lower part of the stem with almost microscopic gland-tipped hairs; pods about 1 cm. long, shorter than the slender spreading pedicels; seeds in 2 rows in each cell.—A weed along railroads, on limestone beaches, roadsides, etc.

2. **D. Sòphia** (L.) Webb. *Hairs on stem not gland-tipped;* pods 2 cm. long; seeds in one row in each cell.—A rare weed.

12. **Hésperis** DAME'S VIOLET

H. matronàlis L. Tall plants with toothed leaves and many showy purple (or sometimes white) flowers.—Garden flowers, introduced from Europe, escaping and becoming locally abundant along roadsides.

13. **Erýsimum** WORM-SEED MUSTARD

Pod linear, 4–sided; the midribs of the carpels keeled; seeds in one row in each carpel.

1. **E. cheiranthoìdes** L. (Fig. 148) Leaves covered with minute

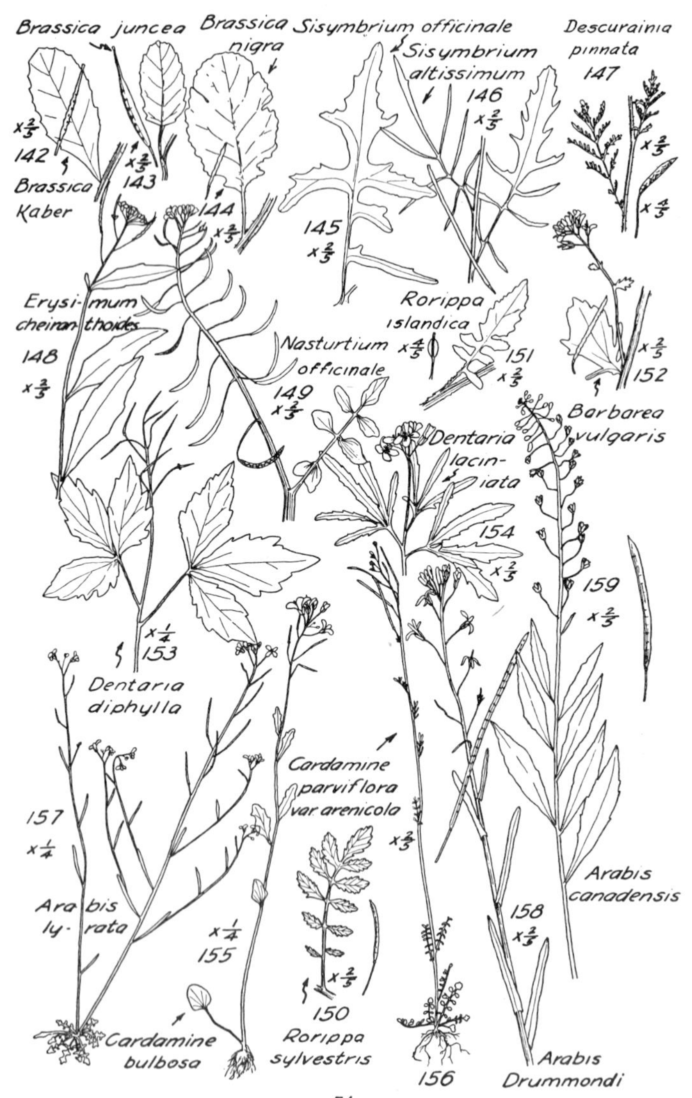
Brassica juncea
Brassica nigra
Sisymbrium officinale
Descurainia pinnata
147
x 2/5
x 4/5
Sisymbrium altissimum
146
x 2/5
x 2/5
142
Brassica Kaber
x 2/5
143
144
x 2/5
145
x 2/5
Erysimum cheiranthoides
148
x 2/5
Rorippa islandica
x 4/5
151
x 2/5
x 2/5
152
Barbarea vulgaris
Nasturtium officinale
149
x 2/5
Dentaria laciniata
154
x 2/5
159
x 2/5
x 1/4
153
Dentaria diphylla
Cardamine parviflora var. arenicola
157
x 1/4
x 2/5
Arabis canadensis
Arabis lyrata
x 1/4
155
158
x 2/5
x 2/5
150
Cardamine bulbosa
Rorippa sylvestris
156
Arabis Drummondi

3-branched hairs, but bright green; stems with closely appressed 2-branched hairs; pods 1–2 cm. long, on spreading pedicels.—Sterile soil.

2. **E. inconspícuum** (S. Wats.) MacM. Similar; hairs more dense, whitening the leaves; pods 2.5–6 cm. long, on short pedicels.—Open soil.—Can be positively distinguished from the preceding species only in the fruiting condition.

14. **Nastúrtium** WATER CRESS

N. officinàle R. Br. (Fig. 149) Plants somewhat fleshy; leaflets often rounded, the edges not toothed, the terminal usually larger than the lateral ones. A European species, cultivated as a salad plant, now naturalized and found commonly in springs and along streams, especially in southern Wisconsin.—Not related to the "Nasturtium" *(Tropaeolum)* of flower gardens.

15. **Roríppa**

Plants 2–5 dm. high; petals yellow; pods varying from slender to elliptic.

1. **R. sylvéstris** (L.) Druce. YELLOW CRESS. Leaflets elliptical, toothed, the terminal on stem-leaves, about as large as the lateral (Fig. 150); on the leaves at the base the terminal leaflet often larger.—Damp ground; introduced from Europe.

2. **R. islándica** (Oeder) Borbas, var. **híspida** (Desr.) Butt. & Abbe. MARSH CRESS. Lower leaves pinnately cleft almost to the midrib (Fig. 151); upper leaves less deeply cleft; stems with scattered spreading hairs; fruit almost globose, about 2 mm. broad.—Common in wet places.—Var. **Fernaldiàna** Butt. & Abbe is without hairs on the stem, and has pods about twice as long as broad.—Common in wet places.

16. **Armoràcia** HORSERADISH

Armoràcia lapathifòlia Gilib. Flowers white; smooth basal leaves often to 4 dm. long, wavy-margined; the thick vertical root is grown commercially. Introduced from Europe.

17. **Barbarèa** WINTER CRESS; YELLOW ROCKET

B. vulgàris R. Br. Lower leaves pinnate, the terminal divisions large and rounded, the lateral very small; upper leaves sometimes deeply cut, but scarcely pinnate (Fig. 152); pods cylindrical or 4-angled, spreading at maturity, with a short beak; seeds in one row in each carpel.—Roadsides; introduced from Europe.—A form with the pods closely appressed is occasionally found.

18. **Dentària** Toothwort

Plants 1.5–3 dm. high, from thick white rootstocks; stems with 2 or 3 leaves borne above the middle; flowers white or purplish; pods flat, lanceolate; seeds in one row in each carpel.

1. **D. diphýlla** Michx. Leaves 2, 3–parted, the leaflets a third to a half as broad as long (Fig. 153).—Rare in rich woods, south to Shawano and Sheboygan Counties.

2. **D. laciniàta** Muhl. Leaves 3, in a single whorl, each palmately 3–cleft, the 2 lateral leaflets usually deeply 2–cleft (Fig. 154).—Common in rich woods, north to Dunn County.

19. **Cardámine** Bitter Cress

Plants with few or no hairs; pod linear, flattened; seeds in one row in each carpel.

a. Leaves simple; plant with a bulb *b*.	
b. Petals white	1. *C. bulbosa*.
b. Petals rose-purple	2. *C. Douglassii*.
a. Leaves pinnately compound; plant without a bulb *c*.	
c. Flowers 1 cm. or more broad	3. *C. pratensis*, var. *palustris*.
c. Flowers 4 mm. or less broad *d*.	
d. Leaflets of the stem-leaves very narrow . .	4. *C. parviflora*, var. *arenicola*.
d. Leaflets ovate or roundish	5. *C. pensylvanica*.

1. **C. bulbòsa** (Schreb.) BSP. Spring Cress. (Fig. 155) Plants about 3 dm. high, unbranched; leaves 5–8, scattered, the lower sometimes petioled; petals 7–10 mm. long.—Common in marshy land, north to La Crosse, Sauk, and Milwaukee Counties.

2. **C. Douglássii** (Torr.) Britton. Similar; stem somewhat hairy; petals 1–1.8 cm. long.—Occasional in shady places, eastern Wisconsin.

3. **C. praténsis** L., var. **palústris** Wimm. & Grab. Cuckoo Flower. Segments of the lower leaves rounded, those of the upper leaves narrow; petals white.—Rare in swamps, or sometimes in dry places.

4. **C. parviflòra** L., var. **arenícola** (Britt.) Schulz. (Fig. 156) Slender, almost simple; flowers very small, white; leaflets not running together on the midrib.—Occasional in wet places.

5. **C. pensylvánica** Muhl. Similar but larger; leaflets tending to run together on the midrib.—Frequent in wet places.

20. **Árabis** Rock Cress

Pods linear, long, flattened; stem-leaves usually simple.—Species determined largely on characteristics of the fruit. (See remarks under *Brassica*.)

a. Stem flexuous, branching at base *b.*	
b. Stem without hairs above	1. *A. lyrata.*
b. Stem rough-hairy above	2. *A. perstellata.*
a. Stem stiff, straight, unbranched below *c.*	
c. Basal leaves with simple or 2–branched hairs, or none *d.*	
d. Flowers yellowish	3. *A. glabra.*
d. Flowers greenish or pinkish or white *e.*	
e. Leaves not long-pointed with large auricles at base *f.*	
f. Stem without hairs except sometimes at base *g.*	
g. Stem-leaves without hairs *h.*	
h. Petals pinkish; basal leaves toothed	4. *A. Drummondi.*
h. Petals creamy-white; basal leaves lobed $\frac{1}{3}$–$\frac{1}{2}$ way to the midrib	8. *A. missouriensis.*
g. Stem-leaves with short hairs . . .	9. *A. canadensis.*
f. Stem rough-hairy	6. *A. hirsuta*, var. *pycnocarpa.*
e. Leaves long-pointed and with large auricles at base.	7. *A. laevigata.*
c. Basal leaves with 3–parted hairs	5. *A. divaricarpa.*

1. **A. lyràta** L. (Fig. 157) Basal rosette of many small, sometimes hairy, pinnatifid leaves, with the terminal lobe much the largest; stem much-branched, smooth; stem-leaves simple, lanceolate, entire or pinnately lobed; flowers small, white; seeds very small, in one row in each carpel.—On sandstone and sand.

2. **A. perstellàta** Braun, var. **Shórtii** Fernald. Stem-leaves rather broad, shallowly toothed; pods widely spreading.—Rich woodlands, not common.

3. **A. glàbra** (L.) Bernh. Tower Mustard. Plants somewhat powdery-whitened; leaves smooth, the midrib conspicuous, but not the branch-veins; pod 8 cm. long; seeds in one row in each carpel.—Dry places, mostly northward.

4. **A. Drummóndi** Gray. (Fig. 158) Similar; stem-leaves toothed or entire; seeds in 2 rows in each carpel.—Dry hills; local.

5. **A. divaricárpa** Nelson. Similar.—Rocky banks, etc.; local.

6. **A. hirsùta** (L.) Scop., var. **pycnocárpa** (M. Hopkins) Rollins. Stem rather slender; plants rough-hairy; pods upright; seeds in one row in each carpel.—Calcareous rocks; not common.—Var. **glabráta** T. & G. has the stem without hairs except near the base. —Grant Co., rare.

7. **A. laevigàta** (Muhl.) Poir. Leaves very long and tapering; pods long and narrow, spreading; seeds in one row in each carpel. —Woods and shaded rocky hillsides, common.

8. **A. missouriénsis** Greene. Similar but with more numerous and smaller leaves; stem glabrous at base.—Baraboo Hills.—Var. **Deàmii** M. Hopkins. Stem pubescent at base.—Rare.

9. **A. canadénsis** L. SICKLE-POD. (Fig. 159) Leaves flat, sometimes 3 cm. broad; pods 4 mm. broad, hanging downward.—Rich woods and bluffs, north to Pierce and Wood Counties.

21. Alliària GARLIC-MUSTARD

A. officinàlis Andrz. Plants with odor of onions; leaves long-petioled, with rounded teeth.—A weed of shady places, introduced from Europe. Recently found along Lake Michigan shore north of Milwaukee, and roadsides near Lake Geneva.

22. Alýssum

A. Alyssoìdes L. Low, hoary, annual weed.—Railway tracks and sandy roadsides.—Not common. Not "Sweet Alyssum".

SARRACENIÀCEAE PITCHER-PLANT FAMILY

Sarracènia purpùrea L. PITCHER-PLANT. (Fig. 160) Leaves hollow, with a wing on the upper side, the lower part of the opening usually covered with downward-pointing hairs; flower solitary, nodding; petals red; stigma very broad, covering the ovary and stamens.—Peat bogs, mostly northward and eastward.

CRASSULÀCEAE ORPINE FAMILY

Sèdum àcre L. MOSSY STONECROP. (Fig. 161) Stems low, spreading on the ground; *leaves small, fleshy, scale-like;* flowers yellow.—Dry soil, not common; a European species, escaping from cultivation.

SAXIFRAGÀCEAE SAXIFRAGE FAMILY

- *a.* Herbs *b.*
  - *b.* Scapes upright, leafless or with few leaves *c.*
    - *c.* Leaves lanceolate, with short broad petioles . . . 1. *Saxifraga.*
    - *c.* Leaves ovate, with long slender petioles *d.*
      - *d.* Stamens 5 *e.*
        - *e.* Scape simple, leafless, with spreading white hairs . . . . 2. *Heuchera.*
        - *e.* Scape branching above, with a few reduced leaves, glabrous . . . . 3. *Sullivantia.*
      - *d.* Stamens 10 . . . . 4. *Mitella.*
  - *b.* Stems creeping, leafy . . . . 5. *Chrysosplenium.*
- *a.* Shrubs *f.*
  - *f.* Leaves opposite. . . . . 6. *Philadelphus.*
  - *f.* Leaves alternate . . . . 7. *Ribes.*

1. Saxífraga

Leaves all clustered in a basal rosette, rough-hairy, 1–2 dm. long, 2–7 cm. wide, blunt; scapes stout, hairy, 4–5 dm. high; flowers on short branches, whitish.

1. **S. pensylvánica** L. SWAMP SAXIFRAGE. The two carpels that comprise the fruit erect throughout most of their length, the tips usually divergent; petals greenish-white.—Wet woods and meadows, north to Sheboygan, Waushara, Burnett, and Iron Counties, and in the Lake Superior region.—The typical variety has petals narrowly lanceolate, 1-nerved, and lanceolate leaves; var. **crassicárpa** (Johnson) Bush, with carpels 4–5 mm. long and styles over 0.5 mm. long, and var. **congésta** Burns, with carpels about 2 mm. long, and styles 0.5 mm. or less long, both have petals ovate-lanceolate, 3-nerved, and ovate leaves.

2. **S. Forbèsii** Vasey. CLIFF SAXIFRAGE. The two carpels divergent; petals white.—Moist sandstone cliffs in the Driftless Area.

2. **Heùchera** ALUM ROOT

H. Richardsònii R. Br. (Fig. 162) Leaves clustered at the base of the scape, the blades rounded, with a broad sinus, 5–9-lobed; the lobes toothed; petioles long, hairy; scape 5-12 dm. high; flowers in a loose panicle, whitish.—Wooded bluffs and prairies, north to Douglas and Lincoln Counties.—Var. **hispídior** RBL. has glandular petals and barely exserted stamens; var. **Grayàna** RBL., with flowers 6–10 mm. long, and var. **affìnis** RBL., with flowers 5–7 mm. long, both have glandular petals with minute bumps and exserted stamens.

3. **Sullivántia**

S. renifòlia Rosendahl. Spreading herbs with bright green rounded and toothed leaves; flowers small and white, in an openly branched inflorescence.—Moist mossy cliffs in the Driftless Area.

4. **Mitélla** BISHOP'S CAP

Leaves mostly at the base of the scape, with long hairy petioles; scapes slender, hairy, bearing a raceme of white flowers; petals delicately fringed.

1. **M. diphýlla** L. (Fig. 163) Scape bearing a pair of opposite scarcely petioled leaves below the raceme; petals 1.5–2 mm. long, the width of the flat body less than the length of the fringes.—Damp woods.

2. **M. nùda** L. (Fig. 164) Scape without leaves; petals 4 mm. long, the body as well as the fringes thread-like.—Northern Wisconsin, and coming southward to Walworth County in tamarack bogs.

5. **Chrysosplènium** GOLDEN SAXIFRAGE

C. americànum Schwein. (Fig. 165) Stems slender; leaves opposite, the blades roundish; flowers inconspicuous, without petals,

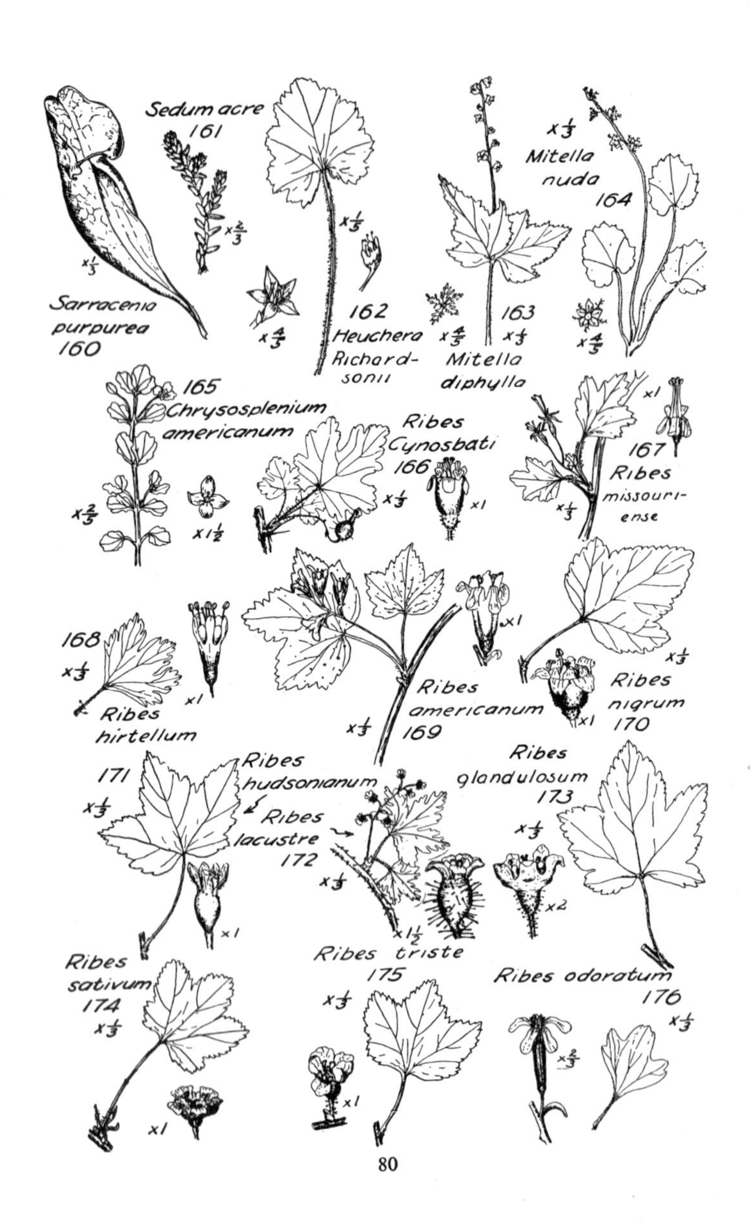
Sarracenia purpurea 160
Sedum acre 161
162 Heuchera Richardsonii
163 Mitella diphylla
Mitella nuda 164
165 Chrysosplenium americanum
Ribes Cynosbati 166
167 Ribes missouriense
168 Ribes hirtellum
Ribes americanum 169
Ribes nigrum 170
171
Ribes hudsonianum
Ribes lacustre 172
Ribes glandulosum 173
Ribes sativum 174
Ribes triste 175
Ribes odoratum 176

the 8–10 anthers purple or yellow.—Northern Wisconsin, and coming south in cold canyons and springy stream-banks to the Baraboo Hills.

6. **Philadélphus** MOCK ORANGE

P. coronàrius L. Flowers large, cream-colored, odorous.—Escaping from cultivation.

7. **Rìbes** GOOSEBERRY; CURRANT

Shrubs, with palmately lobed leaves and white, yellow or greenish flowers; fruit a berry.

a. Flowers solitary or in bunches of 2–4, often with spines at the base of each bunch (Figs. 166, 167, 169) *b.*
  b. Calyx-lobes shorter than the tube; ovary and berries usually prickly; petioles with simple or slightly fringed gland-tipped hairs . . . 1. *R. Cynosbati.*
  b. Calyx-lobes longer than the tube; ovary and berries not prickly; petioles with long branched hairs *c.*
    c. Stamens about twice as long as the calyx-lobes, conspicuous; bracts of the inflorescence fringed by minute stalked red or yellow glands . . . . 2. *R. missouriense.*
    c. Stamens about equaling the calyx-lobes; bracts fringed with minute hairs, and sometimes glands *d.*
      d. Stamens about twice as long as the petals 3. *R. hirtellum.*
      d. Stamens about as long as the petals . . 4. *R. oxyacanthoides.*
a. Flowers in racemes (Fig. 172) *e.*
  e. Calyx-tube about as broad as long *f.*
    f. Leaves with resinous dots or glands beneath *g.*
      g. Calyx-lobes equaling the tube *h.*
        h. Bract at the base of each flower longer than its pedicel . . . . 5. *R. americanum.*
        h. Bract shorter than the pedicel . . . . 6. *R. nigrum.*
      g. Calyx-lobes much longer than the tube . 7. *R. hudsonianum.*
    f. Leaves frequently with hairs, but never with resinous dots beneath *i.*
      i. Stems densely covered with prickles . . 8. *R. lacustre.*
      i. Stems without prickles *j.*
        j. Ovary and fruit with stalked glands . 9. *R. glandulosum.*
        j. Ovary and fruit without glands *k.*
          k. Pedicels and peduncles without stalked glands . . . . 10. *R. sativum.*
          k. Pedicels and peduncles with stalked glands . . . . 11. *R. triste.*
  e. Calyx-tube several times as long as broad . . . 12. *R. odoratum.*

1. **R. Cynósbati** L. PRICKLY GOOSEBERRY. (Fig. 166) *Stems usually with a sharp reddish spine at the base of each leaf;* internodes often covered with slender spines; leaves round-ovate, velvety beneath; berries usually prickly.—Open woods and pastures, common.

2. **R. missouriénse** Nutt. MISSOURI GOOSEBERRY. (Fig. 167) Spines long, stout, and red; flowers white or yellowish; sepals usually

turned back or spreading, longer than the petals and *much shorter than the conspicuous stamens.*—Woods and thickets, north to Barron, Marathon, and Manitowoc Counties.

3. **R. hirtéllum** Michx. SMOOTH GOOSEBERRY. (Fig. 168) Usually unarmed; leaf-blades deeply 3–lobed, usually slightly pubescent beneath; flowers greenish or purplish (*R. oxyacanthoides* of Ed. 7, not L.).—Moist woods northward, and rare in boggy places southward.—Var. **calcícola** Fernald has leaves velvety beneath.—Mostly in Door Co.

4. **R. oxyacanthoìdes** L. Similar but usually more spiny.—Superior and the Barron Hills, rare.

5. **R. americànum** Mill. AMERICAN BLACK CURRANT. (Fig. 169) Stems unarmed; leaf-blades sharply 3–5-lobed, a little longer than broad, with *glands on the upper as well as the lower surface;* bracts of the inflorescence green, hairy, lanceolate; calyx yellow and greenish, *8–10 mm. long;* ovary not glandular.—Open woods and fields, common.

6. **R. nìgrum** L. BLACK CURRANT. (Fig. 170) Similar; calyx *5–6 mm. long;* ovary with sessile glands.—Cultivated, sometimes escaping.

7. **R. hudsoniànum** Richards. HUDSON BAY CURRANT. (Fig. 171) Similar to No. 5, but upper surface of the leaves without glands; ovary, and often the petioles, with sessile glands; *leaf-blade a little broader than long.*—Lake Superior region, rare.

8. **R. lacústre** (Pers.) Poir. SWAMP BLACK CURRANT; PRICKLY CURRANT. (Fig. 172) Leaf-blades heart-shaped at base, deeply 3–5-lobed; *ovary with long-stalked glands.*—Cold woods and swamps, northern Wisconsin.

9. **R. glandulòsum** Weber. SKUNK CURRANT. (Fig. 173) *Stems reclining;* leaf-blades somewhat heart-shaped at base, 3–5-lobed; *fruit ill-scented.*—Swamps and cool woods, south to Dunn and Manitowoc Counties.

10. **R. satìvum** Syme. GARDEN CURRANT. (Fig. 174) Leaf-blades velvety, heart-shaped at base and 3–5-lobed; *the middle lobe ovate, a little longer than broad;* flowers yellow-green. Escaping from cultivation, and sometimes appearing as if native when growing in woods.

11. **R. trìste** Pall. SWAMP CURRANT. (Fig. 175) *Stems reclining;* leaf-blades densely hairy beneath, 3–lobed, the sides almost parallel; *middle lobe triangular, broader than long.*—Less common than var. **albinérvium** (Michx.) Fernald, which has the leaf-blades almost without hairs.—Wet woods, south to Dunn, Washington, and Milwaukee Counties.

12. **R. odoràtum** Wendl. CLOVE CURRANT. (Fig. 176) Stems without spines; leaf-blades usually 3–lobed, wedge-shaped or almost square at base; *flowers trumpet-shaped, golden-yellow, spicy-fragrant.*—Commonly cultivated and often persisting, mostly southward.

PLATANÀCEAE PLANE TREE FAMILY

Plátanus occidentàlis L. SYCAMORE. Tree, with bark splitting off and exposing the *smooth whitish inner bark;* leaves maple-like, very woolly when young.—River-bottoms in southern Wisconsin, rare.

ROSÀCEAE ROSE FAMILY

A large family of trees, shrubs, or herbs; leaves alternate, with stipules; sepals united into a calyx-tube, with distinct lobes; stamens usually many, borne on the edge of the calyx-tube; petals usually 5, showy; pistils 1–many, sometimes more or less enclosed in the calyx-tube.

a. Ovary superior, i.e., with sepals borne at its base *b.*
  b. Trees or shrubs; flowers not yellow *c.*
    c. Pistils solitary or several united *d.*
      d. Leaves roundish, 3–lobed (Fig. 177) . . 1. *Physocarpus.*
      d. Leaves lanceolate or ovate, not lobed *e.*
        e. Inflorescence a compound panicle (Fig. 178) . . . . 2. *Spiraea.*
        e. Inflorescence a raceme or umbel (Figs. 185–190) . . . . 12. *Prunus.*
    c. Pistils many, on a dome-shaped receptacle. 10. *Rubus.*
  b. Herbs, or if shrubs then yellow-flowered *f.*
    f. Bractlets outside of and alternating with calyx-lobes *g.*
      g. Styles jointed, the terminal part silky-hairy or fringed, persisting in fruit. . 9. *Geum.*
      g. Styles not silky-hairy, falling as the fruit ripens *h.*
        h. Leaves 3–foliolate, borne at base of the plant *i.*
          i. Petals white . . . . 6. *Fragaria.*
          i. Petals yellow . . . . 7. *Waldsteinia.*
        h. Leaves 5–many-foliolate, or 3–foliolate on the stem . . . . 8. *Potentilla.*
    f. Calyx without bractlets . . . . 10. *Rubus.*
a. Ovary inferior, i.e., with sepals borne at its summit *j.*
  j. Flowers 4 cm. or less broad *k.*
    k. Petals at least twice as long as broad . . . 4. *Amelanchier.*
    k. Petals hardly longer than broad *l.*
      l. Usually with thorns; leaves usually lobed 5. *Crataegus.*
      l. Without thorns or lobed leaves (except sometimes in *P. ioensis*); leaves simple or compound . . . . 3. *Pyrus.*
  j. Flowers 5 cm. or more broad; leaves compound 11. *Rosa.*

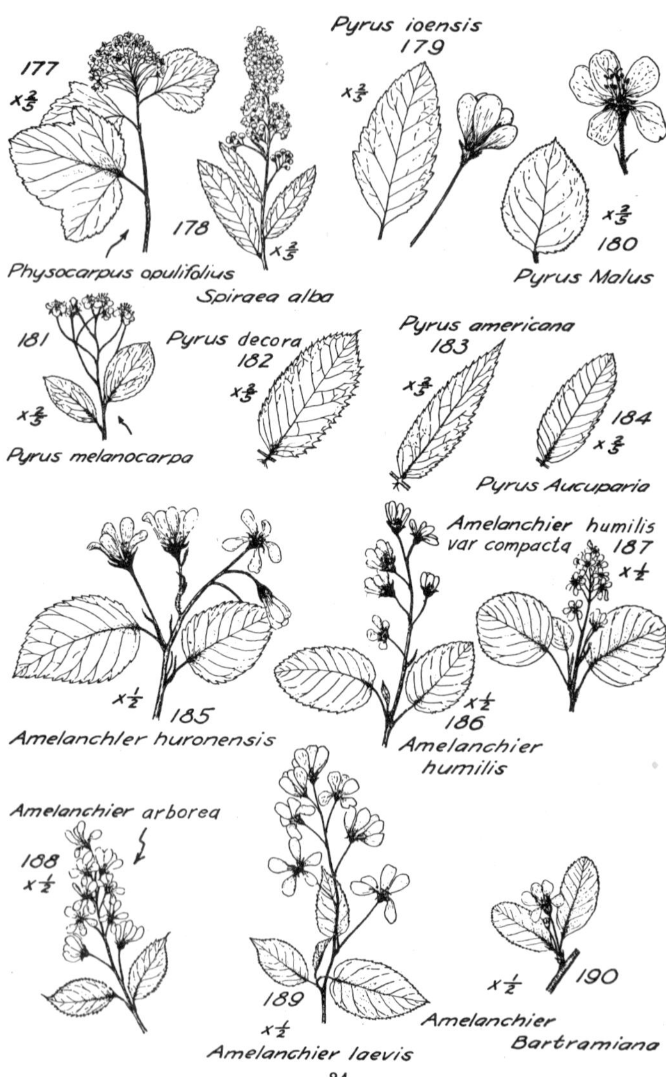
177
x 2/5
Physocarpus opulifolius
178
x 2/5
Spiraea alba
Pyrus ioensis
179
x 2/5
x 2/5
180
Pyrus Malus
181
x 2/3
Pyrus melanocarpa
Pyrus decora
182
x 2/5
Pyrus americana
183
x 2/5
184
x 2/5
Pyrus Aucuparia
x 1/2
185
Amelanchler huronensis
x 1/2
186
Amelanchier humilis
Amelanchier humilis var compacta
187
x 1/2
Amelanchier arborea
188
x 1/2
189
x 1/2
Amelanchier laevis
x 1/2
190
Amelanchier Bartramiana

1. **Physocárpus** NINE-BARK

P. opulifòlius (L.) Maxim. Shrubs, 1–3 m. high; bark loose and separating into thin layers; leaves 3–lobed, the lobes toothed; flowers white, on pedicels longer than the axis of the raceme (Fig. 177); calyx-lobes woolly; fruit of 2–5 dry inflated 2–seeded carpels. —Banks of streams, and rocky places.

2. **Spiraèa** MEADOW-SWEET

S. álba Du Roi. (Fig. 178) Low shrub, with lanceolate pinnately-veined toothed leaves; flowers white, in cylindrical or pyramidal panicles; fruit of several carpels, not inflated *(S. salicifolia* of Ed. 7, not L.). —Low wet meadows and marshes.

3. **Pỳrus**

Trees or shrubs; flowers white or pink; sepals borne at the summit of the ovary; fruit of 2–5 papery carpels, all surrounded by the fleshy calyx-tube. (*Amelanchier Bartramiana* may be confused with this genus.)

- *a.* Leaves simple *b.*
  - *b.* Midrib not glandular *c.*
    - *c.* Leaf-blades coarsely and doubly toothed, and somewhat lobed, narrowed at base *d.*
      - *d.* Calyx and ovary densely woolly . . . . 1. *P. ioensis.*
      - *d.* Calyx and ovary without hairs or very sparsely hairy . . . . 2. *P. coronaria.*
    - *c.* Leaf-blades finely and regularly toothed, rounded or heart-shaped at base . . . 3. *P. Malus.*
  - *b.* Midrib with little red glands on upper surface *e.*
    - *e.* Calyx white-woolly . . . . 4. *P. floribunda.*
    - *e.* Calyx not woolly . . . . 5. *P. melanocarpa.*
- *a.* Leaves pinnate *f.*
  - *f.* Sepals and winter buds densely woolly; underside of leaves hairy . . . . 6. *P. Aucuparia.*
  - *f.* Sepals and winter buds with few scattered hairs or none; underside of leaves without hairs or very slightly hairy *g.*
    - *g.* Leaflets slender (Fig. 183) . . . . 7. *P. americana.*
    - *g.* Leaflets usually shorter and broader (Fig. 182) . . . . 8. *P. decora.*

1. **P. ioénsis** (Wood) Bailey. WILD CRAB. Small much-branched tree or shrub; twigs often short and thorn-like; leaf-blades *coarsely and doubly toothed and somewhat lobed*, narrowed at base (Fig. 179); flowers white or pinkish, very conspicuous and fragrant. Fruit green when ripe, sticky.—Fields and open woods, north to Vernon and Dodge Counties.

2. **P. coronària** L. GARLAND CRAB. Leaves oval, more sharply pointed than No. 1, rounded at the base.

3. **P. Màlus** L. APPLE. Trees; leaf-blades *finely and regularly toothed*, rounded or somewhat heart-shaped at base (Fig. 180); fruit large and edible.—Escaping from cultivation and persisting about old farms.

4. **P. floribúnda** Lindl. PURPLE CHOKEBERRY. Shrub 1–2.5 m. high; leaves usually about 5 cm. long, with red glands along the midrib and at the tip of each tooth; flowers in flat-topped clusters; calyx woolly *(Aronia prunifolia; P. arbutifolia*, var. *atropurpurea)*.—In sandy soil. Probably less common than the next.

5. **P. melanocárpa** (Michx.) Willd. BLACK CHOKEBERRY. (Fig. 181) Similar, but calyx not woolly.—Bogs, rocky places, etc.

6. **P. Aucupària** (L.) Gaertn. ROWAN TREE. Leaflets obtuse, hairy beneath (Fig. 184).—A native of Europe, sometimes escaping from cultivation.

7. **P. americàna** (Marsh) DC. AMERICAN MOUNTAIN ASH. (Fig. 183) Small slender tree; *flowers 5–6 mm. broad*, very many together in a flat-topped cluster; inflorescence and leaves scarcely hairy.—Woods and bluffs, south to Barron, Dane, and Waukesha Counties.

8. **P. decòra** (Sarg.) Hyland. MOUNTAIN ASH. (Fig. 182) Similar; flowers *8–11 mm. broad;* inflorescence and leaf-rachis sometimes hairy, particularly northward.—Woods in northern Wisconsin, occasionally coming south on sandstone bluffs in the Driftless Area.

4. **Amelánchier** JUNEBERRY

Shrubs or small trees, with smooth gray bark; flowers white, rarely pinkish; carpels 5, each divided by a partition so that there are 10 compartments in the fleshy edible fruit, each with one seed. —A variable group, the species probably freely hybridizing. The following treatment describes only the typical form of each species; a large proportion of the individuals in any region will combine to some extent the characters of several species.

a. Flowers in racemes; petioles 8–25 mm. long *b*.
  b. Summit of ovary woolly *c*.
    c. Teeth of leaves 3–5 per cm., usually less than 20 on each side of the leaf *d*.
      d. Petals less than 1 cm. long; veins of leaves usually branching before reaching the teeth . . . . 1. *A. humilis.*
      d. Petals more than 1 cm. long; veins of leaves mostly running to the teeth without branching . . . . 2. *A. huronensis.*
    c. Teeth of leaves 5 or more per cm., more than 20 on each side *e*.
      e. Leaves rounded or squarish at tip. . . . 3. *A. stolonifera.*
      e. Leaves pointed at tip . . . . 4. *A. interior.*
  b. Summit of ovary not woolly; teeth of leaves 5–12 per cm. *f*.
    f. Lower pedicels 7–18 mm. long in flower, 1–2.5 cm. long in fruit (Fig. 188); leaves woolly when young . . . . 5. *A. arborea.*
    f. Lower pedicels 1.5–3.3 cm. long in flower, 3–5 cm. long in fruit (Fig. 189); leaves without wool from the first. . . . . . 6. *A. laevis.*
a. Flowers solitary or 2–3 together; petioles 2–7 mm. long . . . . 7. *A. Bartramiana.*

1. **A. hùmilis** Wiegand. Shrubs 0.3–2 m. tall, forming dense clumps; *leaves densely woolly beneath* at flowering time (*A. spicata*, in part).—Woods northward and eastward, and on rocky cliffs southwestward.—The typical *A. humilis* has open racemes and pointed leaves (Fig. 186); var. **compácta** Nielsen has more dense racemes and usually rounded leaves (Fig. 187).

2. **A. huronénsis** Wiegand. (Fig. 185) Shrubs 1–3 m. tall; *leaves densely woolly beneath* at flowering time.—Woods, mostly northward and eastward.

3. **A. stolonífera** Wiegand. Shrubs 0.5–1.5 m. tall, forming clumps.—Oconto County.

4. **A. intèrior** Nielsen. Shrubs or small trees, usually resembling the next two species but with the top of the ovary woolly.—Scattered.

5. **A. arbòrea** (Michx. f.) Fernald. (Fig. 188) Bushy tree 5–10 m. high, or sometimes a shrub; leaves long-pointed, small and *green at flowering time, woolly beneath when young* and usually when older; petals 10–18 mm. long.—Mostly eastward.

6. **A. laèvis** Wiegand. (Fig. 189) Shrub or small tree; leaves long-pointed, small and *purplish red at flowering time, smooth from the first;* petals 10–18 mm. long.—Common.

7. **A. Bartramiàna** (Tausch) Roemer. (Fig. 190) Shrub 0.5–2.5 m. high; leaves rounded to acute at apex, finely toothed, with irregular veins.—Lake Superior region.

5. **Crataègus** HAWTHORN

Usually thorny shrubs or small trees; leaves simple, usually lobed; flowers white or pink; fruit red, yellow, blue, or black, the carpels bony, surrounded by the thin slightly fleshy receptacle.—The species are numerous and identified with great difficulty, so are not described here.

6. **Fragària** STRAWBERRY

Fruits small achenes scattered over an enlarged pulpy receptacle; plants bearing numerous elongate stolons.

1. **F. virginiàna** Duchesne. (Fig. 191) Inflorescence flattish-topped, the primary branches subequal, usually overtopped by the leaves; *flowers about 2 cm. in diameter; sepals appressed to the young fruit;* achenes in pits in the mature receptacle; petioles and scapes with appressed or spreading hairs; pedicels with appressed hairs.—Common in sunny fields.—Var. **illinoénsis** (Prince) Gray. Pedicels and sometimes the scapes with spreading hairs.—Mostly southward; less common.

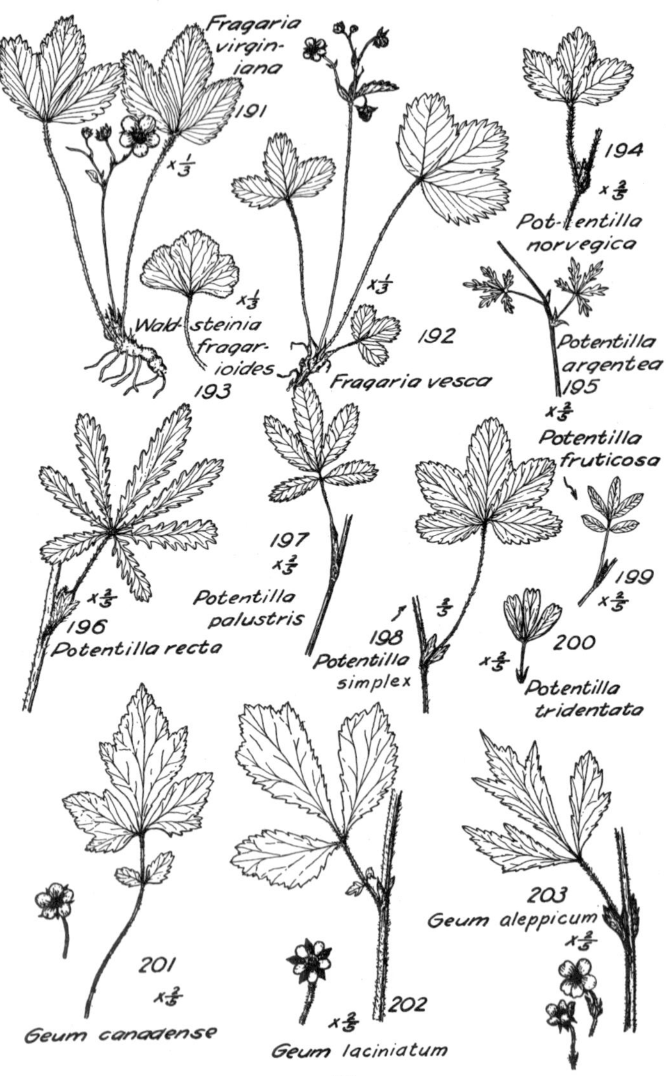
Fragaria virgin- iana
191
x 1/3
Wald-steinia fragar- ioides
x 1/3
193
192
x 1/3
Fragaria vesca
194
x 2/5
Pot-entilla norvegica
Potentilla argentea
195
x 2/5
Potentilla fruticosa
199
x 2/5
196
x 2/5
Potentilla recta
197
x 2/5
Potentilla palustris
198
2/5
Potentilla simplex
200
x 2/5
Potentilla tridentata
201
x 2/5
Geum canadense
202
x 2/5
Geum laciniatum
203
Geum aleppicum
x 2/5

2. **F. vésca** L. (Fig. 192) Inflorescence more irregular, the primary branches unequal, usually overtopping leaves; *flowers about 1.3 cm. in diameter; sepals turned back from the young fruit;* achenes superficial on the mature receptacle; hairs of petioles and scapes wide-spreading.—Not common.—Var. **americàna** Porter. Hairs appressed on the petioles and scapes.—Frequent.

7. **Waldsteìnia** BARREN STRAWBERRY

W. fragarioìdes (Michx.) Trattinick. Perennial herbs, 1–1.8 dm. high; leaves mostly from the base of the plant, the blades almost round, 3–parted; the leaflets short-stalked and shallowly lobed at tip (Fig. 193); flowers several on the bracted scapes, yellow; achenes dry, 2–6 on a dome-shaped receptacle.—Dry sandy woods and barrens, northern Wisconsin.

8. **Potentílla** CINQUEFOIL; FIVE-FINGER

Achenes dry, many on a dome-shaped receptacle.

a. Leaflets 3 *b.*
  b. Petals yellow; leaflets toothed along the sides . 2. *P. norvegica.*
  b. Petals white; leaflets 3–toothed at tip . . . . 9. *P. tridentata.*
a. Leaflets 5 or more, at least on lower leaves *c.*
  c. Leaves palmately compound *d.*
    d. Leaflets not woolly beneath, but often with long spreading hairs *e.*
      e. Flowers many, in a much branched inflorescence. . . . . 6. *P. recta.*
      e. Flowers few, each on a long peduncle in the axil of a leaf . . . . 11. *P. simplex.*
    d. Leaflets woolly beneath *f.*
      f. Leaflets with margins strongly inrolled; calyx and pedicels densely white-woolly . . . . 3. *P. argentea.*
      f. Leaflets with flat margins; calyx and pedicels silky-hairy *g.*
        g. Surface of nutlets marked with a network of fine ridges . . . . 4. *P. intermedia.*
        g. Surface of nutlet smooth . . . . . . 5. *P. gracilis.*
  c. Leaves pinnately compound *h.*
    h. Stems woody . . . . 8. *P. fruticosa.*
    h. Stems not woody *i.*
      i. Stems leafy, erect or reclining at base but not rooting at each node; flowers several or many in a branched inflorescence *j.*
        j. Petals purple; leaflets several times as long as wide. . . . . 7. *P. palustris.*
        j. Petals yellow; leaflets seldom more than twice as long as wide . . . 1. *P. arguta.*
      i. Stems mostly flat on the ground, radiating from a rosette of leaves and rooting at each node; flowers borne singly or a few together at each node or in the rosette . . . . 10. *P. Anserina.*

1. **P. argùta** Pursh. Stems 3–10 dm. high, stout, rough-hairy; basal leaves long-petioled, the petioles decreasing in length in the upper leaves; leaflets velvety beneath; flowers many, crowded, the petals cream-colored.—Dry open ground, mostly southward.

2. **P. norvégica** L. (Fig. 194) Stems erect, 2–9 dm. high, with *stiff spreading hairs;* petals small, about as long as the sepals.—Dry soil.

3. **P. argéntea** L. SILVERY CINQUEFOIL. (Fig. 195) Plants usually low, sometimes 5 dm. high, much branched; *sepals and lower surfaces of the leaflets whitened with a silky wool;* petals a little longer than the sepals.—Dry soil.

4. **P. intermèdia** L. A rare weed along railroads; introduced from Europe.

5. **P. grácilis** Dougl. A rare weed along railroads; introduced from the west.

6. **P. récta** L. Plant coarse, erect, hairy; leaflets 5–7, with many coarse blunt teeth (Fig. 196).—A European plant recently introduced into this region, and locally abundant.

7. **P. palústris** (L.) Scop. MARSH FIVE-FINGER. Stems somewhat woody at base; *leaves pinnately compound* (Fig. 197); bases of the petioles sheathing the stem.—Bogs, northward and eastward.

8. **P. fruticòsa** L. SHRUBBY CINQUEFOIL. Stem much branched, *woody,* 1–8 dm. high; leaves pinnately compound; leaflets 5–7, small, entire, whitened beneath (Fig. 199); flowers bright yellow, conspicuous.—Occasional in springy meadows and borders of bogs southward and eastward.

9. **P. tridentàta** Ait. THREE-TOOTHED FIVE-FINGER. Stems 3–22 dm. high, somewhat woody at base; leaflets 3, entire except for the *3 teeth at the apex* (Fig. 200); flowers white.—Dry sterile rocky or sandy soil, south to the Wisconsin Dells and rarely to Dane County.

10. **P. anserìna** L. SILVER WEED. *Spreading by long runners;* leaflets whitened beneath with silky hairs.—Sandy shores, Lake Michigan and occasionally inland.

11. **P. símplex** Michx. FIVE-FINGER. Stems erect or reclining, often rooting at the nodes; leaflets 3, the 2 lateral deeply cleft so that there appear to be 5 leaflets (Fig. 198); flowers bright yellow (*P. canadensis* of 7th ed., *Gray's Manual,* not L.).—Very common in pastures, roadsides, etc.—The stem usually has spreading hairs; var. **calvéscens** Fernald has stems glabrous or with appressed hairs and is found occasionally, while var. **argyrísma** Fernald has leaflets silvery-silky and has been collected in Richland County.

9. **Gèum** AVENS

Perennial herbs; leaves pinnate, the largest often in a basal rosette; stipules large, kidney-shaped; stamens 20 or more; calyx with bractlets outside the lobes and alternating with them; achenes many, with long plumose persistent styles.

The character of the receptacle, important in the first four species, may be seen by removing some of the fruits and examining the structure on which they were borne.

a. Calyx-lobes green, turned back (Fig. 203) *b.*
- *b.* Petals white or greenish yellow; stipules 7–15 mm. long *c.*
  - *c.* Petals equaling the calyx-lobes (Fig. 201); receptacle densely hairy . . . . 1. *G. canadense.*
  - *c.* Petals about half as long as the calyx-lobes (Fig. 202); receptacle nearly glabrous. . 2. *G. laciniatum.*
- *b.* Petals bright yellow; stipules longer, deeply cut *d.*
  - *d.* Lower internode of style not glandular; receptacle densely hairy . . . . . . 3. *G. aleppicum.*
  - *d.* Lower internode of style with minute stalked glands; receptacle nearly glabrous. . . . . 4. *G. macrophyllum.*

a. Calyx-lobes purple, ascending (Fig. 204) *e.*
- *e.* Bractlets about half as long as the calyx-lobes (Fig. 204). . . . . 5. *G. rivale.*
- *e.* Bractlets longer than the calyx-lobes (Fig. 205) 6. *G. triflorum.*

1. **G. canadénse** Jacq. Stem 6–11 dm. high, forked above, slightly hairy or woolly; leaves pinnately 3–5-foliolate (Fig. 201).—Woods and thickets.

2. **G. laciniàtum** Murr., var. **trichocárpum** Fernald. Stems and petioles bristly-hairy; lowest leaves compound, or often simple with blades heart-shaped at base; stem-leaves 3–cleft (Fig. 202). (*G. virginianum* of Ed. 7, not L.)—Mostly northward.

3. **G. aléppicum** Jacq., var. **stríctum** (Ait.) Fernald. Stem 9–15 dm. high, hairy; leaflets of stem-leaves much like those of No. 2, but narrower (Fig. 203); petals conspicuous.—Moist openings in woods.

4. **G. macrophýllum** Willd., var. **perincìsum** (Rydb.) Raup. Similar to No. 3.—Rare, Washburn Co.

5. **G. rivàle** L. Stems with few leaves; leaflets of lower leaves roundish, toothed all around, the terminal 3–lobed; style about 1 cm. long in fruit (Fig. 204).—Moist meadows.

6. **G. triflòrum** Pursh. (Fig. 205) Plants with soft hairs; leaves mostly at the base of the stem; leaflets many, narrowed at base, coarsely toothed toward the apex only; sepals about 1 cm. long, exceeding the purplish petals; style becoming 5 cm. long in fruit. —Dry fields and prairies, north to Pierce, Waupaca, and Marinette Counties.

10. **Rùbus**

Mostly shrubs; stems of the first year, in the raspberries and blackberries, with 3– or 5–foliolate leaves and without flowers, their axillary buds in the second year forming short flowering branches with 3–foliolate leaves; fruits fleshy, each with a single stone, cohering, many on a dome-shaped receptacle.

a. Leaves compound *b.*
b. Plants woody *c.*
c. **Leaves woolly-whitened beneath, those of the first year's growth pinnately compound** ***d.***
d. **Pedicels with glands and slender bristles;** sepals bristly on the back . . . . . 1. *R. idaeus.*
d. Pedicels with stout hooked prickles but no glands; sepals without bristles . . . 2. *R. occidentalis.*
c. **Leaves sometimes velvety beneath, but not woolly-whitened, the first year's growth 3- or 5-foliolate** ***e.***
e. Plants erect or arching, sometimes rooting at tip . . . . 5. The blackberries.
e. Plants low, creeping, rooting at the nodes or tip . . . . 6. The dewberries.
b. Plants low, herbaceous, soft-woody at base . . 4. *R. pubescens.*
a. Leaves simple . . . . 3. *R. parviflorus.*

1. **R. idaèus** L., var. **strigòsus** (Michx.) Maxim. RED RASPBERRY. *Stems upright*, covered with needle-like prickles; fruit red, easily detached from the receptacle (var. *aculeatissimus*, in part).—Common.—Var. **canadénsis** Richards. has the stems of the first year's growth minutely hairy beneath the slender prickles.—Usually growing with var. *strigosus* but most common along our northern borders.—Var. **aculeatíssimus** Regel & Tiling has the prickles broadened at base, and is approached by material from northern Wisconsin.

2. **R. occidentàlis** L. BLACK RASPBERRY. *Stems recurved, rooting at tip;* leaves usually 3–foliolate; fruit purple-black, easily detached from the receptacle; whole plant somewhat powdery-whitened.—Common in openings in woods.

3. **R. parviflòrus** Nutt. THIMBLEBERRY. *Shrubs without prickles*, but the new growth densely glandular; leaves *maple-like;* flowers large, white.—Rich woods, south to Lincoln and Manitowoc Counties.

4. **R. pubéscens** Raf. Stems 1–4 dm. high, trailing or ascending; leaflets 3–5, thin, coarsely toothed; petals small, white or pinkish.—Bogs.

5. THE BLACKBERRIES. Erect or arching shrubs; leaves palmate; stems and often petioles and pedicels with large, hooked prickles; flowers white; mature fruit black, not separating from the receptacle at maturity.—The species of blackberries and dewberries are too difficult for the beginner to attempt.

6. THE DEWBERRIES. Usually smaller and more delicate than the blackberries.

11. **Ròsa** Rose

Shrubs; leaves pinnate, the leaflets toothed and mostly blunt or rounded at apex; stipules joined for most of their length with the petiole, the free part triangular; calyx-tube (or receptacle) urn-shaped, constricted at apex, becoming red and fleshy in fruit, enclosing the bony achenes; stamens very numerous; petals 5, usually pink or white.—A variable, probably freely hybridizing group, in which many species and varieties have been described, and many more doubtless will be described. The present treatment is necessarily very conservative, including only the more well-marked forms.

a. Styles all together in a column as long as the stamens . . . . 1. *R. setigera.*
a. Styles distinct from one another, shorter than the stamens *b*.
  b. Pedicels and receptacle without stalked glands *c*.
    c. Leaflets 5–7 *d*.
      d. Stems without prickles . . . . 2. *R. blanda.*
      d. Stems with prickles *e*.
        e. Teeth of leaflets incurved, so that the outer side of each is convex and the inner slightly concave (Fig. 206) . . . . 2. *R. blanda*, var. *hispida.*
        e. Teeth of leaflets rather spreading, so that each side is somewhat convex (Fig. 207) . . . . 3. *R. acicularis.*
    c. Leaflets 9–11 *f*.
      f. Rachis and leaflets glabrous on both surfaces . . . . 4. *R. arkansana.*
      f. Petiole, rachis, and lower leaf-surface soft-pilose . . . . 4. *R. arkansana*, var. *suffulta.*
  b. Pedicels and receptacle with stalked glands *g*.
    g. Rachis of leaves with stalked glands . . . 5. *R. rubiginosa.*
    g. Rachis of leaves without stalked glands *h*.
      h. Prickles stout, curved, broad-based; terminal leaflet with 14–20 fine teeth on each side above the middle (Fig. 208) 6. *R. palustris.*
      h. Prickles slender, straight, not very broad-based; terminal leaflet with 9–13 coarser teeth on each side above the middle (Fig. 209) . . . . 7. *R. carolina.*

1. **R. setígera** Michx. Prairie Rose. *Stems climbing or arching*, with stout flattened prickles; leaflets mostly 3 on flowering stems.—Rare, escaping from cultivation.

2. **R. blánda** Ait. Meadow Rose. (Fig. 206) Plants usually less than a meter high; leaf-rachis sometimes smooth, often hairy or woolly, rarely with stalked glands; flowers usually 3 or more at the end of a branch 1 dm. or more long, white or pink. Usually in moist places.—Var. **híspida** Farw. is more or less armed with prickles.

3. **R. aciculàris** Lindl. (Fig. 207) *Leaf-rachis usually glandular;* flowers 1–3 at the end of a branch 1 dm. or less long. Fruit *pyri-*

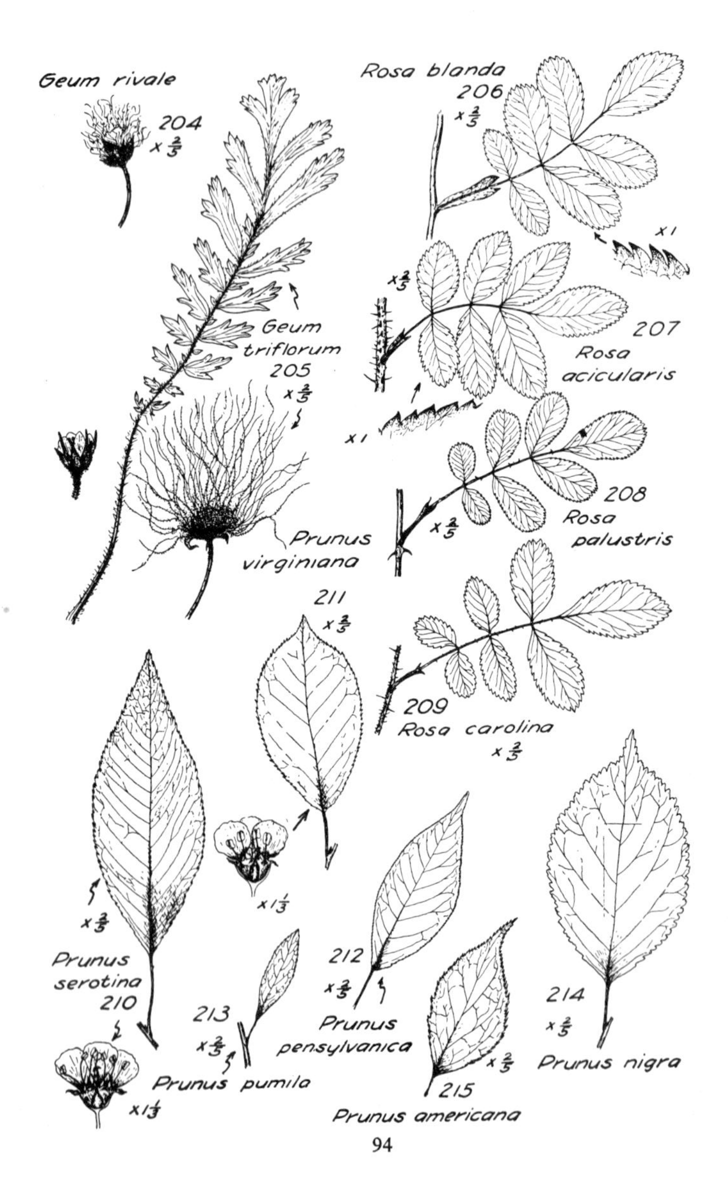
Geum rivale
204
x 2/3
Geum
triflorum
205
x 2/3
Prunus
virginiana
Rosa blanda
206
x 2/3
x 1
x 2/3
207
Rosa
acicularis
x 1
208
Rosa
palustris
x 2/5
211
x 2/3
209
Rosa carolina
x 2/3
x 1 1/3
x 2/3
Prunus
serotina
210
x 1 1/3
213
x 2/3
Prunus pumila
212
x 2/3
Prunus
pensylvanica
x 2/3
215
Prunus americana
214
x 2/5
Prunus nigra

form, contracted to a neck below the beak of sepals. Var. **Bourgeauiàna** Crepin has *subglobose fruit*, the neck less developed.—Sandy shores, etc., south to Jackson and Door Counties.

4. **R. arkansàna** Porter. Stems 3–5 dm. high, usually simple, covered rather densely with straight prickles. Var. **suffúlta** (Greene) Cockerell, has petiole, rachis, and lower leaf-surface *soft-pilose*.—Rocky slopes, thickets, and dry prairies, southern Wisconsin.

5. **R. rubiginòsa** L. SWEETBRIAR. Stems usually arching, armed with *very broad-based flattened prickles;* leaflets dark-dotted with glands beneath, *aromatic (R. Eglanteria)*.—Occasionally escaping from cultivation.

6. **R. palústris** Marsh. SWAMP ROSE. (Fig. 208) Stems 0.7–2 m. high; prickles somewhat flattened at base or occasionally absent.—Borders of swamps and streams.

7. **R. carolìna** L. PASTURE ROSE. (Fig. 209) Stems 3–6 dm. high, with slender prickles.—Borders of woods, and roadsides.

12. **Prùnus** CHERRY; PLUM

Trees or woody shrubs; leaves finely toothed; flowers white or pinkish; fruit fleshy, with a stone enclosing the single seed.

a. Flowers coming with the leaves, in racemes *b.*	
b. Petals fan-shaped, decidedly narrowed to the attachment (Fig. 210); calyx persisting on the fruit	1. *P. serotina.*
b. Petals nearly round, not narrowed to the attachment (Fig. 211); calyx not persisting on the fruit	2. *P. virginiana.*
a. Flowers coming before the leaves, in umbels *c.*	
c. Petals 4–6 mm. long; branches without thorns *d.*	
d. Leaf-blades toothed nearly to the base (Fig. 212)	3. *P. pensylvanica.*
d. Leaf-blades not toothed below the middle (Fig. 213)	4. *P. pumila.*
c. Petals 6–16 mm. long; some branches thorny *e.*	
e. Calyx-lobes glandular-margined, not woolly	5. *P. nigra.*
e. Calyx-lobes woolly, not glandular	6. *P. americana.*

1. **P. seròtina** Ehrh. BLACK CHERRY. Large tree with aromatic inner bark; *leaves with incurved teeth;* midrib with rusty pubescence, thickest at base (Fig. 210); fruit black.—Woods and fencerows.

2. **P. virginiàna** L. CHOKE CHERRY. Shrubs or small trees, the inner bark with a disagreeable odor; *leaves with sharp spreading teeth* (Fig. 211); *glabrous*, except in axils of veins along the midrib; fruit dark red. Forma **Deàmii** G. N. Jones is pubescent on new branchlets, rachis, petioles, and lower leaf-surfaces.—Woods, thickets, and fencerows.

3. **P. pensylvánica** L. f. PIN CHERRY. Shrub or small tree; leaves oval or lanceolate, rounded or broadly wedge-shaped at base (Fig. 212); fruit light red, sour.—Woods and clearings.

4. **P. pùmila** L. SAND CHERRY. Erect or prostrate small shrub; leaf-blades somewhat whitened beneath, 3–4 times as long as broad (Fig. 213).—Sandy or rocky ground.—Broader-leaved forms are often separated as var. **susquehánae** (Willd.) Jaeg. (includes *P. susquehanae* Willd.).

5. **P. nìgra** Ait. CANADA PLUM. Shrub or small tree; some twigs short and leafless, serving as thorns; *leaves with rounded teeth* (Fig. 214); calyx green or pink.—North to Douglas and Vilas Counties.

6. **P. americàna** Marsh. WILD PLUM. Small tree, with thorns as in No. 5; *leaves sharply toothed; glabrous* (Fig. 215). Var. **lanàta** Sudw. has branchlets, petioles, and lower leaf-surfaces *pubescent*.—Pastures, fencerows, and borders of woods.

LEGUMINÒSAE PEA FAMILY

Flowers sometimes nearly regular, but usually bilaterally symmetrical, the upper petal *(standard)* largest and usually erect, the two lateral ones *(wings)* oblique and outside the two lower which are united to form the *keel*, which ordinarily encloses the 10 (rarely 5) stamens and single pistil; fruit a pod which usually splits lengthwise into two parts, thus releasing the seeds.

a. Trees or shrubs *b*.
- *b*. Ultimate divisions of leaves broadest below the middle, gradually tapering into a long point (Fig. 216) . . . . 1. *Gymnocladus*.
- *b*. Ultimate divisions of leaves oval or with nearly parallel sides, blunt or with a short abrupt point (Figs. 217 and 227) *c*.
  - *c*. Plants low, slightly woody, whitened with copious hairs . . . . 10. *Tephrosia*.
  - *c*. Plants definitely woody, the stems scarcely hairy *d*.
    - *d*. Ultimate divisions of leaves on stipes 1 mm. or less long . . . . 2. *Gleditsia*.
    - *d*. Ultimate divisions of leaves on stipes 2–4 mm. long *e*.
      - *e*. Flowers small, hardly pediceled, in a close cylindrical spike (Fig. 226) . 9. *Amorpha*.
      - *e*. Flowers large, usually less than 20 in a loose raceme, on pedicels 5 mm. or more long (Fig. 228) . . . . . 11. *Robinia*.

a. Herbs *f*.
- *f*. Stamens not joined to one another . . . . . 3. *Baptisia*.
- *f*. Stamens joined in 1 or 2 groups *g*.
  - *g*. Leaves palmately 5–11-foliolate *h*.
    - *h*. Calyx 2–lobed . . . . 4. *Lupinus*.
    - *h*. Calyx 5–lobed . . . . 8. *Psoralea*.

g. Leaves not palmately 5–11-foliolate *i.*
  i. Leaves 3–foliolate, with no tendrils *j.*
    j. Flowers in a close globular head . . 5. *Trifolium.*
    j. Flowers in an elongate head or spike *k.*
      k. Spike many times as long as broad 6. *Melilotus.*
      k. Spike not over 3 times as long as broad . . . . 7. *Medicago.*
  i. Leaves more than 3–foliolate, or else with one or more of the terminal leaflets modified as tendrils *l.*
    l. Leaves without tendrils *m.*
      m. Each leaflet with many conspicuous lateral veins running from mid-rib to margin . . . . 10. *Tephrosia.*
      m. Each leaflet with a few obscure and irregular veins which seldom reach the margin *n.*
        n. Keel not tipped with a sharp point . . . . 12. *Astragalus.*
        n. Keel tipped with an abrupt sharp point . . . . 13. *Oxytropis.*
    l. Leaves with tendrils *o.*
      o. Lateral petals joined to the keel . 14. *Vicia.*
      o. Lateral petals not joined to the keel 15. *Lathyrus.*

1. **Gymnócladus** KENTUCKY COFFEE TREE

G. dioíca (L.) Koch. Tall tree, without thorns; leaves 6–9 dm. long, once or twice pinnate (Fig. 216); flowers nearly regular, about 2 cm. long, short-hairy; pod oblong, 1.5–2.5 dm. long, 3–4 cm. broad, pulp inside, with flattish seeds.—Rather rare; southern Wisconsin, and north to Buffalo, Dane, and Outagamie Counties.

2. **Gledítsia** HONEY LOCUST

G. triacánthos L. Tree with long stout often 3–branched thorns; leaves once or twice pinnate (Fig. 217); flowers small, nearly regular, in a long dense spike; fruit a broad flat pod 2–4.5 dm. long. —River-bottoms, north to Crawford and Dane Counties; sometimes planted.

3. **Baptísia** FALSE INDIGO

Large coarse herbs; leaves 3–foliolate, 5–8 cm. long; pods short, inflated, nearly round in cross section, many-seeded; calyx persistent in fruit.

1. **B. leucophaèa** Nutt. *Plants hairy;* stipules large, persistent (Fig. 218); flowers large, cream-colored.—Common on prairies north to Eau Claire and Juneau Counties.—Var. **glabréscens** Larisey has the stem without hairs and leaves less hairy; it is less common, apparently, in sandy places.

2. **B. leucántha** T. & G. *Plants without hairs;* stipules soon dropping (Fig. 219); flowers white.—Prairies, southern and western Wisconsin.

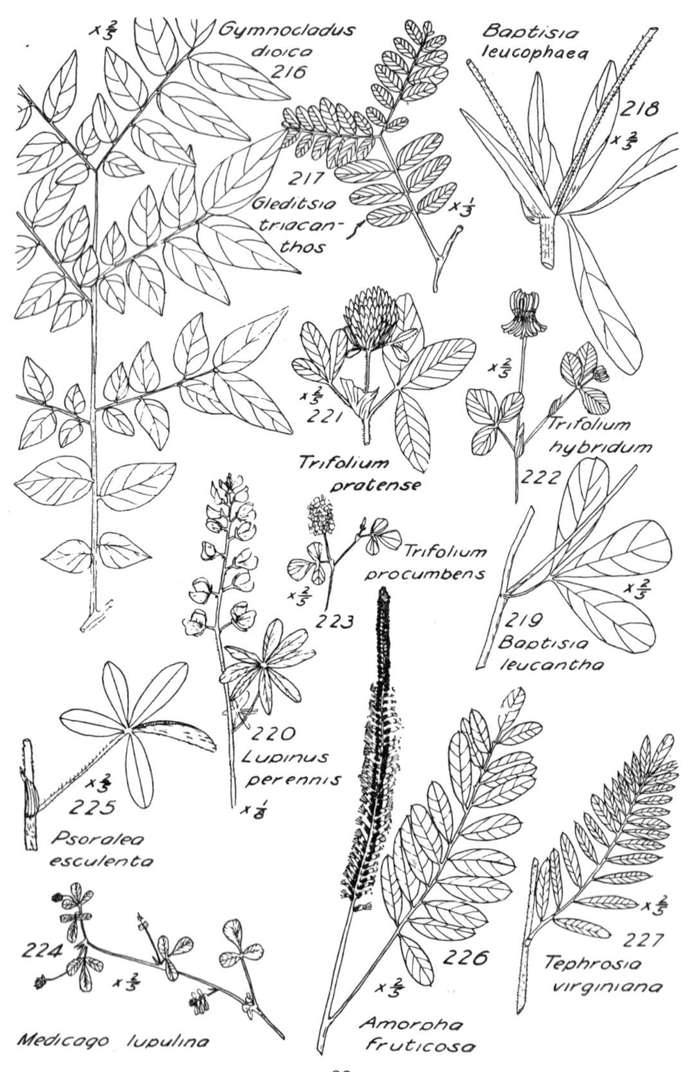
Gymnocladus dioica 216
x 2/5
217 Gleditsia triacanthos
x 1/3
Baptisia leucophaea
218
x 2/5
221
x 2/5
Trifolium pratense
x 2/5
Trifolium hybridum
222
Trifolium procumbens
x 2/5
223
x 2/5
219 Baptisia leucantha
220 Lupinus perennis
x 1/8
x 2/5
225
Psoralea esculenta
224
x 2/5
Medicago lupulina
226
x 2/5
Amorpha fruticosa
x 2/5
227
Tephrosia virginiana

4. **Lupìnus** WILD LUPINE

L. perénnis L. (Fig. 220) Tall herbs; flowers blue, in a long raceme; pod oblong, flattened, often constricted between the seeds. —Dry sand; less common than var. **occidentàlis** S. Wats.; stems and petioles with long silky hairs.

5. **Trifòlium** CLOVER

Pods small and membranous, often shorter than the persistent calyx, 1–6-seeded.

a. Flowers without pedicels . . . . 1. *T. pratense.*
a. Flowers on short pedicels *b.*
  b. Flowers red or white; terminal leaflet not stalked *c.*
    c. Stems creeping, rooting at the nodes . . . 2. *T. repens.*
    c. Stems erect or ascending, not rooting at the nodes . . . . 3. *T. hybridum.*
  b. Flowers yellow; terminal leaflet short-stalked . 4. *T. procumbens.*

1. **T. praténse** L. RED CLOVER. (Fig. 221) Plant rather hairy; leaflets with a pale spot on the upper surface; flowers magenta to white.—Introduced from Europe, and escaped from cultivation to fields and roadsides.

2. **T. rèpens** L. WHITE CLOVER. Plants without hairs; leaflets nearly as broad as long, often notched at the apex; flowers white or pink; calyx-lobes about equaling the tube.—Common everywhere; introduced from Europe.

3. **T. hýbridum** L. ALSIKE CLOVER. (Fig. 222) Similar to No. 2, but not rooting at the nodes; calyx-lobes 1.5–2 times as long as the tube.—Common; introduced from Europe.

4. **T. procúmbens** L. LOW HOP CLOVER. (Fig. 223) Stems low, 1–1.5 dm. high, hairy; leaflets often notched at apex; heads small, close, globular, with 20–40 flowers; *petals furrowed.*—Introduced from Europe.—See *Medicago lupulina*, specimens of which may key to this species.

6. **Melilòtus** SWEET CLOVER

Pods ovoid, wrinkled, longer than the calyx, 1–2 seeded.

1. **M. álba** Desr. WHITE SWEET CLOVER. Tall plants; leaflets several times as long as broad; flowers white.—Very common along roadsides, in fields and waste ground, and on railroad embankments; introduced from Europe.

2. **M. officinàlis** (L.) Lam. YELLOW SWEET CLOVER. Similar to No. 1; flowers yellow.—Less common, but becoming abundant as it escapes from cultivation.

7. Medicàgo

Pods curved or coiled.

1. **M. satìva** L. ALFALFA; LUCERNE. Plants smooth; leaflets several times as long as broad; flowers bluish-purple.—Escaping from cultivation along roadsides and in fields; introduced from Europe.

Sometimes hybrids with **M. falcàta** L., the SICKLE ALFALFA, are found; the flowers range through cream to yellow, and the pods are only slightly coiled or sickle-shaped.

2. **M. lupulìna** L. BLACK MEDICK. (Fig. 224) Plants finely hairy; leaflets not over twice as long as broad; heads with 10–12 yellow flowers; *petals not furrowed.*—Roadsides, about dwellings, and borders of city streets; adventive from Europe.

8. Psoràlea POMME DE PRAIRIE

P. esculénta Pursh. (Fig. 225) Perennial herbs, from a deep spindle-shaped taproot; stem and leaves very rough-hairy; flowers bluish or whitish, in dense spike-like racemes; pod thick, usually shorter than the persistent calyx, 1-seeded, with glandular dots.—Prairies, southward and westward. Rare.

9. Amórpha FALSE INDIGO

A. fruticòsa L., var. **angustifòlia** Pursh. (Fig. 226) Tall shrubs; leaves with 9–25 leaflets, each about 2 cm. long; flowers in a long slender dense spike, each with but one petal, purple; pod oblong, longer than the persistent calyx, roughened, 1–2 seeded.—River bottoms, up the Wisconsin River to Sauk County, and up the Mississippi and St. Croix Rivers to St. Croix Falls.

10. Tephròsia HOARY PEA; GOAT'S RUE

T. virginiàna (L.) Pers. (Fig. 227) Whole plant somewhat whitened with silky hairs; stem rather woody at base, 3–6 dm. high; flowers 1–1.5 cm. long, yellowish, marked with purple; pod linear, flat, several-seeded.—Dry sandy or rocky ground, north to Jackson and Juneau Counties.—Typical *T. virginiana*, with leaflets perfectly glabrous above, is rare in Wisconsin; our common plant, with leaflets finely pubescent above, is var. **holoserícea** (Nutt.) T. & G.

11. Robínia LOCUST

1. **R. Pseùdo-acàcia** L. (Fig. 228) Branchlets scarcely hairy; flowers showy, white, fragrant, in drooping racemes in the leaf-axils; fruit flat, about 1 dm. long and 1 cm. wide.—Often planted.

2. **R. viscòsa** Vent. CLAMMY LOCUST. Branchlets with sticky hairs; flowers pink.—Occasionally planted.

3. **R. híspida L.** Branchlets bristly-hispid; flowers pink.—Occasionally escaping from cultivation.

12. **Astrágalus** MILK VETCH

Perennial herbs, often slightly woody at base; leaves pinnate, with 11–25 leaflets; flowers in a spike; pods mostly swollen.

a. Flowers purple; pod short-stalked in the calyx *b.*
  b. Flowers 15–20 mm. long . . . . 1. *A. caryocarpus.*
  b. Flowers 10–12 mm. long . . . . 2. *A. alpinus.*
a. Flowers white; pod not stalked in calyx . . . . 3. *A. neglectus.*

1. **A. caryocárpus** Ker. GROUND PLUM. Stems many from a taproot, 1–3 dm. high; leaflets narrowly oblong, covered with stiff white hairs, as is the calyx.—Prairies, Pierce County.

2. **A. alpìnus** L. Low, branching, sprawling; leaflets oval, over half as broad as long, with rather silky hairs; calyx with close jet-black hairs.—Gravelly shores of Pigeon Lake, near Drummond.

3. **A. negléctus** (T. & G.) Sheldon. (Fig. 229) Erect, 3–6 dm. high; leaflets about 2 cm. long, elliptic or oblong, without hairs; calyx with a few white hairs.—Counties bordering on Lake Michigan.

13. **Oxýtropis**

O. chartàcea Fassett. Leaves all at the base of the plant, silky with fine close white hairs; leaflets lanceolate; scapes with spreading silky or woolly hairs; calyx whitened with dense hairs; corolla blue, or sometimes white; pods leathery, silky-hairy, cylindrical and long-pointed.—Shores of Pigeon Lake, near Drummond, and lake shores east of Plainfield.

14. **Vícia** VETCH; TARE

Trailing or climbing herbs; pod flat, 2–several-seeded.

a. Leaflets with 10 or more pairs of veins *b.*
  b. Racemes without peduncle . . . . 1. *V. angustifolia.*
  b. Racemes peduncled . . . . 4. *V. americana.*
a. Leaflets with 6 or fewer pairs of veins *c.*
  c. Flowers barely 1 cm. long, white with blue tip 3. *V. caroliniana.*
  c. Flowers 10–15 mm. long, blue, rarely white *d.*
    d. Flowers less than 4 times as long as thick *e.*
      e. Limb of standard equaling the claw . . 2. *V. Cracca.*
      e. Limb longer than claw . . . . 2. *V. Cracca*, var. *tenuifolia.*
    d. Flowers more than 5 times as long as thick 5. *V. villosa.*

1. **V. angustifòlia** Reichard. (Fig. 230) Flowers solitary or in pairs in the upper leaf-axils, 1–1.8 cm. long.—Occasional along railroads and in thickets; adventive from Europe.

2. **V. Crácca** L. Leaflets with a short abrupt tip; flowers 1–1.2 cm. long, in dense one-sided racemes.—Occasionally adventive in fields. Var. **tenuifòlia** (Roth) G. Beck is less common.

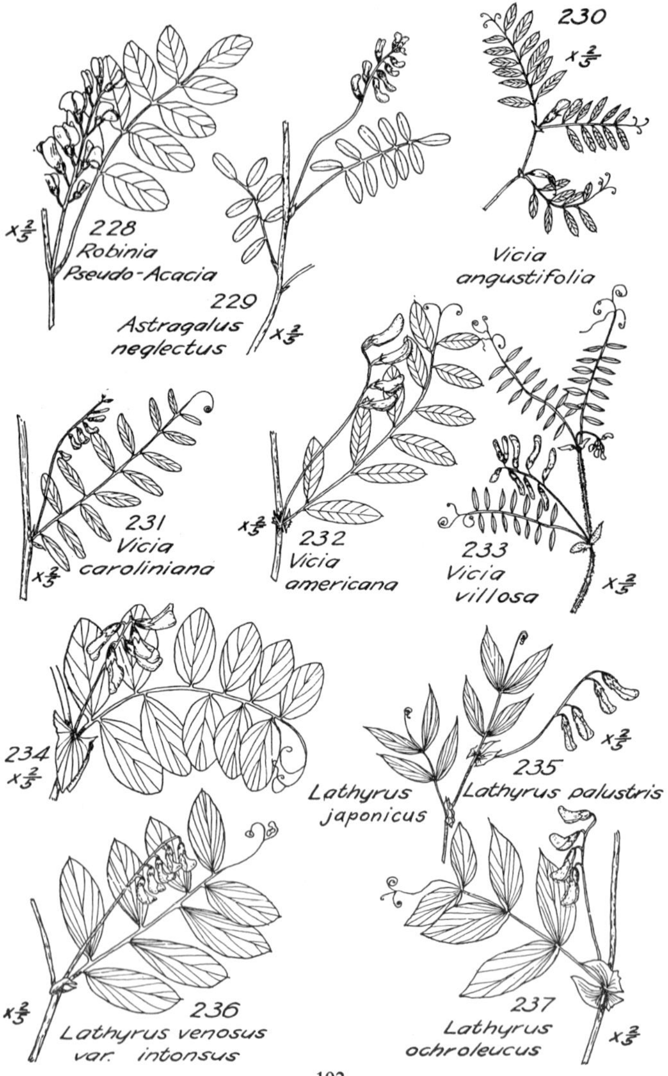
230
x 2/5
228
Robinia
Pseudo-Acacia
x 2/5
229
Astragalus
neglectus
x 2/5
Vicia
angustifolia
231
Vicia
caroliniana
x 2/5
x 2/5
232
Vicia
americana
233
Vicia
villosa
x 2/5
234
x 2/5
x 2/5
235
Lathyrus palustris
Lathyrus
japonicus
x 2/5
236
Lathyrus venosus
var. intonsus
237
Lathyrus
ochroleucus
x 2/5

3. **V. caroliniàna** Walt. (Fig. 231) Leaflets oblong, blunt; flowers whitish, tipped with blue.—Low rich thickets, north to Vernon, Adams, and Winnebago Counties.

4. **V. americàna** Muhl. (Fig. 232) Plants nearly or quite without hairs; leaflets elliptical or ovate, rounded at tip, wavy-veined; flowers purplish.—In woods and grassy places.

5. **V. villòsa** Roth. (Fig. 233) Hairy throughout; flowers white and violet.—Introduced from Eurasia, and occasional in fields.

15. **Láthyrus** WILD PEA

Similar in aspect to *Vicia;* leaflets larger in our species.

a. Stipules not more than 5 mm. broad, or wanting *b.*	
b. Principal leaves with 4–8 leaflets; peduncles 2–8-flowered	2. *L. palustris.*
b. Principal leaves with 8–12 leaflets; peduncles 6–18-flowered	3. *L. venosus*, var. *intonsus.*
a. Stipules 1 cm. or more broad *c.*	
c. Each stipule shaped like half an arrowhead, with 1 basal lobe	4. *L. ochroleucus.*
c. Each stipule shaped like an arrowhead, with 2 basal lobes	1. *L. japonicus.*

1. **L. japónicus** Willd. BEACH PEA. (Fig. 234) Flowers pink when young, purple in age, 1.8–2.5 cm. long; leaves slightly fleshy.—Var. **pellìtus** Fernald, covered with fine hairs, is very rare with us; var. **glàber** (Seringe) Fernald, without hairs, is common along beaches of Lake Michigan and Lake Superior.

2. **L. palústris** L. (Fig. 235) Flowers pale purple, rather loosely arranged, with slender pedicels 3–6 mm. long; calyx smooth.—Moist ground. The leaflets in this species vary greatly in width and length, and the described varieties intergrade. Vars. **linearifòlius** Ser., **pilòsus** (Cham.) Ledeb., and **myrtifòlius** (Muhl.) Gray are covered in detail by Norman C. Fassett, *The Leguminous Plants of Wisconsin* (Madison, Wis.: University of Wisconsin Press, 1939).

3. **L. venòsus** Muhl., var. **intónsus** Butters & St. John. (Fig. 236) Flowers magenta, closely crowded on rather stout pedicels; calyx densely hairy.—Common.

4. **L. ochroleùcus** Hook. (Fig. 237) Stems 3–9 dm. high; flowers 1.5–1.8 cm. long, yellowish-white.—Common in rich open woods.

LINÀCEAE FLAX FAMILY

Lìnum FLAX

Plants 3–10 dm. high, slender, branched above; leaves narrow, sharp-pointed.

1. **L. usitatíssimum** L. Flowers blue.—Roadsides and railroad embankments; introduced from Europe.

2. **L. sulcàtum** Riddell. Flowers yellow; leaves usually with 2 dark glands at base.—Prairies and dry hills, southward and westward.

OXALIDÀCEAE WOOD SORREL FAMILY

Óxalis WOOD SORREL

Small herbs with sour juice; leaves long-petioled, with 3 heart-shaped leaflets, each of which is attached by its point; sepals 5; petals 5, delicate; stamens 10; styles 5; fruit a small pod.

a. Leaves all at the base of the plant; flowers on naked scapes *b*.
  b. Flower solitary on each scape . . . . 1. *O. montana.*
  b. Flowers several in an umbel . . . . 2. *O. violacea.*
a. Leaves on the stem; petals yellow *c*.
  c. Fruits with dense ascending white hairs . . . 3. *O. dillenii.*
  c. Fruits glabrous or with spreading hairs . . . 4. *O. stricta.*

1. **O. montàna** Raf. COMMON WOOD SORREL. (Fig. 238) *Plant with a thick creeping rootstock;* petals white with purple lines.—Cool damp woods in northern Wisconsin.

2. **O. violàcea** L. VIOLET WOOD SORREL. (Fig. 239) *Plants from scaly bulbs* and slender taproot (the latter sometimes thick and fleshy when diseased); petals violet.—Sandy and stony banks, north to St. Croix, Eau Claire, Columbia, and Walworth Counties.

3. **O. dillénii** Jacq. Plants much branched, usually 1 dm. tall or less; *repent*, often rooting at the nodes; pedicels strongly deflexed in fruit (*O. stricta* sensu Am. auth. Native to N. America, rare in Europe).–Common weed.

4. **O. strícta** L. (Fig. 240) Similar, but usually taller; erect; pedicels ascending or spreading in fruit (*O. europaea* Jord., *O. cymosa* Small).

GERANIÀCEAE GERANIUM FAMILY

Geránium

Herbs with palmately compound or deeply lobed leaf-blades on long petioles; petals 5; stamens 10, 5 of them longer and with a gland at base; fruit a long slender cylindrical pod.

a. Stem simple or little branched below, from a stout rootstock . . . . 1. *G. maculatum.*
a. Stem much branched below, spreading, from a taproot *b*.
  b. Petals about 1 cm. long, twice the length of the sepals . . . . 2. *G. Robertianum.*
  b. Petals 3–6 mm. long, 1–1.5 times the length of the sepals *c*.
    c. Sepals with a long bristle-like point *d*.

d. Pedicels not more than twice as long as sepals *e.*
e. Larger sepals 3–4.5 mm. wide, 3–nerved . . . . 3. *G. carolinianum.*
e. Larger sepals 5–8 mm. wide, 5–nerved 4. *G. sphaerospermum.*
d. Pedicels several times as long as the sepals 5. *G. Bicknellii.*
c. Sepals without a long bristle-like point . . 6. *G. pusillum.*

1. **G. maculàtum** L. CRANESBILL. (Fig. 241) Perennial; stem simple below, *above with several peduncles and leaves arising from one point;* leaves about 1 dm. wide, deeply 5–7-parted, the wedge-shaped divisions lobed and cut at the end; petals light purple, 1 cm. or more long.—Common in woods and thickets, north to Douglas and Lincoln Counties.

2. **G. Robertiànum** L. HERB ROBERT. Stems a little hairy; *leaves compound,* the 3–5 divisions pinnately divided, these divisions themselves pinnately lobed.—Door County.

3. **G. caroliniànum** L. *Flowers crowded;* fruit with a stout persistent style about 2 mm. long.—Rare in southern Wisconsin.

4. **G. sphaerospérmum** Fernald. Similar to No. 3.—Rare in northern Wisconsin.

5. **G. Bicknéllii** Britton. (Fig. 242) Leaf-blades about 5–parted, the *divisions forking and cut into somewhat ribbon-like segments;* fruit with a slender persistent style 4–6 mm. long.—In dry ground and clearings, mostly northward.

6. **G. pusíllum** L. Leaf-blades cut about two-thirds of the way to the base, the divisions with rounded lobes; petals little if at all exceeding the sepals.—Rare; adventive from Europe.

RUTÀCEAE RUE FAMILY

Leaves with transparent dots and a pungent oil.

1. Xanthóxylum PRICKLY ASH

X. americànum Mill. Shrubs or small trees with many broad-based prickles; *leaves pinnate,* dioecious flowers yellow, in little clusters appearing before the leaves.—Low ground.—Forma **impùniens** Fasset is without prickles.

2. Ptèlea HOP TREE

P. trifoliàta L. Tall shrubs, or sometimes tree-like; *leaves with 3 leaflets;* flowers in a terminal panicle; fruit surrounded by a wing about 1 cm. broad.—Native from Milwaukee southward, and planted elsewhere.

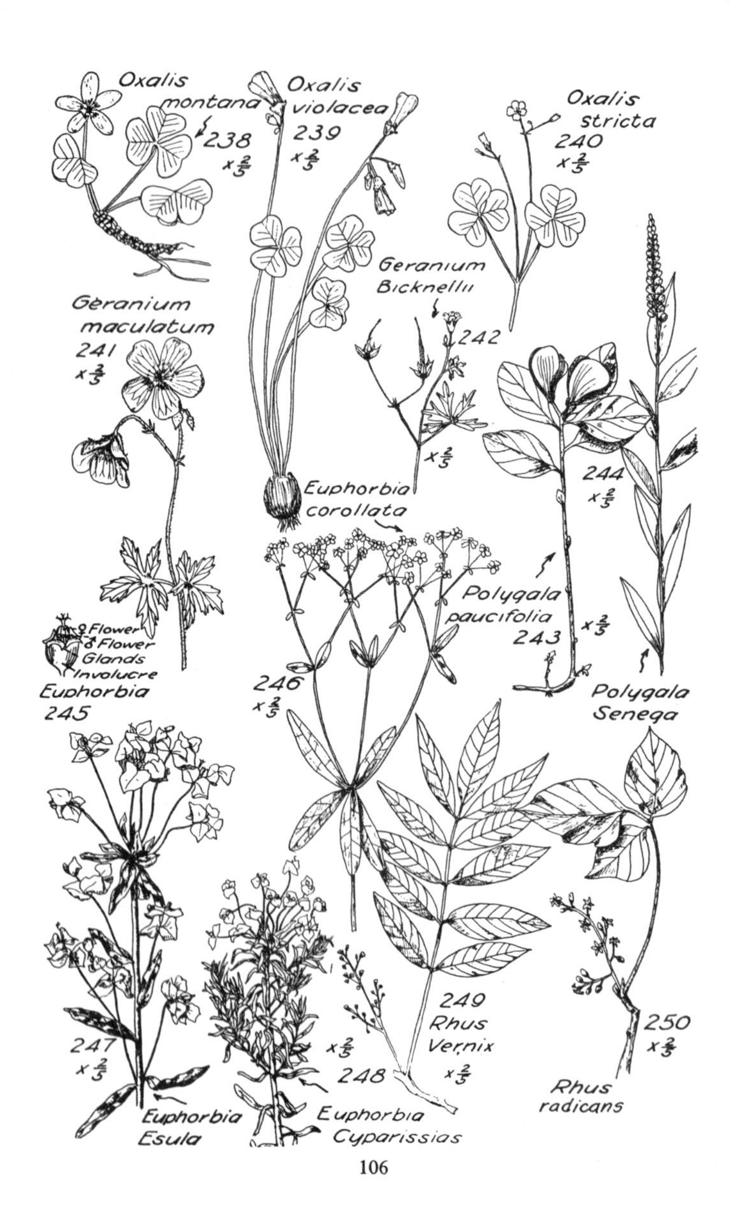
Oxalis montana
238
x 2/5
Oxalis violacea
239
x 2/5
Oxalis stricta
240
x 2/5
Geranium Bicknellii
242
x 2/5
Geranium maculatum
241
x 2/5
244
x 2/5
Euphorbia corollata
Polygala paucifolia
243
x 2/5
♀ Flower
♂ Flower
Glands
Involucre
Euphorbia
245
246
x 2/5
Polygala Senega
249
Rhus Vernix
x 2/5
250
x 2/5
247
x 2/5
x 2/5
248
Rhus radicans
Euphorbia Esula
Euphorbia Cyparissias

POLYGALÀCEAE MILKWORT FAMILY

Polýgala

Herbs; stamens 6 or 8, their stalks more or less united below with each other and with the petals; leaves alternate, not toothed.

a. Flowers 1–2 cm. long, in the axils of upper leaves 1. *P. paucifolia.*
a. Flowers about 0.5 cm. long, in a terminal spike *b.*
  b. Flowers usually pink; one petal with a crest . 3. *P. polygama.*
  b. Flowers white; petals not crested . . . . . . 2. *P. Senega.*

1. **P. paucifòlia** Willd. FRINGED POLYGALA. (Fig. 243) Stems solitary, 7–10 cm. high, from a rootstock; lower leaves small and scale-like, the upper ovate, stalked, crowded; flowers 1–3, 1–2 cm. long, pink.—Woods, south to Barron and Wood Counties, and on dunes to Manitowoc County.

2. **P. Sénega** L. SENECA SNAKEROOT. (Fig. 244) Stems clustered, 1.5–3 dm. high; leaves about 5 mm. broad, 1–3 cm. long; flowers white, in a terminal spike.—Prairies, north to Washburn and Marquette Counties.

3. **P. polýgama** Walt. Stems densely tufted from a slender taproot; underground stems with white fleshy flowers which are self-fertilized without opening.—Sandy regions, common except in the north-central area.

EUPHORBIÀCEAE SPURGE FAMILY

Euphórbia SPURGE

Plants 1–5 dm. tall; leaves simple, alternate, not toothed; juice milky; flowers clustered, each cluster containing a pistillate flower and many staminate flowers, each reduced to a single stamen, the whole cluster simulating a single flower, with a 4–5-lobed corolla-like or calyx-like involucre, and 4 or 5 two-horned glands (Fig. 245); fruit a capsule of 3 compartments; plants poisonous.

a. Involucre white . . . . 1. *E. corollata.*
a. Involucre greenish or yellowish *b.*
  b. Foliage leaves at least 3 times as long as wide *c.*
    c. Floral leaves 5 mm. wide . . . . 2. E. *Cyparissias.*
    c. Floral leaves 1–1.5 cm. wide . . . . 3. *E. Esula.*
  b. Foliage leaves nearly or quite as wide as long 4. *E. commutata.*

1. **E. corollàta** L. FLOWERING SPURGE. (Fig. 246) Stems usually several from a deep woody root, simple below, much branched in the inflorescence; leaves linear-oblong.—Open sandy soil, north to St. Croix and Columbia Counties, and occasionally adventive northward.

2. **E. Cyparíssias** L. CYPRESS SPURGE. (Fig. 248) Plants perennial from rootstocks; leaves narrowly ribbon-like, very numerous, 0.5–2 cm. long; floral leaves yellowish-green.—Cemeteries and about abandoned houses; introduced from Europe.

3. **E. Ésula** L. (Fig. 247) Perennial from rootstocks; leaves 2–6 cm. long; floral leaves heart-shaped, yellow.—Becoming an abundant weed in fields and along roadsides; adventive from Europe.

4. **E. commutàta** Engelm. Leaves round-obovate; floral leaves ovate, green, 7–10 mm. broad.—Beloit.

LIMNANTHÀCEAE False Mermaid Family

Floèrkea proserpinacoìdes Willd. Stems 1–3 dm. high, lax; leaves pinnate; leaflets 3–5, lanceolate; flowers solitary in the leaf-axils, minute, on long pedicels.—Locally abundant in moist shady maple woods.

ANACARDIÀCEAE Cashew Family

Trees or shrubs with resinous or milky juice; flowers green in a panicle or head; sepals and petals 5; the species here described poisonous to the touch.

Rhùs

1. **R. Vérnix** L. Poison Sumach; Poison Dogwood. (Fig. 249) Shrub 2–3 m. high; leaves pinnately compound; leaflets 7–13, not toothed.—Swamps, mostly southward.

2. **R. radìcans** L. Poison Ivy; Poison Oak. (Fig. 250) Small erect shrub, or trailing or climbing vine; leaflets 3, often few-toothed, red and shining when expanding.—Common.

AQUIFOLIÀCEAE Holly Family

Nemopánthus mucronàta (L.) Trel. Mountain Holly. Shrub 0.3–3 m. high; leaves alternate, the petioles 5–10 mm. long, the blades broadest above the middle, round-tipped, *with a small abrupt point* (Fig. 251); fruit a red berry.—Swamps, northward and eastward.

CELASTRÀCEAE Staff Tree Family

Shrubs; leaves simple, petioled; flowers very small; fruit a pod; seeds with a colored appendage.

a. Leaves opposite . . . . 1. *Euonymus.*
a. Leaves alternate . . . . 2. *Celastrus.*

1. Euónymus Wahoo

E. atropurpùreus Jacq. Small tree; leaves finely and sharply toothed (Fig. 252); flowers several on branched peduncles, which come from the lower part of the current season's growth.—Southward and westward.

2. **Celástrus** CLIMBING BITTERSWEET

C. scándens L. (Fig. 253) Twining shrub; leaves finely toothed, pointed; flowers greenish, in clusters at the ends of the branches. —Thickets and along fences.

STAPHYLEÀCEAE BLADDERNUT FAMILY

Staphylèa trifòlia L. BLADDERNUT. (Fig. 254) Shrub or small tree; leaves of 3 leaflets, the terminal one stalked, each narrowed to a long point, finely toothed; flowers in drooping racemes terminating the branches; pod large, 3–parted, papery, and much inflated.—Woods and bluffs, north to Polk, Sawyer, and Brown Counties.

ACERÀCEAE MAPLE FAMILY

Àcer MAPLE

Trees or shrubs, with opposite, palmately lobed or pinnately compound leaves; ovary of 2 carpels, each becoming winged, easily separable from each other at maturity.

a. Stamens on a definite disk; leaves palmately lobed *b*.	
b. Flowers in long racemes	1. *A. spicatum.*
b. Flowers in umbel-like or panicle-like clusters *c*.	
c. Flowers yellowish or greenish, long-pediceled *d*.	
d. Inflorescence irregular and little branched	2. *A. saccharum.*
d. Inflorescence rather flat-topped and several times branched.	3. *A. platanoides.*
c. Flowers red, almost without pedicels, appearing before the leaves *e*.	
e. Petals none; leaves lobed more than halfway to the midrib (Fig. 257)	4. *A. saccharinum.*
e. Petals present; leaves lobed ⅓ of the way to the midrib (Fig. 258)	5. *A. rubrum.*
a. Stamens not on a disk; leaves pinnately compound	6. *A. Negundo.*

1. **A. spicàtum** Lam. MOUNTAIN MAPLE. A shrub or small tree; leaves slightly heart-shaped at the base of the blade, 3–5-lobed, toothed, *downy beneath* (Fig. 255); fruit reddish.—Mostly northward, coming south on cool bluffs.

2. **A. sáccharum** Marsh. SUGAR MAPLE. Tree with scaly bark; buds slender, pointed; *juice not milky;* flowers hang vertically on *weak pedicels;* leaf-blades whitish and smooth beneath, 3–5-lobed with rounded sinuses, the lobes themselves somewhat lobed and wavy-margined (Fig. 256).—Woods.—Var. **nìgrum** (Michx. f.) Britton. BLACK MAPLE. Leaves green and downy beneath, mostly 3–lobed.—With the Sugar Maple.

3. **A. platanoìdes.** NORWAY MAPLE. Large tree with ridged bark; buds fat, blunt; *juice milky; pedicels spreading* to form umbel-like clusters; leaf-blades 5–lobed, the lobes cut into long-pointed coarse

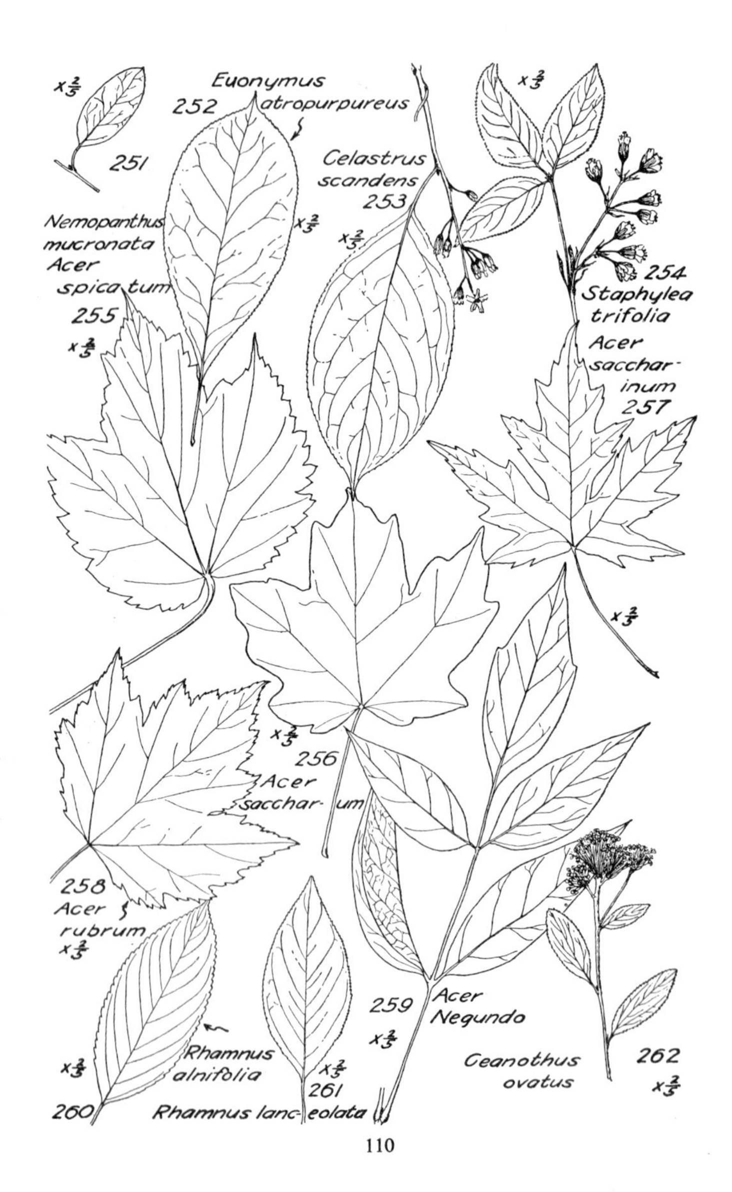
x 2/5
251
Euonymus
252
atropurpureus
x 2/5
Celastrus
scandens
253
x 2/5
x 2/5
254
Staphylea
trifolia
Nemopanthus
mucronata
Acer
spicatum
255
x 2/5
Acer
sacchar-
inum
257
x 2/5
x 2/5
256
Acer
sacchar- um
258
Acer
rubrum
x 2/5
259
Acer
Negundo
x 2/5
x 2/5
Rhamnus
alnifolia
x 2/5
261
260
Rhamnus lanceolata
Ceanothus
ovatus
262
x 2/5

teeth or lobes.—Mostly cultivated as a shade tree; introduced from Europe.

4. **A. saccharìnum** L. SILVER MAPLE. Usually a large tree with flaky bark; leaf-blades much whitened beneath, 3–5-lobed, the lobes coarsely and sharply toothed (Fig. 257); fruit 5 cm. long.—Mostly along river-bottoms; also common as a shade tree along city streets.

5. **A. rùbrum** L. RED MAPLE. Similar to No. 4; leaves (Fig. 258) whitened beneath; fruit 2 cm. long.—Common except southwestward.

6. **A. Negúndo** L. BOX ELDER. Tree with close bark; leaflets 3–5, very veiny (Fig. 259); flowers dioecious; petals none.—Mostly southwestward; frequently planted.

HIPPOCASTANÀCEAE BUCKEYE FAMILY

Aèsculus HORSE-CHESTNUT

A. glàbra Willd. OHIO BUCKEYE. Small tree; opposite, palmate leaves with 5–7 leaflets. Flowers showy, in a terminal panicle; yellowish; the upper *petals shorter than the stamens*. Fruit prickly. —Yahara River bottom near Fulton, Rock County, and woods near Coon Valley, Vernon County. **A. octándra** Marsh, with dark yellow *petals longer than the stamens*, and **A. Hippocástanum** L., with *white petals*, are frequently cultivated in Wisconsin. The latter is a European plant.

RHAMNÀCEAE BUCKTHORN FAMILY

Shrubs with mainly alternate, finely toothed leaves. Flowers perfect or dioecious.

a. Flowers scattered toward the base of the current year's growth . . . . 1. *Rhamnus*.
a. Flowers in a compound panicle at the tip of the current year's growth . . . . 2. *Ceanothus*.

1. Rhámnus BUCKTHORN

Petals small or wanting; calyx free from the ovary; fruit black, 2–4 seeded, berry-like.

a. Leaves toothed *b*.
  b. Calyx-lobes and stamens 5; petals none . . . 1. *R. alnifolia*.
  b. Calyx-lobes, petals, and stamens 4 *c*.
    c. Leaves with 3–4 pairs of veins . . . . . . 2. *R. cathartica*.
    c. Leaves with 6–7 pairs of veins . . . . . . 3. *R. lanceolata*.
a. Leaves not toothed . . . . 4. *R. Frangula*.

1. **R. alnifòlia** L'Her. Leaves oval to elliptic, the *shallow blunt teeth 4–8 per cm.* (Fig. 260).—Swamps.

2. **R. cathártica** L. Branchlets rigid, often spine-like; leaf-blades broadly ovate, the *shallow somewhat incurved teeth 8–12 per cm.* —Occasionally escaping from cultivation.

3. **R. lanceolàta** Pursh. Leaves narrowly ovate to lanceolate, the *teeth 13–20 per cm.*, larger on the young growth (Fig. 261).—Hillsides, Grant County.

4. **R. Frángula** L. ALDER BUCKTHORN. Leaves broadly oval, with 7–8 straight or slightly curved veins; flowers in sessile umbels in the axils of leaves.—Rare in southeastern Wisconsin and in Taylor County; introduced from Europe.

2. **Ceanòthus** NEW JERSEY TEA

C. ovàtus Desf. Low shrubs; leaf-blades finely toothed, the teeth ending in a dark tip (Fig. 262); flowers white.—In sand, mostly northward.—Forma **pubéscens** (S. Wats.) Soper has leaf-blades hairy beneath.—Dry rocky soil, rare.

VITÀCEAE VINE FAMILY

Trailing or extensively climbing vines, with tendrils; leaves alternate, palmately lobed or divided; flowers in clusters, small and greenish; calyx very small and often lacking lobes; petals falling very early; fruit a berry.

a. Leaves compound . . . . 1. *Parthenocissus.*
a. Leaves simple . . . . 2. *Vitis.*

1. **Parthenocíssus** WOODBINE

Leaves compound, of 5 (often 3 on young growth) stalked, coarsely toothed leaflets; petioles as long as the leaflets; flowers many in a much-branched long-stalked inflorescence; fruit a small blue berry.

1. **P. insérta** (Kerner) K. Fritsch. Inflorescence regularly forking, its main branches equal or nearly so; tendrils without well-developed adhesive disks.—Throughout the state, but more common southward.

2. **P. quinquefòlia** (L.) Planch. Inflorescence a panicle, not regularly forking; tendrils often with well-developed adhesive disks. —Northern.—Common in cultivation and occasionally escaping to roadsides.

2. **Vìtis** GRAPE

Flowers in a much-branched drooping panicle, fragrant; calyx reduced to a small disk at the base of the flower; petals separating only at the base and falling off without expanding; fruit a pulpy berry; leaves somewhat heart-shaped at base, sometimes both shallowly and deeply lobed on the same plant.

1. **V. aestivàlis** Michx. SUMMER GRAPE. Teeth of leaves broader than long, somewhat narrowed to a short abrupt point (Fig. 263); leaves red-woolly beneath, especially when young.—Rare in Rock and Kenosha Counties.—Var. **argentifòlia** (Munson) Fernald. SILVERLEAF GRAPE. Leaves whitened but not woolly beneath.—North to Clark and Fond du Lac Counties.

2. **V. ripària** Michx. FROST GRAPE. Teeth of leaves longer than broad, drawn out to a long point which is often slightly curved (Fig. 264); leaves green beneath and without hairs.—Common.—Var. **syrtícola** (Fernald & Wiegand) Fernald. DUNE GRAPE. Leaves hairy beneath.—Rare.

TILIÀCEAE LINDEN FAMILY

Tília LINDEN; BASSWOOD

T. americàna L. Tree; leaf-blades heart-shaped, without hairs except for minute tufts on the lower surface at the junctions of the conspicuous veins; flowers in a branching cluster in the axil of a *leaf-like bract* about 1 dm. long, which is *partly fused with the peduncle;* sepals 5; petals 5.—Rich woods.

MALVÀCEAE MALLOW FAMILY

Herbs with alternate long-petioled palmately veined or lobed leaves; the numerous stamens united to form a column.

a. Petals notched at apex . . . . 1. *Malva.*
a. Petals rounded at apex . . . . 2. *Napaea.*

1. Málva

Carpels united in a ring around a central axis, from which they separate at maturity.

a. Leaves rounded (Fig. 265) *b.*
  b. Sepals margined with hairs longer than the sepals; petals only a little exceeding the sepals . . . . 1. *M. rotundifolia.*
  b. Sepals margined with short hairs; petals 3–4 times as long as the sepals. . . . . 2. *M. neglecta.*
a. Leaves cleft into ribbon-like segments . . . . . 3. *M. moschata.*

1. **M. rotundifòlia** L. Stems reclining; leaf-blades shallowly lobed, the lobes toothed (Fig. 265); flowers pink, in clusters in the axils of the leaves, fruits marked with a network on the back.—Not common; a naturalized weed.

2. **M. neglécta** Wallr. MALLOW; CHEESES. Similar; fruits finely velvety and without net-like markings on the back.—A common weed, naturalized from Europe.

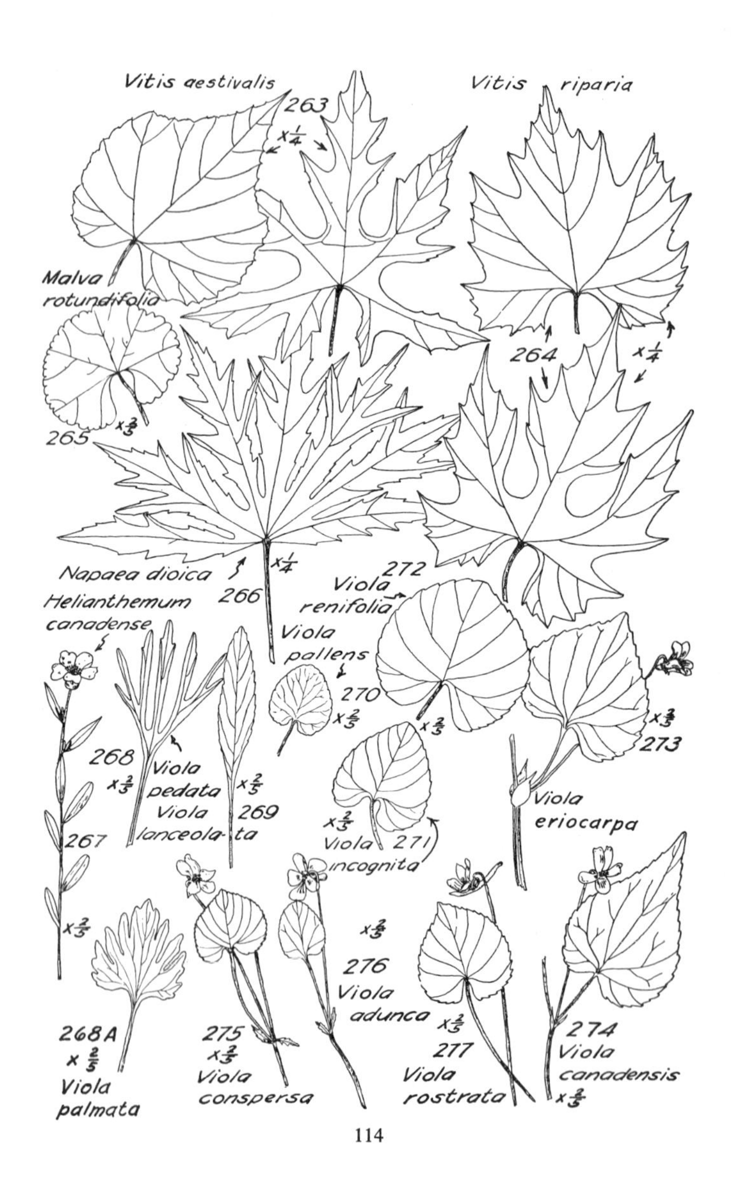

Vitis aestivalis
263
x 1/4
Vitis riparia
Malva rotundifolia
264
x 1/4
265
x 2/5
Napaea dioica
x 1/4
266
272
Viola renifolia
Helianthemum canadense
Viola pallens
270
x 2/5
x 2/5
x 2/5
273
268
x 2/5
Viola pedata
Viola lanceolata
x 2/5
269
x 2/5
Viola incognita
271
Viola eriocarpa
267
x 2/5
x 2/5
276
Viola adunca
x 2/5
268A
x 2/5
Viola palmata
275
x 2/5
Viola conspersa
277
Viola rostrata
274
Viola canadensis
x 2/5

3. **M. moschàta** L. MUSK MALLOW. Flowers rose-colored or white, in racemes, only the lowest in the axils of leaves.—Introduced from Europe, and rarely escaping from cultivation.

2. **Napaèa** GLADE MALLOW

N. dioìca L. Stems nearly simple, 1.5–3 m. high; leaves large, deeply 9–11-cleft, the divisions coarsely toothed (Fig. 266); flowers white, dioecious; fruit a pod of 5 carpels.—Moist places and along railroads, north to Dane and Vernon Counties.

CISTÀCEAE ROCKROSE FAMILY

a. Leaves flat, narrow, green . . . . 1. *Helianthemum.*
a. Leaves scale-like, woolly . . . . 2. *Hudsonia.*

1. **Heliánthemum** FROSTWEED

H. canadénse (L.) Michx. (Fig. 267) Stems simple, later becoming branched; leaves about 2 cm. long, rather narrow, ascending; first flower solitary, 2.5 cm. broad, bright yellow, *soon wilting;* later flowers very numerous, small, clustered on small branches which rise from branches that overtop the first flower.—Dry prairies and sand barrens.

2. **Hudsònia**

H. tomentòsa Nutt., var. **intermèdia** Peck. Plants 1–2 dm. high, much branched; flowers short-pediceled, bright yellow.—In open sand.

VIOLÀCEAE VIOLET FAMILY

a. Flowers blue, white, or yellow. . . . . 1. *Viola.*
a. Flowers greenish . . . . 2. *Hybanthus.*

1. **Vìola** VIOLET

Plants small and delicate, seldom more than a few dm. high; petals 5, somewhat unequal, the lowest with a spur.*

a. Leaves and scapes rising directly from the base of the plant *b*.
  b. Petals blue or violet *c*.
    c. Leaf-blades not divided or incised *d*.
      d. Plants hairy *e*.
        e. Rhizome thread-like; leaves slightly hairy above, heart-shaped, blunt, the rounded basal lobes nearly meeting or overlapping; petioles and peduncles smooth; petals not bearded . . . . 8. *V. Selkirkii.*

---

* The stemless blue violets as revised by Margaret S. Bergseng (1955).

e. Rhizome stout, vertical or branching; leaves conspicuously hairy; heart-shaped, oval, or arrow-shaped; basal lobes spreading; petioles and top of peduncles hairy *f.*

f. Leaves heart-shaped, as wide as, or wider than long, the basal lobes merely rounded; lateral petals heavily bearded; spurred petal smooth or with a few hairs; sepals ciliate at the base, the auricles rounded; flowers light or dark blue with white centers 4. *V. sororia.*

f. Leaves arrow-shaped (or early leaves oval), longer than wide, the basal lobes frequently with 2–6 large teeth (in older leaves); lateral and spurred petals bearded; sepals mostly glabrous, the auricles elongated; flowers deep purple 7. *V. sagittata.*

d. Plants smooth *g.*

g. Flowering stems above the leaves; sepals smooth, 1 mm. long (or 2–6 mm. long in No. 9); spurred petal smooth or bearded *h.*

h. Flowers small, violet (or sometimes appearing faded in dry places), with a conspicuous dark center; spurred petal smooth, lateral petals with club-shaped hairs; sepals with auricles 2–6 mm. long, extending straight backwards . . . . 9. *V. cucullata.*

h. Flowers larger, violet, without a conspicuous dark center; the three lower petals bearded; sepals with auricles rounded, 1 mm. long, appressed . . . . 6. *V. nephrophylla.*

g. Flower stems equaling the leaves; sepals short, with few or no cilia; spurred petal smooth . . . . . . 5. *V. papilionacea.*

c. Leaf-blades deeply divided (or only incised in No. 3) *i.*

i. Leaf not cordate at the base; 3-divided nearly to the base, each division cleft again into ribbon-like segments *j.*

j. Petals all beardless, of two colors, the upper two dark purple, the lower three lighter in color; a flat-faced, pansy-like flower with conspicuous orange anthers (see also var. *lineariloba* with petals alike in color) . 1. *V. pedata.*

j. Lateral petals bearded, the upper and lower petals alike in color. . . . 2. *V. pedatifida.*

i. Leaf cordate at base, the blade cleft into 5–11 lobes from margin toward mid-rib, but not nearly to the base, the segment at the tip wider than the lateral lobes (1 cm.). . . . . 3. *V. palmata.*

b. Petals white *k.*

k. Leaf-blades long and narrow, *widest at the middle,* tapering narrowly at the base (Fig. 269) . . . . 10. *V. lanceolata.*

k. Leaf-blades rounded, heart-shaped, or arrow-shaped *l.*
l. Leaf-blades without hairs *m.*
m. Leaf-blades rounded or with a short, blunt tip, often as broad as long; heart-shaped at the base . . . . 12. *V. pallens.*
m. Leaf-blades mostly not more than twice as long as wide, nearly straight across at the base, where it is the widest, the blade extending narrowly down at the summit of the petiole to make a short asymmetrical wing . . . . 11. *V. primulifolia.*
l. Leaf-blades with hairs on at least one surface *n.*
n. The two lateral petals with hairy tufts; leaves pointed, with basal lobes spreading . . . . 13. *V. incognita.*
n. Lateral petals without hairs; leaves blunt, rounded . . . . 14. *V. renifolia.*
a. Both leaves and flowers arising from the stem *o.*
o. Stipules with low shallow wavy teeth or none *p.*
p. Flowers yellow; at least the upper stipules flat, green, persistent, somewhat oval with the outer side more curved, short-pointed at tip (Fig. 273) *q.*
q. Blades of the stem leaves with 15 or more teeth on each side; whole plant hairy 15. *V. pubescens.*
q. Blades of the stem leaves with less than 15 teeth on each side; plant hairy only on upper part . . . . 16. *V. eriocarpa.*
p. Flowers white, tinged with violet; stipules brownish, withering, long-triangular, broadest at the base and tapering gradually to a long tip (Fig. 274) *r.*
r. Leaf-blades velvety beneath . . . . . . 17. *V. rugulosa.*
r. Leaf-blades with scattered weak appressed hairs or none . . . . 18. *V. canadensis.*
o. Stipules with fringe-like teeth *s.*
s. Spur not over 8 mm. long; lateral petals with a tuft of hairs on the inner surface *t.*
t. Leaf-blades definitely heart-shaped at base, nearly as broad as long (Fig. 275); plant smooth . . . . 19. *V. conspersa.*
t. Leaf-blades nearly straight across the base or slightly heart-shaped, longer than broad (Fig. 276); plant with short hairs . . . . 20. *V. adunca.*
s. Spur about 1 cm. long; lateral petals without hairs (Fig. 277) . . . . 21. *V. rostrata.*

1. **V. pedàta** L. BIRD-FOOT VIOLET. Leaf-blades 3–divided, the divisions cleft into ribbon-like segments (Fig. 268); flowers flattened, pansy-like; upper petals dark-purple, the lower lilac-purple. —Occurs very rarely, usually with the following variety.—Var. **linearíloba** DC. has all the petals colored alike, deep blue or rarely white.—Abundant in dry soil, especially in sand barrens.

2. **V. pedatífida** G. Don. Leaves divided much as in No. 1; petals violet, flower not pansy-like.—Dry fields and prairies, mostly southern, north to Washburn County in the west.

3. **V. palmàta** L. (Fig. 268a) Leaves heart-shaped in outline, *the base cordate*, each side with 5–11 narrow lobes, but *not cut to the base* as in the bird-foot violet; the tip or middle segment about 1 cm. wide.—Rich woods and calcareous slopes. Found in Racine, Jefferson, Dane, Green, and Lafayette Counties.

4. **V. soròria** Willd. Hairy Blue Violet. Leaves heart-shaped, long-hairy beneath and on the stems. The rounded sepals ciliate toward the base; lateral petals bearded, spurred petal smooth or only slightly hairy. This is the common, widely ranging *blue violet of rich woods, meadows, and river bottoms.*

5. **V. papilionàcea** Pursh. Leaves and peduncles numerous, especially in shady, damp places; young leaves often hairy; flowers below the leaves; the spurred petal beardless, the lateral ones heavily bearded; sepals with rounded auricles and few cilia. Our commonest violet, found everywhere, in borders of woods, meadows, roadsides, and near dwellings. It is often planted on city lots. Many color variations appear, such as white with blue veins or blue speckles.

6. **V. nephrophýlla** Greene. Plant glabrous; early leaves round or reniform, often bluish beneath; later leaves heart-shaped, cordate, bluntly pointed, with low teeth. All petals hairy, the two upper ones only slightly so; sepals blunt, rounded at the base; auricles without ciliae.—Cold mossy bogs and borders of streams and lakes.

7. **V. sagittàta** Ait. Arrow-leaved Violet. Plants mostly small, the flowers usually slightly overtopping the leaves; leaf-blades on long petioles, more than twice as long as broad, slightly to very hairy, often with coarse elongated teeth on the basal lobes.—In sand and wet, rocky woods, north to Polk, Chippewa, Wood, and Winnebago Counties.—**V. fimbriátula** Sm. has been collected a very few times in tamarack bogs in Wisconsin.

8. **V. Selkírkii** Pursh. Small and delicate; rootstock slender; leaf-blades heart-shaped, the lobes approaching each other or overlapping.—Along our northern borders, south to Clark and Door Counties, and in cold canyons at Devil's Lake and the Dells of the Wisconsin River.

9. **V. cucullàta** Ait. Long-stemmed Marsh Violet. *Plant smooth; flowers on long stems above the leaves;* petals purple-violet, with darker centers; *spurred petal beardless*, shorter than the two lateral ones which are bearded. Lobed auricles of the sepals pointing straight back. Leaves in general small, heart-shaped, pointed or blunt at the tips; teeth varying in size and number.—Widely ranging *plant of cold springs, streams, and marshes*, sometimes spreading to dryer ground.

10. **V. lanceolàta** L. LANCE-LEAVED VIOLET. Leaf-blades long, rather narrow, tapering to the petiole (Fig. 269).—Moist sandy shores, mostly northward, south along the Wisconsin River to Iowa County.

11. **V. primulifòlia** L. var. **acùta** (Bigel.) T. & G. *Leaf-blades* bluntly arrow-shaped, *without hairs, 1.5–3.5 cm. broad;* blunt at tip, *widest at base*, which is *abruptly rounded* or mostly *straight across above the broadened summit of the petiole;* teeth broad, flattened or none. Flowers similar to those of *V. lanceolata.*—Open shores.

12. **V. pállens** (Banks) Brainerd. SWEET WHITE VIOLET. Plants stoloniferous; leaf-blades rounded at tip, often as broad as long (Fig. 270), usually smaller than in the next, 1–3 cm. broad; petals with purple lines.—Cold, wet springs and brooks, mostly northward, south to Iowa, Dane, and Green Lake Counties.

13. **V. incógnita** Brainerd. SWEET WHITE VIOLET. Plants stoloniferous; *leaf-blades 2–6 cm. broad, pointed* (Fig. 271), *dull*, with delicate appressed white hairs.—Damp rich woods, mostly northward, south to Dane County.—Most of our plants belong to the var. **Forbèsii** Brainerd, with hairs only on the upper leaf-surface.

14. **V. renifòlia** Gray. Plants without stolons; *leaf-blades nearly round* (Fig. 272), 3–9 cm. broad, *shining*, with stiff white appressed hairs on both surfaces.—Woods, northern Wisconsin, less common than var. **Brainérdii** (Greene) Fernald, which lacks hairs on the upper leaf-surface.

15. **V. pubéscens** Ait. DOWNY YELLOW VIOLET. Plants softly hairy; one or no leaves arising from the base of the stem; blades of stem leaves usually 7 cm. or more wide; pods woolly.—Woods.—A form with smooth pods has been named var. **Péckii** House.—When growing alone this species and the next are said to be distinct, but when both occur in a region there may be a confusing exchange of characters.

16. **V. eriocárpa** Schwein. SMOOTH YELLOW VIOLET. (Fig. 273) Less hairy; one or two leaves arising from the base of the stem; blades of stem leaves usually less than 7 cm. wide; pods woolly (*V. pensylvanica*).—Woods.—The form with smooth pods is called var. **leiocárpa** (Fernald & Wiegand) Deam; this is more frequent.

17. **V. rugulòsa** Greene. Plants with slender, branching underground stolons; leaf-blades less tapering than in the next, more abruptly pointed, those of the lower leaves often broader than long; upper part of plant hairy; stipules somewhat persistent, seldom over 3 times as long as broad.—West and south. Rare in the southern third of the state.

18. **V. canadénsis** L. CANADA VIOLET. (Fig. 274) Plants from a creeping rootstock; leaf-blades heart-shaped, taper-pointed; stipules usually 4–5 times as long as broad, withering; corolla white with purple lines.—Rich woods, mostly northeastward, south to Rusk, Marathon, and Fond du Lac Counties.

19. **V. conspérsa** Reichenb. AMERICAN DOG VIOLET. (Fig. 275) Stems several, 8–16 cm. high; leaf-blades roundish, 2–4.5 cm. wide, without hairs; flowers small, blue.—Common.

20. **V. adúnca** Smith. SAND VIOLET. (Fig. 276) Stems not often over 1 dm. high, tufted; the whole plant almost microscopically woolly; leaf-blades 1–2 cm. wide; flowers small, blue.—Dry sand and ledges throughout the state.

21. **V. rostràta** Pursh. LONG-SPURRED VIOLET. (Fig. 277) Stems usually tufted, 1–1.5 dm. high; leaves roundish-heart-shaped, without hairs.—Rare in counties bordering Lake Michigan.

2. **Hybánthus** GREEN VIOLET

H. cóncolor (Forster) Spreng. Leaves on the stem, pointed both ends, with small, green flowers in their axils.—Wooded slope, Platteville.

THYMELAEÀCEAE MEZEREUM FAMILY

Dírca palústris L. LEATHERWOOD; WICOPY. Shrub 1–2 m. high; wood brittle, but *bark exceedingly tough and flexible;* flowers light yellow, appearing before the alternate short-petioled leaves.—Rich, wet woods, commoner northward.

ELAEAGNACEAE OLEASTER FAMILY

Shephérdia canadénsis (L.) Nutt. Dioecious shrub, 1–2 m. high; twigs, leaves, and sepals covered with a silvery down and rusty scales; flowers coming before the leaves.—Lake Superior and Lake Michigan regions.

ONAGRÀCEAE EVENING PRIMROSE FAMILY

Oenothèra perénnis L. SUNDROPS. Stems solitary or several in a cluster, 15–35 cm. tall; leaves alternate, 3–4 cm. long and 5–10 mm. wide, entire, rounded at tip; petals 4, bright yellow; fruit club-shaped and with several ridges.—Dry ground.

ARALIÀCEAE GINSENG FAMILY

Herbs, or somewhat woody plants; leaves compound; stamens and petals 5; fruit berry-like.

a. Leaves alternate or basal . . . . 1. *Aralia*.
a. Leaves whorled . . . . 2. *Panax*.

1. Aràlia

Leaves 3–parted, the divisions pinnately divided, ultimate leaf-segments toothed; flowers in umbels.

a. Umbels very numerous, in a raceme . . . . . . 1. *A. racemosa*.
a. Umbels 2–12, each on a long stalk *b*.
  b. Ultimate leaf-segments not over 2 cm. wide. . 2. *A. hispida*.
  b. Ultimate leaf-segments at least 5 cm. wide . . 3. *A. nudicaulis*.

1. **A. racemòsa** L. SPIKENARD. Plants 1–2 m. tall; ultimate leaf-segments heart-shaped (Fig. 278); flowers greenish, about 2 mm. broad.—Rich woods.

2. **A. híspida** Vent. BRISTLY SARSAPARILLA. (Fig. 279) Stems 4–9 dm. high, *bristly on the woody base*, openly branched above, each branch terminated by an umbel; flowers white, 2 mm. broad.—Common northward in woods and clearings, rare southward.

3. **A. nudicaùlis** L. WILD SARSAPARILLA. (Fig. 280) Stem mostly underground; *leaf long-petioled, overtopping the scape;* branches of the scape rising all from one point; flowers greenish, 3 mm. broad.—Rich woods and bluffs. Common.

2. Pànax

1. **P. quinquefòlius** L. GINSENG. Roots large and spindle-shaped; stem simple, 3 dm. high; leaves, mostly 3, *large*, palmately divided into 5 leaflets (Fig. 281) with *long-pointed tips;* flowers greenish, about 2 mm. broad; fruit a cluster of scarlet berries.— Rich woods, becoming rare.

2. **P. trifòlius** L. DWARF GINSENG; GROUNDNUT. Tuber globular; stem 1–2 dm. high; the 3–5 leaflets usually much *smaller than the above*, and *with blunt* or *rounded tips* (Fig. 282); fruit a cluster of small, greenish pods (carpels).—Woods, south to Dunn, Clark, and Calumet Counties, and along the Lake Michigan shore.

UMBELLÍFERAE PARSLEY FAMILY

Herbs; flowers small, in umbels; fruit of 2 seed-like dry carpels which split at maturity. The genera are based primarily on fruit characters.

a. **Petals white (rarely purplish; greenish in *Angelica*) *b*.**
  b. **Leaves twice or more compound *c*.**
    c. Sheaths seldom over 2 cm. long *d*.
      d. Bracts of the umbel rounded or obtuse at tip *e*.

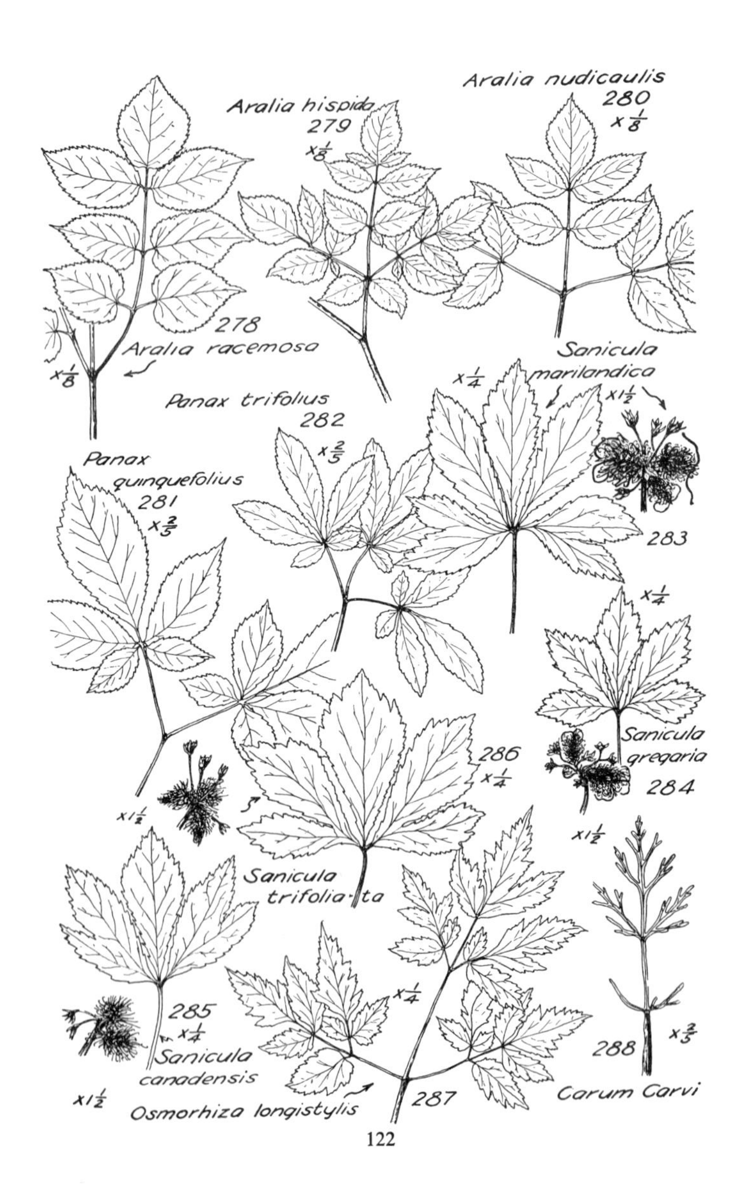

Aralia nudicaulis
280
x 1/8
Aralia hispida
279
x 1/8
278
Aralia racemosa
x 1/8
Sanicula
marilandica
x 1/4
x 1 1/2
Panax trifolius
282
x 2/5
Panax
quinquefolius
281
x 2/5
283
x 1/4
Sanicula
gregaria
284
286
x 1/4
x 1 1/2
x 1 1/2
Sanicula
trifolia-ta
285
x 1/4
Sanicula
canadensis
x 1/4
x 1 1/2
Osmorhiza longistylis
287
288
x 2/5
Carum Carvi

e. Stipules without hairs . . . . 2. *Erigenia.*
e. Stipules fringed with hairs . . . . . 3. *Chaerophyllum.*
d. Bracts of the umbel acuminate at tip, or lacking *f.*
f. Divisions of leaves flat, toothed (Fig. 287) . . . . 4. *Osmorhiza.*
f. Divisions of leaves narrowly ribbon-like (Fig. 288) . . . . 5. *Carum.*
c. Sheaths 5–10 cm. long *g.*
g. Leaflets with teeth or lobes 1 cm. or more wide, these sharply toothed; stalks of leaflets with coarse flattened hairs. . 13. *Heracleum.*
g. Leaflets obscurely double-toothed, their stalks with delicate very short hairs or none . . . . 14. *Angelica.*
b. Leaves (except when submerged) once compound *h.*
h. Leaves pinnately 5–many-foliolate . . . . 6. *Sium.*
h. Leaves palmately 3–foliolate . . . . 7. *Cryptotaenia.*
a. Petals yellow or greenish *i.*
i. Stem-leaves pinnate, the leaflets not divided . 12. *Pastinaca.*
i. Stem-leaves divided into 3 parts above the sheath, each part simple or again compound *j.*
j. Ultimate divisions of leaves not toothed . . 9. *Taenidia.*
j. Ultimate divisions of leaves toothed *k.*
k. Each tooth ending in a fine bristle . . . 1. *Sanicula.*
k. Teeth not ending in a bristle *l.*
l. Divisions of leaves somewhat ribbon-like, the sides roughly parallel . . 11. *Polytaenia.*
l. Divisions of leaves ovate, the sides curved *m.*
m. All flowers on short stalks . . . . 10. *Thaspium.*
m. Central flower of each cluster without a stalk . . . . 8. *Zizia.*

1. **Sanícula** Black Snakeroot

Plants 3–10 dm. high; leaves mostly basal and long-petioled; leaves of stem sometimes 1–3, with petioles short or none; blades palmately 3–5-foliolate, the two lateral leaflets often deeply 2–cleft, all sharply and somewhat doubly toothed, more or less narrowed to the base; umbels several times few-branched; pistillate flowers with very short pedicels or none; staminate flowers intermixed with the pistillate or in different heads, rather slender-pediceled; fruits with copious hooked bristles.

a. Styles longer than the bristles, conspicuous, recurved; some heads entirely staminate *b.*
b. Staminate calyx 1.5–2 mm. long after stamens fall . . . . 1. *S. marilandica.*
b. Staminate calyx about 1 mm. long after stamens fall . . . . 2. *S. gregaria.*
a. Styles shorter than the bristles, obscure; all heads with some pistillate flowers *c.*
c. Pedicels of staminate flowers shorter than the entire pistillate flower . . . . 3. *S. canadensis.*
c. Pedicels of staminate flowers longer than the entire pistillate flower . . . . 4. *S. trifoliata.*

1. **S. marilándica** L. (Fig. 283) Leaves usually 5–parted (appearing 7–parted); calyx-lobes of staminate flowers very narrow and acute; fruit 5–7 mm. long, not stipitate.—Rich woods.

2. **S. gregària** Bickn. (Fig. 284) Leaves usually 3–parted (appearing 5–parted); staminate flowers with calyx-lobes not over twice as long as broad, obtuse or acute; fruit 3–4 mm. long, short-stipitate.—Rich woods.

3. **S. canadénsis** L., var. **grándis** Fernald. (Fig. 285) Leaf-blades 3–parted (appearing 5–parted); terminal leaflet 2–3 times as long as broad; fruit nearly globose, without conspicuous persistent calyx.—Southwestward, mostly along the Mississippi and lower Wisconsin Rivers; not common.

4. **S. trifoliàta** Bickn. (Fig. 286) Terminal leaflet 1.5–2 times as long as broad; fruit tapering at both ends, somewhat stipitate, with a conspicuous persistent beak-like calyx.—Known in Wisconsin only from Marshfield, Ludington, and Glenhaven.

2. **Erigenìa** HARBINGER-OF-SPRING

E. bulbòsa (Michx.) Nutt. Stem 1–2.3 dm. high, *from a solid corm;* leaves palmately much-divided.—Rare; Milwaukee, Racine, and Kenosha Counties.

3. **Chaerophýllum**

C. procùmbens (L.) Crantz. Stems slender, often spreading, 1–5 dm. high, somewhat hairy; leaflets ovate, stalked, pinnately divided; their divisions stalked, wedge-shaped at base, often 2–3-lobed; umbels with few flowers; fruit narrowly oblong, 5–10 mm. long.—Wooded bottoms of the Sugar River, Rock County.

4. **Osmorhìza** SWEET CICELY

Stems 3–12 dm. high; upper leaves practically sessile, divided into 3 leaflets which are rather long-stalked and pinnately 3–5-divided (Fig. 287); fruit long and narrow, tapered to both ends, often curved, ribbed, with ascending hairs.

a. Umbels with bracts at base of branches *b*.
  b. Anthers 0.2–0.3 mm. long; enlarged base of style shorter than the petals, 0.8–1.5 mm. long in fruit. . . . . 1. *O. Claytoni.*
  b. Anthers about 0.5 mm. long; enlarged base of styles longer than the petals, becoming 3–4 mm. long in fruit . . . . 2. *O. longistylis.*
a. Umbels without bracts . . . . 3. *O. chilensis.*

1. **O. Clàytoni** (Michx.) Clarke. Stems and leaves with soft white hairs; body of fruit 1–1.3 cm. long.—Woods throughout the state.

2. **O. longistỳlis** (Torr.) DC. (Fig. 287) Stem glabrous, or rarely with spreading hairs; body of fruit 1.2–1.5 cm. long.—Woods throughout the state, less abundant than No. 1.

3. **O. chilénsis** H. & A. Umbels with only 3–7 rays.—In Bayfield County near Lake Superior.

5. **Càrum** CARAWAY

C. Cárvi L. Leaves pinnate, the leaflets once or twice pinnate (Fig. 288).—Roadsides; naturalized from Europe.

6. **Sìum** WATER PARSNIP

S. suàve Walt. (Fig. 289) Plant usually erect, 0.8–2 m. high; leaves pinnate, the leaflets pointed, sharply toothed; submerged leaves, when present, usually finely dissected; fruit 2.5–3 mm. long, ovate, with prominent corky nearly equal ribs.—Marshy land.

7. **Cryptotaènia** HONEWORT

C. canadénsis (L.) DC. Plants 3–9 dm. high, not hairy; leaves long-petioled; blades 3-parted; leaflets ovate, tapered at base, doubly toothed, the two lateral ones often deeply 2-cleft; pedicels very unequal; fruit 4–6 mm. long, often curved.—Rich woods.

8. **Zízia** GOLDEN ALEXANDER

1. **Z. aùrea** (L.) Koch. Lower leaves long-petioled, *compound;* leaflets of upper leaves again 3–5-divided with stalked divisions; rays 2–5 cm. long; fruit oblong, 4 mm. long.—Woods and fields.

2. **Z. áptera** (Gray) Fernald. Lower leaves not divided, the *blades heart-shaped;* upper leaves 3–5-parted, the divisions toothed or deeply cleft.—Prairies and barrens, and along railroad tracks.—Var. **occidentàlis** Fernald, an immigrant from the west, with leaflets of stem-leaves irregularly jagged-toothed, has been found along railroad tracks in Milwaukee County.

9. **Taenídia** YELLOW PIMPERNEL

T. integérrima (L.) Drude. Plants 5–10 dm. high; leaves long-petioled, 3-divided, the leaflets often twice 3-divided (making theoretically 27 ultimate divisions); rays of the primary umbel 1.5–6 cm. long; secondary umbels, in flower, less than 1 cm. in diameter; fruit short-oblong, 4 mm. long.—Dry woods and open ground, not common.

10. **Tháspium** MEADOW PARSNIP

Closely resembling *Zizia*, from which it is positively distinguished by its coarsely winged fruits.

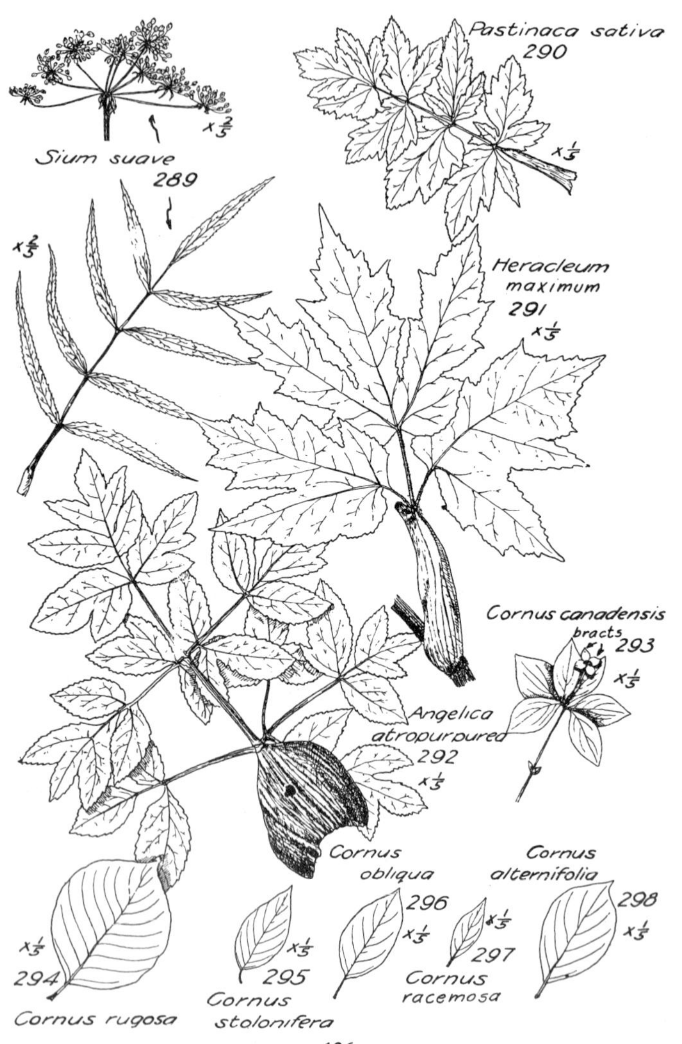
Pastinaca sativa
290
x 1/5
Sium suave
289
x 2/5
x 2/5
Heracleum
maximum
291
x 1/5
Cornus canadensis
bracts
293
x 1/5
Angelica
atropurpurea
292
x 1/5
Cornus
obliqua
Cornus
alternifolia
296
x 1/5
x 1/5
297
298
x 1/5
x 1/5
x 1/5
294
295
Cornus
racemosa
Cornus
stolonifera
Cornus rugosa

1. **T. trifoliàtum** (L.) Gray, var. **flàvum** Blake. Leaflets with firm white glabrous margins.—Rather uncommon along the Rock, Sugar, and Pecatonica Rivers. Easily confused, when fruit is not present, with the more abundant *Zizia aurea;* both have the flowers in little umbels which terminate long peduncles, but in *Thaspium* all the flowers are pediceled while in *Zizia* each little umbel has one central flower sessile.

2. **T. barbinòde** (Michx.) Nutt. Leaflets with thin green minutely ciliate margins.—Prairie du Chien.

11. Polytaènia

P. Nuttállii DC. Stem 5–10 dm. high; leaves twice pinnate; fruit obovate to oval, flattened.—Open ground, north to Monroe and Columbia Counties; not common.

12. Pastinàca PARSNIP

P. satìva L. Plants stout, often tall; leaves pinnate, the leaflets coarsely toothed, sometimes deeply cleft (Fig. 290); rays 2–6 cm. long; fruit flattened, oval.—Introduced from Europe and often escaping from cultivation.

13. Heraclèum COW PARSNIP

H. máximum Bartr. Plants 1–2.8 m. high, coarse, woolly; leaves 3–parted, the *leaflets usually 1 dm. or more broad*, deeply 3–cleft (Fig. 291); fruit flattened, obovate.—Roadsides and woods.

14. Angélica

A. atropurpùrea L. Plants stout, often 2 m. high; *stem streaked with purple and green, with a powdery bloom;* leaves 3–parted, the divisions stalked and pinnately divided (Fig. 292), without hairs; *umbels spherical*, long-stalked, many, aggregated into a large spherical umbel.—Wet open ground, from Lafayette, Dane, Columbia, and Shawano Counties southeastward.— Var. **occidentàlis** Fassett has the leaflets very finely hairy beneath.—From Lafayette, Dane, and Milwaukee Counties northwestward.

CORNÀCEAE DOGWOOD FAMILY

Leaves simple; calyx-lobes minute; petals 4 or 5; stamens as many as the petals, borne on a disk; style one; fruit 1–2 seeded, fleshy.

a. Stamens and petals 4 . . . . 1. *Cornus*.
a. Stamens and petals 5 . . . . 2. *Nyssa*.

1. Córnus DOGWOOD

a. Herb-like plants with petal-like bracts below the close cluster of flowers; fruits red . . . . 1. *C. canadensis.*
a. Shrubs; flowers in open, flat-topped or pyramidal clusters, without large petal-like bracts *b.*
  b. Leaves alternate, crowded toward the tips of the branches; ripe fruit blue-black . . . . . . 6. *C. alternifolia.*
  b. Leaves opposite, scattered along the stems; ripe fruit blue or white *c.*
    c. Pubescence more or less spreading, often woolly; leaves broadly ovate generally with 7 to 9 pairs of veins (Fig. 294), white woolly below; branchlets yellow-green, more or less streaked with purplish dots; fruit blue . . 2. *C. rugosa.*
    c. Either with closely appressed, straight and silky pubescence, or lacking hairs; leaves ovate or ovate-lanceolate, generally with 3 to 6 pairs of veins (Fig. 295), branchlets gray, brown, or reddish *d.*
      d. Sepals 1–1.5 mm. long; style with club-shaped tip; fruit pale blue . . . . 4. *C. obliqua.*
      d. Sepals 0.7 mm. long or less; style cylindrical; fruit white *e.*
        e. Twigs gray, slender; young twigs lacking hairs; inflorescence pyramidal, about as tall as broad; fruiting pedicels bright red . . . . 5. *C. racemosa.*
        e. Twigs red, rarely green, stout; young twigs with appressed white pubescence, becoming hairless; inflorescence flat-topped; pedicels of fruit green . . . . 3. *C. stolonifera.*

1. **C. canadénsis** L. BUNCHBERRY. (Fig. 293) Stems not branched, 9–22 cm. high, from a slender creeping rootstock; *leaves crowded in an apparent whorl of 6* (rarely one or more pairs also on the stem); bracts white, petal-like, usually 4; petals small, long-triangular.—Common northward; local southward along the Lake Michigan shore, and on sandstone bluffs to Dane County.

2. **C. rugòsa** Lam. ROUND-LEAF DOGWOOD. Shrub 2–3 m. high; *twigs green;* leaf-blades reaching 12 cm. in length and 10 cm. in width (Fig. 294); petals 3–4 mm. long.—Thickets and open woods; south to Vernon, Sauk, Walworth, and Racine Counties.

3. **C. stolonífera** Michx. RED-OSIER DOGWOOD. Shrubs 1.5–3 m. high, strongly stoloniferous and making large thickets in open swamps; *twigs stout, red* (especially in winter), sometimes green, or rarely gray; leaves (Fig. 295) with fine close hairs beneath; petals about 3.5 mm. long.—Common, usually in moist places, but occasionally on dry slopes.

4. **C. oblìqua** Raf. Shrub 1.5–3.5 m. high; *twigs greenish when young, soon becoming brown;* leaves (Fig. 296) slightly roughened beneath with minute hairs; *petals 4–5 mm. long.*—Wet places, north to Pierce, Wood, and Waushara Counties.

5. **C. racemòsa** Lam. Shrub 1–2.5 m. high; *twigs gray, slender;* leaf-blades narrower than those of *C. stolonifera*, tapering at base and apex (Fig. 297); *petals 3–4 mm. long.*—In sunny places in rich woods.

6. **C. alternifòlia** L. f. Shrub or small tree 2.5–8 m. high; young twigs greenish; leaf-blades oval, 4–10 cm. long and 2–6 cm. wide,

short-pointed at apex (Fig. 298); petals 3–3.5 mm. long.—Not uncommon in rich woods.

2. **Nýssa** BLACK GUM

N. sylvática Marsh. Tree; branches horizontal; leaf-blades not toothed, broadest above the middle, narrowed to a short point; fruit bluish-black, about 1.2 cm. long.—Berryville, Kenosha County.

PYROLÀCEAE SHINLEAF FAMILY

Herbaceous or partly woody plants, from perennial slender rootstocks. Leaves mostly simple, some evergreen. Petals separate; fruit a capsule of several carpels. Stamens 10.

a. Leaves evergreen, scattered on the stem, tapered to a very short petiole, sharply toothed; about three times as long as wide . . . . 1. *Chimaphila*.
a. Leaves all basal, definitely petioled, rarely more than twice as long as wide *b*.
 b. Flowers solitary. . . . . 2. *Moneses*.
 b. Flowers several in a raceme . . . . 3. *Pyrola*.

1. **Chimáphila** PRINCE'S PINE; PIPSISSEWA

C. umbellàta (L.) Nutt., var. **cisatlántica** Blake. Slightly woody plants from a horizontal rootstock; leaves leathery and evergreen, shining above, 4–5 cm. long, sharply toothed above the middle (Fig. 299), flowers 2–8, pink.—Common northward; rare southward to Iowa, Rock, and Walworth Counties.

2. **Monèses** ONE-FLOWERED PYROLA

M. uniflòra (L.) Gray. (Fig. 300) Plant rarely 1 dm. high; leaf-blades almost round, scallop-toothed, narrowed at base to a long petiole; flower 1–2 cm. wide.—Mostly in evergreen woods, south to Rusk, Shawano, Sheboygan, and very rarely to Grant Counties.

3. **Pýrola** SHINLEAF

Low herbs, without hairs, from a rootstock; leaf-blades mostly rounded; *flowers nodding, in a raceme*, on a naked or few-bracted scape.

a. Bracts intermingled with the leaves at the base of the stem, usually 1 cm. or more long, rounded or blunt at tip *b*.
 b. Cályx-lobes longer than broad *c*.
  c. Calyx-lobes with rounded sides, blunt, twice as long as wide (Fig. 301) . . . . . . 1. *P. rotundifolia*, var. *americana*.
  c. Calyx-lobes triangular, with straight sides, sharp-pointed, about 1½ times as long as wide (Fig. 302) . . . . 2. *P. asarifolia*.
 b. Calyx-lobes about as broad as long (Fig. 303) *d*.
  d. Style curved, slightly club-shaped below the small stigma . . . . 3. *P. elliptica*.

d. Style straight, ending in a flat shield-shaped stigma . . . . 4. *P. minor.*
a. Basal bracts 2–4 mm. long and long-pointed, or absent *e.*
e. Flowers on all sides of the stem; style curved (Fig. 304). . . . . 5. *P. virens.*
e. Flowers all turned in the same direction; style straight (Fig. 305) . . . . 6. *P. secunda.*

1. **P. rotundifòlia** L., var. **americàna** (Sweet) Fern. (Fig. 301) Scape 1–3.5 dm. high, with 1–5 bracts; *leaf-blades shining, not as long as the petiole; petals white* or rarely pink, 6.5–10.5 mm. long.—Mostly northward, coming south to the Dells of the Wisconsin River, and rarely to Lafayette County.

2. **P. asarifòlia** Michx. Similar, but *petals pink*, about 5 mm. long; leaf-blades as broad as long, heart-shaped or tapered at the base.—Woods and swamps, south to Barron, Adams, Milwaukee, and Racine Counties.—Includes var. **purpùrea** (Bunge) Fern.

3. **P. ellíptica** Nutt. Scape without bracts or with 1–3 very narrow bracts; *leaf-blades thin, not shining, 3–7 cm. long, longer than the petiole;* flowers white.—Common in rich woods.

4. **P. mìnor** L. Scape without bracts; leaf-blades round, 2–4 cm. long, rounded at base.—Lake Superior shore; rare.

5. **P. vìrens** Schweigger. (Fig. 304) Scape 0.5–3 dm. high, naked or with 1–2 minute hair-like bracts; leaf-blades shorter than the petiole, *not toothed*, sometimes wavy-margined; *flowers greenish.*—Douglas to Forest Counties, and south along the Lake Michigan shore to Racine.—The typical form has a rosette of 4–11 leaves with rounded blades 1.5–3.3 cm. wide and anthers not over 3 mm. long; forma **paucifòlia** Fernald, leafless or with 1–7 leaves with blades 0.7–2.5 cm. wide, and var. **convolùta** (Barton) Fernald, with blades 2–4.5 cm. wide and anthers 3–4 mm. long, are less common.

6. **P. secúnda** L. (Fig. 305) Scape 1–2.5 dm. high, with usually 2–4 bracts; leaf-blades narrowed at tip, 1.5–6 cm. long, *with scalloped margins and usually minute teeth;* flowers small, greenish.—Mostly northward and eastward, local southwestward.—Var. **obtusàta** Turcz., with leaf-blades rounded at tip, 0.8–3 cm. long, comes south to Rusk, Taylor, and Shawano Counties.

ERICÀCEAE Heath Family

Mostly woody small shrubs, prostrate or erect; flowers regular or nearly so; petals united, at least at base, into a bell-shaped corolla (except in *Rhododendron*); stamens 8–10; fruit a capsule or berry of several carpels.

a. Stems mostly erect, smooth or hairy but not with rusty hairs (except in *Ledum*) *b*.
b. Calyx borne at the base of the ovary; leaves evergreen *c*.
c. Shrubs *d*.
d. Flowers violet *e*.
e. Leaves alternate, with minute rusty scales . . . . 2. *Rhododendron.*
e. Leaves opposite, without scales . . . 3. *Kalmia.*
d. Flowers white or pinkish *f*.
f. Stems erect *g*.
g. Leaves with rusty wool beneath . 1. *Ledum.*
g. Leaves not woolly *h*.
h. Leaves white-hairy beneath . . 4. *Andromeda.*
h. Leaves with tiny round scales beneath . . . . 5. *Chamaedaphne.*
f. Stems prostrate . . . . 8. *Arctostaphylos.*
c. Herbs . . . . 7. *Gaultheria.*
b. Calyx borne at the summit of the ovary; leaves not evergreen (except in Cranberries) *i*.
i. Leaves yellow resinous dotted beneath. . . 9. *Gaylussacia.*
i. Leaves not resinous dotted beneath . . . . 10. *Vaccinium.*
a. Stems creeping, with scattered rusty hairs *j*.
j. Leaf-blades oval, cordate at base, 1–3 inches long . . . . 6. *Epigaea.*
j. Leaf-blades pointed at both ends, 0.5–3 cm. long . . . . 7. *Gaultheria.*

1. Lèdum LABRADOR TEA

L. groenlándicum Oeder. Leaves without teeth, the margins inrolled, *aromatic when bruised;* flowers clustered, white.—Mostly northern, south in bogs to Wood and Sheboygan Counties; on sandstone ledges at the Wisconsin Dells and in Richland County.

2. Rhododéndron

R. lappónicum (L.) Wahlenb. LAPLAND ROSE BAY. Much-branched shrub; leaves 2 cm. or less long, dotted above and below with glands, each of which is on a minute scale.—Trailing down the face of cliffs, Wisconsin Dells, where it is known as ROCK ROSE. An Arctic-Alpine plant; this is the only known locality west of the Adirondacks and south of Hudson Bay.

3. Kálmia PALE LAUREL

K. polifòlia Wang. (Fig. 306) Shrub 1–6 dm. high; *branches somewhat 2-edged;* leaves opposite, scarcely petioled, nearly veinless except for the conspicuous midrib, with inrolled margins; flowers on long slender pedicels, 1–2 cm. wide, rose-purple.—Cold bogs, south to Barron, Lincoln, Waupaca, and Kewaunee Counties.

4. Andrómeda BOG ROSEMARY

A. glaucophýlla Link. (Fig. 307) Shrub 5–50 cm. high; stems round in cross section; leaves alternate, 2–4 cm. long, 2–4 mm.

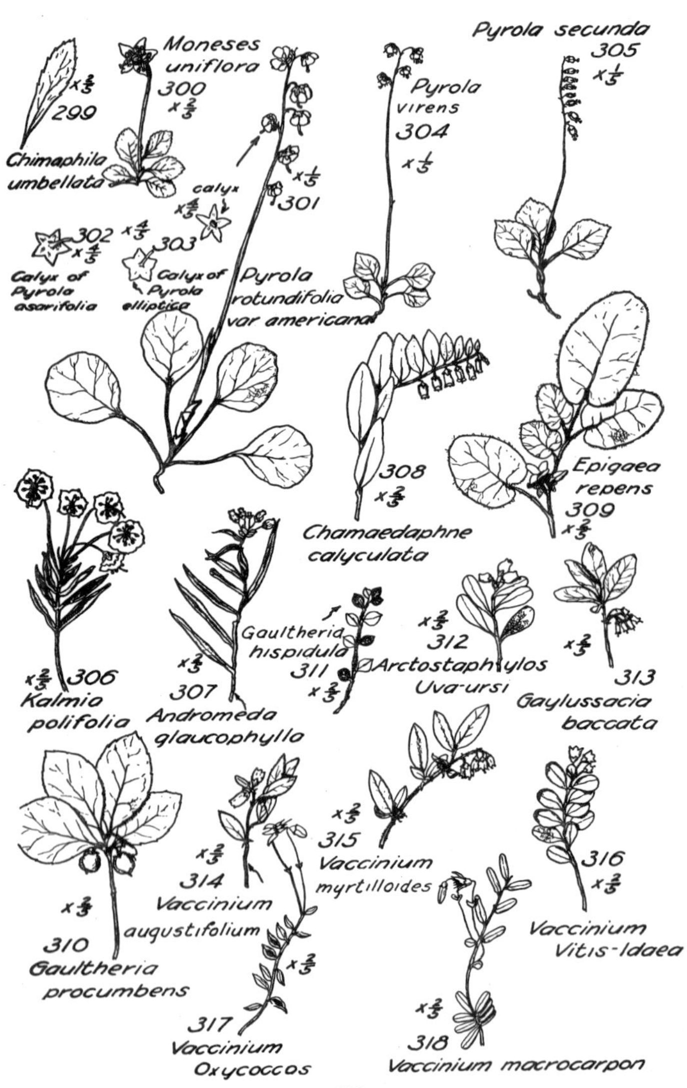
x 2/5
299
Chimaphila
umbellata
Moneses
uniflora
300
x 2/5
x 1/5
301
calyx
x 4/5
302 x 4/5
x 4/5
303
Calyx of
Pyrola
asarifolia
Calyx of
Pyrola
elliptica
Pyrola
rotundifolia
var americana
Pyrola
virens
304
x 1/5
Pyrola secunda
305
x 1/5
308
x 2/5
Chamaedaphne
calyculata
Epigaea
repens
309
x 2/5
x 2/5
306
Kalmia
polifolia
x 4/5
307
Andromeda
glaucophylla
Gaultheria
hispidula
311
x 2/5
x 2/5
312
Arctostaphylos
Uva-ursi
x 2/5
313
Gaylussacia
baccata
x 2/3
310
Gaultheria
procumbens
x 2/5
314
Vaccinium
augustifolium
x 2/5
315
Vaccinium
myrtilloides
316
x 2/5
Vaccinium
Vitis-Idaea
x 2/5
317
Vaccinium
Oxycoccos
x 2/5
318
Vaccinium macrocarpon

wide, strongly bluish-whitened beneath and nearly veinless except for the conspicuous midrib, the *margins strongly inrolled;* flowers 3–5 mm. wide, pink or white.—Bogs, south to Barron County in the west, and to Jefferson and Racine Counties in the east.

5. **Chamaedáphne** LEATHER-LEAF

C. calyculàta (L.) Moench. (Fig. 308) Low shrubs; flowers white, small, *in a single row in the axils of foliage leaves along the last dm. at the tips of the branches.*—Bogs; locally abundant except in the unglaciated area.

6. **Epigaèa** TRAILING ARBUTUS; MAYFLOWER

E. rèpens L. (Fig. 309) Plants bristly with rusty hairs; flowers in dense clusters, pink and white, very fragrant.—Dry woods, south to the Wisconsin Dells, the Baraboo Hills, and rarely on bluffs to Dane and Green Counties.

7. **Gaulthèria** WINTERGREEN

1. **G. procúmbens** L. WINTERGREEN. (Fig. 310) Stems erect from woody rootstocks; leaves leathery, shining, *aromatic*, the youngest red; flowers white; berry red, edible.—Pine woods and in bogs; common northward, and rare southward.

2. **G. hispídula** (L.) Bigel. CREEPING SNOWBERRY. (Fig. 311) Creeping evergreen; leaves 0.5–1 cm. long, on very short petioles, *the blades pointed at both ends and beset beneath with scattered rusty hairs;* flowers very small, solitary in the axils of leaves; berry white. —Bogs; south to Chippewa County in the west, and rarely to Walworth and Milwaukee Counties in the east.

8. **Arctostáphylos** BEARBERRY

A. Ùva-úrsi (L.) Spreng. (Fig. 312) Stems woody, trailing; *plants making mats;* fruit a red dry berry.—On sand and sandstone bluffs, mostly northward.

9. **Gaylussàcia** HUCKLEBERRY

G. baccàta (Wang.) C. Koch. (Fig. 313) *Flowers reddish, sticky;* leaves sticky when young; berry black, 10-seeded.—Rocky woodlands, sandstone bluffs, and southward in bogs.

10. **Vaccìnium**

Corolla white or pink, not sticky, united at base, tubular in the Blueberries, with 4 long lobes in the Cranberries.

a. Lobes of the corolla 5, shorter than the united part; leaves not evergreen *b.*
  b. Flowers clustered; anthers without bristles *c.*
    c. Leaves finely toothed . . . . 1. *V. angustifolium.*
    c. Leaves not toothed . . . . 2. *V. myrtilloides.*
  b. Flower solitary; anthers with 2 bristles. . . . 3. *V. cespitosum.*
a. Lobes of the corolla 4; leaves evergreen *d.*
  d. Corolla bell-shaped, with short lobes (Fig. 316) 4. *V. Vitis-idaea,* var. *minus.*
  d. Lobes of the corolla much longer than the united part (Fig. 317) *e.*
    e. Leaves with margins strongly inrolled, becoming triangular in outline (Fig. 317) 5. *V. Oxycoccos.*
    e. Leaves with margins but slightly inrolled, elliptic in outline (Fig. 318). . . . . . 6. *V. macrocarpon.*

1. **V. angustifòlium** Ait. EARLY BLUEBERRY. (Fig. 314) Stems 2–6 dm. high; *twigs green, warty,* with 2 narrow lines of hairs running down from each node; teeth of leaves finely bristle-tipped; berry sweet, blue, with a bloom.—Common northward, coming south to Dane and Racine Counties in bogs, and on sand and sandstone ledges.—Var. **nìgrum** (Wood) Dole has black berries without a bloom, and somewhat thicker leaves which are somewhat bluish-white beneath.

2. **V. myrtilloìdes** Micht. VELVET-LEAVED BLUEBERRY. (Fig. 315) Shrub 2–6 dm. high; *leaves and twigs soft-downy;* fruit ripening later than in the preceding, not so sweet.—More frequent than the preceding northward but not common southward.

3. **V. cespitòsum** Michx. DWARF BILBERRY. Tufted shrub 0.5–3 dm. high; leaves smooth and shining, toothed; *flowers solitary,* nodding.—On dry ledges and sand, rare; known from Barron, Holcombe, Stevens Point, and Wisconsin Dells.

4. **V. Vìtis-idaèa** L., var. **mìnus** Lodd. MOUNTAIN CRANBERRY. (Fig. 316) Dwarf shrub, rarely more than 10 cm. high; leaves leathery, 5–18 mm. long, 3–9 mm. wide, dark green above, *pale beneath and smooth except for scattered black bristly hairs;* flowers pink, in a small cluster; berry dark red, hard.—Bogs and dry rocks in northwestern Wisconsin; rare.

5. **V. Oxycóccos** L. SMALL CRANBERRY. (Fig. 317) Stems very slender; leaf-blades 3–8 mm. long, 1–3 mm. wide, *much whitened beneath;* pedicels 1–4, from a *rachis 1–4 mm. long which terminates the stem;* berry 6–8 mm. in diameter.—Bogs, south to Barron, Lincoln, and Manitowoc Counties.—Var. **ovalifòlium** Michx. is coarser, intermediate between this and the next species; leaf-blades 6.5–15 mm. long, 3–6.5 mm. wide, less strongly inrolled; pedicels 2–10, from a rachis 5–10 mm. long; berry 8–10 mm. in diameter. —Occasional in bogs throughout the state except in the unglaciated area.

6. **V. macrocárpon** Ait. AMERICAN CRANBERRY. (Fig. 318) *Leaf-blades blunt or rounded at tip*, 6–17 mm. long and 2–8 mm. wide, only slightly whitened beneath; pedicels 1–10, from *a rachis 1–3 cm. long, beyond which a leafy branch continues;* berry 1–2 cm. long.—In bogs, where often cultivated, south to Polk, Jackson, Columbia, Waukesha, and Racine Counties.

PRIMULÀCEAE PRIMROSE FAMILY

Leaves simple; corolla 5–7-lobed; stamens opposite the corolla-lobes; fruit a pod, with the many seeds on a central knob arising from the base.

a. Corolla with erect or spreading segments *b*.
  b. Leaves all near the ground in a basal rosette *c*.
    c. Corolla longer than the calyx . . . . . . 1. *Primula.*
    c. Corolla shorter than the calyx . . . . . . 2. *Androsace.*
  b. Leaves on the stem *d*.
    d. Leaves along the entire stem . . . . 3. *Lysimachia.*
    d. Leaves in a single whorl near the summit of the stem . . . . 4. *Trientalis.*
a. Corolla with segments strongly turned back (Fig. 322) . . . . 5. *Dodecatheon.*

1. Prímula PRIMROSE

P. mistassínica Michx. (Fig. 319) Plants 0.5–2 dm. high; leaves 1–4 cm. long; corolla pink or blue (rarely white), with a slender tube and spreading lobes.—Damp ledges, Dells of the Wisconsin River and of the St. Croix River; Door County; Bayfield Peninsula.

2. Andrósace

A. occidentàlis Pursh. (Fig. 320) Plants less than 1 dm. high; leaves in a close rosette about 1 cm. in diameter; flowers usually numerous, in a dense cluster.—Bare hills, local; Sauk, Dane, Columbia, Rock, Manitowoc, and Pepin Counties.

3. Lysimáchia LOOSESTRIFE

Corolla yellow, *saucer-shaped*, with short pointed lobes.

a. Flowers less than 1 cm. in diameter; leaf-blades pointed, longer than broad *b*.
  b. Flowers in the axils of the whorled leaves . . 1. *L. quadrifolia.*
  b. Flowers in dense axillary spikes . . . . 2. *L. thyrsiflora.*
a. Flowers more than 1 cm. in diameter; leaf-blades rounded, about as broad as long . . . . . . 3. *L. Nummularia.*

1. **L. quadrifòlia** L. WHORLED LOOSESTRIFE. Stem erect, 3–8 dm. high; leaves in whorls of 4–5; *corolla dark-dotted or streaked.*—Dry rocky ground.

2. **L. thyrsiflòra** L. Tufted Loosestrife. Leaves opposite, *the lower scale-like;* corolla purplish-dotted.—Swampy ground, occasional.

3. **L. Nummulària** L. Moneywort. *Stem creeping;* corolla bright yellow, not dotted or streaked.—An occasional weed in shady places; introduced from Europe.

4. Trientàlis Star Flower

T. boreàlis Raf. (Fig. 321) Stems 1–2 dm. high, with a few scales below the single whorl of leaves; flowers solitary or few, white, star-like.—Deep woods, mostly northward; south to Sauk, Kenosha, and rarely Grant Counties.

5. Dodecátheon Shooting Star

Leaves all near the ground in a basal rosette, the blades without hairs, narrowed to a winged petiole; flowers in an umbel, nodding at flowering time, with a bract at the base of each pedicel; *anthers extending forward* in a compact group, while the *corolla-lobes bend backward.*

1. **D. Meàdia** L. Shooting Star. (Fig. 322) Plant stout, 2.5–6 dm. high; umbel with 6–30 pale lilac to white flowers; calyx-lobes in the unfolding flower at least half as long as the corolla; capsule stout, dark brown, woody.—Low prairies, woods, and along railroads, north to Brown, Sauk, and St. Croix Counties.

2. **D. amethýstinum** Fassett. Jewelled Shooting Star. Plant slender, 2–3.5 dm. high; umbel with 2–11 (rarely –18) deep purple flowers; calyx-lobes in the unfolding flower not more than two-thirds as long as the corolla; capsule slender, pale brown, papery.—Bluffs along the Mississippi and La Crosse Rivers.

OLEÀCEAE Olive Family

Trees or shrubs; leaves opposite; flowers in racemes or panicles.

a. Leaves pinnately compound . . . . 1. *Fraxinus.*
a. Leaves simple . . . . 2. *Syringa.*

1. Fráxinus Ash

Trees; stamens and pistils in different flowers, on the same or different trees; calyx present or absent; fruit dry, flattened, winged.

a. Lateral leaflets narrowed to at least a short stalk *b.*
  b. Twigs round in cross section *c.*
    c. Leaflets pale beneath, rounded at base; leaf-scars deeply concave on upper side . . 1. *F. americana.*

c. Leaflets green on both sides, tapered to the base; leaf-scars nearly straight on upper side . . . . 2. *F. pennsylvanica.*
b. Twigs square in cross section . . . . 3. *F. quadrangulata.*
a. Lateral leaflets with no stalk . . . . 4. *F. nigra.*

1. **F. americàna** L. WHITE ASH. Leaflets 5–9, with stalks 5–10 mm. long, somewhat rounded at base; calyx present; body of fruit round in cross section, the wing extending only a short distance down its side.—In rich moist soil, north to Douglas, Lincoln, and Brown Counties.

2. **F. pennsylvánica** Marsh. RED ASH. Leaflets with stalks 2–5 mm. long, narrowed at base; rachis of leaves and young branches velvety; calyx present; body of fruit round in cross section, the wings extending down at least two-thirds of its length.—Throughout the state in rich moist soils, less common than var. **lanceolàta** (Borkh.) Sarg., the GREEN ASH, which lacks the hairs on the rachis and branchlets.

3. **F. quadrangulàta** Michx. BLUE ASH. Leaflets 7–11, with slender stalks; calyx absent or much reduced; fruit oblong, blunt. Big Bend, Waukesha County.

4. **F. nìgra** Marsh. BLACK ASH. Leaflets 7–11, each with a tuft of brown hairs at its base; calyx absent; fruit with a flat body.—Banks of streams and in swamps.

2. **Syrínga** LILAC

S. vulgàris L. Shrub; leaf-blades heart-shaped; flowers in a raceme, lilac-purple or white.—Occasionally escaping from cultivation.

GENTIANÀCEAE GENTIAN FAMILY

Herbs with usually simple opposite leaves (our single spring-flowering species is an exception); flowers regular; stamens as many as the corolla-lobes; fruit a capsule.

Menyánthes trifoliàta L. BUCKBEAN. (Fig. 323) Petioles with sheathing bases; corolla-lobes white, with *many wavy hairs on their upper surface.*—Bogs.

ASCLEPIADÀCEAE MILKWEED FAMILY

Mostly large herbs, with milky juice; filaments and stigma united into a massive central structure which encloses the ovary and conceals the waxy pollen-masses.

a. Stems erect; corolla-lobes cup-shaped, reflexed . 1. *Asclepias.*
a. Stems twining; corolla spreading . . . . 2. *Cynanchum.*

1. **Asclèpias*** MILKWEED

Flowers fragrant, in umbels; anthers form 5 cup-like appendages (hoods), each of which in most species contains a curved horn.

a. Flowers brightly colored *b.*
b. Flowers orange; leaves alternate . . . . 1. *A. tuberosa.*
b. Flowers pink, red, or purple; leaves opposite *c.*
c. Leaves smooth beneath *d.*
d. Leaf tapered gradually to the tip; branch-veins ascending (Fig. 325) . . . . . 3. *A. incarnata.*
d. Leaf abruptly narrowed to a sharp point at the broadly rounded tip; branch-veins spreading (as in Fig. 326). . . 5. *A. Sullivantii.*
c. Leaves minutely velvety-hairy beneath *e.*
e. Flowers bright red or purple; umbels erect, hemispherical, at or close to tip of stem and above the leaves when in bloom . . . . 2. *A. purpurascens.*
e. Flowers dull pink; umbels forming complete spheres, borne laterally and exceeded by the upper leaves when in bloom . . . . 7. *A. syriaca.*
a. Flowers greenish, yellowish, whitish, or rarely pinkish *f.*
f. Umbel on a terminal peduncle longer than uppermost leaf *g.*
g. Leaves rounded toward tip except for small sharp point. . . . . 8. *A. amplexicaulis.*
g. Leaves tapered to acute tip . . . . 9. *A. Meadii.*
f. Peduncles shorter than the leaves and often axillary *h.*
h. Leaves profusely hairy or downy beneath; stems scattered, from rootstocks *i.*
i. Stems with minute curved hairs or none *j.*
j. Leaves 1–2 dm. long, elliptic oblong . 7. *A. syriaca.*
j. Leaves much shorter, ovate . . . . . 6. *A. ovalifolia.*
i. Stems with spreading hairs 1 mm. or more long . . . . 11. *A. lanuginosa.*
h. Leaves with few or no hairs; stems 1–few, all from the same point, without long rootstocks *k.*
k. Leaves broadly ovate, thin, smooth. . . 4. *A. exaltata.*
k. Leaves lanceolate, thick, rough. . . . . 10. *A. viridiflora.*

1. **A. tuberòsa** L. BUTTERFLY WEED; PLEURISY ROOT. Leaves linear to oblong, hairy, stems 3–6 dm. high, often branched at the tip, where the flat-topped umbels are borne.—Prairies and sand barrens, north to Burnett, Wood, and Marinette Counties.

2. **A. purpuráscens** L. PURPLE MILKWEED. Leaves broad (Fig. 324) but the upper ones are often narrower and taper more gradually to the tip than do those of No. 7 (Fig. 326), which it resembles. Hoods 5–6 mm. long.—Dry to damp woods, thickets, and openings, mostly in the southern counties.

3. **A. incarnàta** L. SWAMP MILKWEED. Stems 5–15 dm. high, without rootstocks, smooth except for the pedicels and 2 downy

---

* *Asclepias* revised by J. H. Zimmerman.

lines along the upper stem. Leaves lanceolate (Fig. 325); umbels flat-topped, borne above the leaves on branches. Flowers vary from pink to purplish red; hoods 2–3 mm. long.—Low, wet places.

4. **A. exaltàta** L. POKE MILKWEED. Plants 5–15 dm. tall, smooth or nearly so; petioles about 1 cm. long; leaves tapered to a long point. Umbels mostly axillary; pedicels long, drooping; flowers whitish with some green or pink.—The only milkweed of rich woods.

5. **A. Sullivántii** Engelm. Resembles No. 7 except for lack of hairs. The oblong leaves are always very broadly rounded, with very abrupt short tips (those of No. 7 taper to the tip as in Fig. 326); the branch veins are less conspicuous. Flowers purple to whitish; hoods 5–6 mm. long.—Low prairies, southward; rare.

6. **A. ovalifòlia** Dcne. Stems 1.5–6 dm. high. Leaves usually taper gradually to acute tips. Flowers white, tinged with yellow, green, or pink.—Prairies and open woods, especially in the southwest half of the state.

7. **A. syrìaca** L. COMMON MILKWEED; SILKWEED. Coarse, downy plants; stems 0.5–1.5 m. high, from deep-seated, branching rootstocks; leaves thick, broad (Fig. 326). Flowers old-rose to whitish; corolla-lobes 6–9 mm. long; hoods 3–4 mm. long. Umbels axillary, many-flowered, numerous along upper half of the stem.—Common along roadsides and in fields.

8. **A. amplexicaùlis** Sm. Stem often solitary; plants smooth; leaves blue-green, heart-shaped at the base, the lower rather triangular (Fig. 327), the upper more oblong and rounded at the tip; umbel large, spherical, solitary, greenish.—Dry sand, north to Eau Claire and Waushara Counties.

9. **A. Meàdii** Torr. Similar to No. 8 but with sharply triangular, acute leaves only 3–8 cm. long.—Collected once in Grant County.

10. **A. viridiflòra** Raf. GREEN MILKWEED. Leaves 4–15 mm. wide, mostly opposite; umbels several, axillary, sessile or on short, down-curved peduncles.—Dry, sandy prairies and open woods, north to Dunn, Portage, and Fond du Lac Counties.

11. **A. lanuginòsa** Nutt. Plant covered with soft, spreading hairs; stems only 1–3 dm. high, often curved; leaves numerous, lanceolate, either alternate or opposite; umbel solitary, erect, terminal; flowers greenish-white, 6–8 mm. long.—Sandy or gravelly prairies and hilltops, north to Waukesha and Portage Counties.

2. **Cynánchum**

C. nìgrum (L.) Pers. Scarcely hairy herbs; flowers small, dark purple, in peduncled axillary clusters.—Potosi; introduced from Europe.

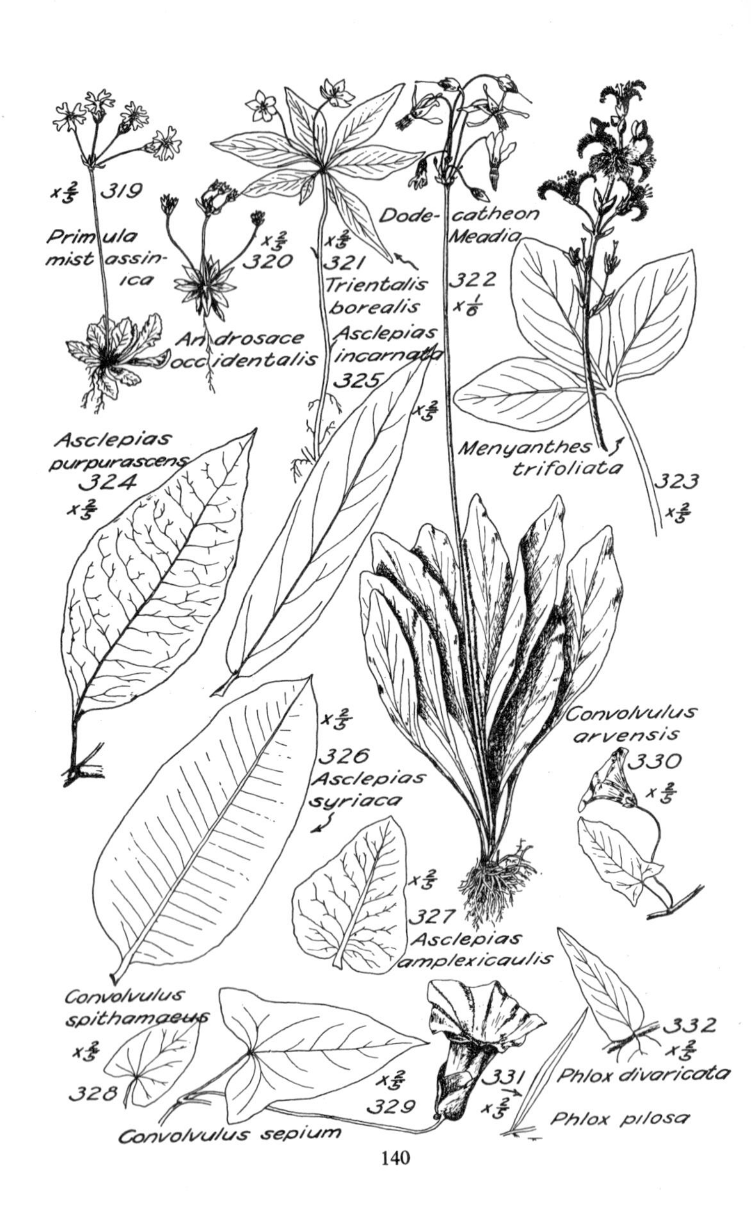
x 2/5 319
Primula
mistassinica
x 2/5
320
Androsace
occidentalis
x 2/5
321
Trientalis
borealis
Dodecatheon
Meadia
322
x 1/6
Asclepias
incarnata
325
x 2/5
Menyanthes
trifoliata
323
x 2/5
Asclepias
purpurascens
324
x 2/5
x 2/5
326
Asclepias
syriaca
Convolvulus
arvensis
330
x 2/5
x 2/5
327
Asclepias
amplexicaulis
Convolvulus
spithamaeus
x 2/5
328
x 2/5
329
331
x 2/5
332
x 2/5
Phlox divaricata
Phlox pilosa
Convolvulus sepium

CONVOLVULÀCEAE Convolvulus Family

Herbs, mostly climbing or trailing; leaves alternate; calyx of 5 sepals; corolla 5–plaited or 5–lobed, pink or white, tubular and flaring, of delicate texture; fruit a capsule.

Convólvulus Bindweed

a. Pedicels with 2 broad bracts enclosing the calyx (Fig. 329); corolla 3–5 cm. long *b*.
  b. Erect plants . . . . 1. *C. spithamaeus.*
  b. Trailing vines. . . . . 2. *C. sepium.*
a. Pedicels without bracts enclosing the calyx (Fig. 330); corolla 1.5–2 cm. long . . . . 3. *C. arvensis.*

1. C. **spithamaèus** L. Plants 1.5–3 dm. high, downy; stems mostly simple, erect or nearly so; petioles short; leaf-blades rounded or truncate at base; corolla white.—Open sandy or rocky ground, locally abundant.—Var. **stáns** (Michx.) Fogelberg has the leaves heart-shaped at base (Fig. 328) and densely velvety.

2. C. **sèpium** L. Hedge Bindweed. (Fig. 329) Stems trailing, twining, or climbing; leaf-blades triangular-arrow-shaped, on long petioles; corolla white or rose-color. The more abundant phase is var. **commùnis** Tryon, with basal lobes of the leaves angled, and peduncles usually not longer than the leaves; var. **americànus** Sims, less common, is often velvety, has rounded or slightly pointed basal lobes, and peduncles often longer than the leaves. Var. **rèpens** (L.) Gray is the narrowest-leaved extreme.

3. C. **arvénsis** L. Field Bindweed. (Fig. 330) Similar to No. 2; nearly smooth; flowers and leaves smaller; lobes of the leaf-blades acute.—Waste places in southern Wisconsin. Naturalized from Eurasia. Forma **cordifòlius** Lasch (heart-leaved) has the broad blade cordate, with rounded basal lobes; forma **auriculàtus** Desr. (eared) has linear-oblong to lanceolate blades with the auricles acute. The forms are less common than the typical plant.

POLEMONIÀCEAE Polemonium Family

Stamens and calyx-lobes 5; ovary of 3 carpels; stigma 3–lobed.

a. Leaves opposite, not divided . . . . 1. *Phlox.*
a. Leaves alternate, pinnately compound . . . . . . 2. *Polemonium.*

1. Phlóx

Corolla-tube long and narrow, the 5 lobes spreading widely.

a. Leaves mostly over 2 cm. long, without axillary tufts *b*.
  b. Leaves at least 10 times as long as broad. . . 1. *P. pilosa.*
  b. Leaves not over 5 times as long as broad. . . 2. *P. divaricata.*
a. Leaves 0.5–1.5 cm. long, with axillary tufts *c*.
  c. Notch in corolla-lobes about 1 mm. deep . . 3. *P. subulata.*
  c. Notch in corolla-lobes about 3 mm. deep . . 4. *P. bifida.*

1. **P. pilòsa** L. Stems erect; leaves narrow (Fig. 331); corolla pink, purple, or white, the tube woolly.—Prairies and open woods.—Var. **fúlgida** Wherry, with glandless hairs in the inflorescence, is common, and var. **vírens** (Michx.) Wherry, with gland-tipped hairs, is rare.

2. **P. divaricàta** L. Stems reclining at base; leaves oblong-ovate (Fig. 332); flowers usually blue.—In woods, north to Barron, Taylor, and Kewaunee Counties. The common form is var. **Lap-hámi** Wood, with corolla-lobes not notched; var. **canadénsis** (Sweet) Wherry, with notched corolla-lobes, is rare in Racine County.

3. **P. subulàta** L. MOSS PINK. Plants low, forming mats.—Occasionally escaping from cultivation.

4. **P. bífida** Beck. Native in Rock County, and occasionally escaping from cultivation northward.

2. Polemònium JACOB'S LADDER

P. réptans L. Stems 2–4 dm. high, branching; leaves pinnate; leaflets alternate or opposite, ovate; *corolla bell-shaped*, blue or white, 1–1.5 cm. broad; calyx bell-shaped, becoming inflated in fruit.—Woods, north to Barron, Marathon, and Brown Counties.

HYDROPHYLLÀCEAE WATERLEAF FAMILY

Herbs; leaves mostly alternate; pistil with but one carpel.

a. Flowers in terminal branched clusters . . . . . 1. *Hydrophyllum.*
a. Flowers long-pediceled in the leaf axils . . . . . 2. *Ellisia.*

1. Hydrophýllum WATERLEAF

Calyx-lobes narrowly ribbon-like, bristly-hairy; corolla longer than the calyx, with the stamens more or less extending beyond its mouth. Leaves variously patterned with white.

1. **H. virginiànum** L. Plants with mostly appressed hairs, 2–7 dm. high; *leaves all pinnate* (Fig. 333), the leaflets sharply and coarsely toothed; flowers bluish-purple, pink, or white.—Rich woods, north to Douglas, Lincoln, and Shawano Counties.

2. **H. appendiculàtum** Michx. Plants hairy; lower leaves pinnately divided; *upper leaves shallowly lobed* (Fig. 334), the lobes toothed (resembling a small grapevine leaf); flowers bluish-purple, pink, or white.—Rich woods, less common; north to Pierce, Dane, Brown, and Calumet Counties.

2. Ellísia

E. Nyctélea L. Rough-hairy, much-branched, 1–4 dm. high; leaves pinnately lobed nearly to the midrib, the lobes coarsely

1–3-toothed; *corolla scarcely longer than the calyx*, whitish.— Occasional as a weed in southern Wisconsin; adventive from farther south.

BORAGINÀCEAE Borage Family

Herbs, *usually rough-hairy*, with simple alternate leaves; flowers usually on one side of a branch which is rolled up from the tip and straightens as the blossoms open; ovary deeply 4–lobed, the single style arising from the middle; fruit of 4 1–seeded nutlets.—Genera based largely on fruit characters. The following key is based on superficial characters, and plants should be carefully checked, when possible, with the description of mature fruit given under each genus.

a. Corolla 1 cm. or more in length or breadth *b.*
  b. Plants hairy *c.*
    c. Upper leaves with a wing extending down the stem . . . . 4. *Symphytum.*
    c. Leaves without such wings *d.*
      d. Flowers reddish-purple . . . . 1. *Cynoglossum.*
      d. Flowers yellow or orange . . . . 8. *Lithospermum.*
  b. Plants without hairs . . . . 7. *Mertensia.*
a. Corolla 5 mm. or less in length or breadth *e.*
  e. Throat of the corolla closed by 5 scales *f.*
    f. Flowers not in the axils of bracts . . . . . 1. *Cynoglossum.*
    f. Flowers, or at least some of them, in the axils of bracts *g.*
      g. Hairs on the stem slender, curved, somewhat ascending *h.*
        h. Pedicels short, erect in fruit . . . . . 2. *Lappula.*
        h. Pedicels recurved or deflected in fruit 3. *Hackelia.*
      g. Hairs on the stem stout, bristle-like, straight, spreading . . . . 5. *Lycopsis.*
  e. Throat of the corolla without scales, open or with crests *i.*
    i. Flowers, or at least the uppermost, not in the axils of bracts . . . . 6. *Myosotis.*
    i. Flowers all in the axils of bracts . . . . . 8. *Lithospermum.*

1. **Cynoglóssum**

Corolla about equaling the calyx, with 5 rounded lobes; the throat closed by 5 scales; stamens included; nutlets attached by their sides, widely spreading in one plane, covered with barbed prickles and thus adhering to clothes, fur of animals, etc.

1. **C. officinàle** L. Hound's Tongue. Stout plants, *much branched above*, copiously leafy and covered with soft hairs; *corolla reddish-purple.*—Pastures, etc.; naturalized from Europe.

2. **C. boreàle** Fernald. Northern Wild Comfrey. Rather slender plants, *once or twice forked above in the bractless inflorescence*, with white spreading hairs; lower leaves with petioles, the upper with a broad clasping base; *corolla pale blue.*—Woods, south to Sawyer and Door Counties.

2. **Láppula** STICKSEED

Corolla with a slender tube and spreading lobes, the throat closed by 5 scales; stamens included; nutlets attached by their sides, erect, the margins or backs armed with barbed prickles; whole plant covered with minute stiff appressed hairs.—Mature fruit is almost indispensable for the determination of species.

a. Fruit with a double row of bristles along the margin . . . . 1. *L. echinata.*
a. Fruit with a single row of bristles along the margin . . . . 2. *L. Redowskii*, var. *occidentalis.*

1. **L. echinàta** Gilbert. Stem 1.5–6 dm. high; leaves very rough to the touch; flowers blue.—A weed in pastures, along railroads, etc.; naturalized from Europe.

2. **L. Redówskii** (Hornem.) Greene, var. **occidentàlis** (S. Wats.) Rydb. Similar; flowers blue.—Along railroads, Muscoda and Avoca; probably adventive from farther west.

3. **Hackèlia** NODDING STICKSEED

H. americàna (Gray) Fern. Stem 0.3–1 m. high, much branched above. Basal leaves narrowly ovate-lanceolate. Stem leaves narrowly to broadly lanceolate, mostly more than 1 cm. wide. Flowers white.—Occasional in shady ground.

4. **Sýmphytum** COMFREY

S. officinàle L. Plants with white stiff short hairs; lower leaves broad, abruptly narrowed at base; upper leaves narrowed at both ends; corolla yellowish or pinkish-white to bluish or roseate-purple, with 5 short spreading teeth, the throat closed by 5 scales; stamens included; nutlets nearly smooth, erect, with a hollow scar where attached, the scar finely toothed on its margin.—Occasional; introduced from Europe.

5. **Lycópsis** BUGLOSS

L. arvénsis L. Plant 1–6 dm. high, with copious spreading white flattened hairs; corolla blue, funnel-shaped, somewhat curved and irregular; stamens included; nutlets wrinkled, erect, with a hollow scar where attached.—Weed in a cultivated field, Ozaukee County; adventive from Europe.

6. **Myosòtis** FORGET-ME-NOT

Small herbs; stem-leaves without petioles, not toothed; upper flowers without bracts; corolla with blunt appendages opposite each of the 5 rounded lobes; nutlets compressed.

a. Calyx not 2–lipped; flowers usually blue *b*.
  b. Calyx with straight close hairs *c*.
    c. Calyx-lobes shorter than the tube. . . . . 1. *M. scorpioides.*
    c. Calyx-lobes about equalling the tube . . . 2. *M. laxa.*
  b. Calyx with curved spreading hairs. . . . . . 3. *M. arvensis.*
a. Calyx 2–lipped; flowers white . . . . 4. *M. verna.*

1. **M. scorpioìdes** L. Corolla 5–9 mm. broad, blue with yellow center.—Wet ground; naturalized from Europe.

2. **M. láxa** Lehm. Corolla 5 mm. or less broad, pale blue.—Wet ground along the lower Wisconsin River.

3. **M. arvénsis** (L.) Hill. Corolla 1.5–4 mm. broad, light blue or occasionally white.—Well-drained soil, rare; introduced from Europe.

4. **M. vérna** Nutt. (Fig. 335) Corolla 1–2 mm. broad; calyx hairs hooked or gland-tipped.—Dry open places, lower Wisconsin River and eastward.

7. **Merténsia** LUNGWORT; BLUEBELLS

M. virgínica (L.) Pers. (Fig. 336) Plants 2–6 dm. high; lower leaves long-petioled, the upper without petioles; *corolla light blue, pinkish in the bud*, trumpet-shaped, without scales in the throat; nutlets ovoid, fleshy, with small scar, the surface dull and roughish. —Mostly in damp wooded river-bottoms, along the Mississippi, St. Croix, Kickapoo, Rock, and Pecatonica. Known in La Crosse as "Hokah Bluebells."

8. **Lithospérmum**

Nutlets bony, often ivory-like, smooth or roughened, the scar nearly flat.

a. Corolla pale, about equalling the calyx *b*.
  b. Midrib of leaf conspicuous, branch veins obscure. . . . . 1. *L. arvense.*
  b. Branch veins of leaf conspicuous *c*.
    c. Leaves 0.6–1.2 cm. broad . . . . 2. *L. officinale.*
    c. Leaves 1.2–4.5 cm. broad . . . . 3. *L. latifolium.*
a. Corolla yellow or orange, several times exceeding calyx *d*.
  d. Corolla-lobes finely toothed . . . . 4. *L. incisum.*
  d. Corolla-lobes not toothed *e*.
    e. Plants with fine white silky hairs . . . . . 5. *L. canescens.*
    e. Plants with bristly hairs which have swollen bases . . . . 6. *L. croceum.*

1. **L. arvénse** L. CORN GROMWELL. Corolla white or yellowish, the lobes glabrous on outer surface.—Rare; naturalized from Europe.

2. **L. officinàle** L. GROMWELL. Corolla greenish, 4.5 mm. or less long, pubescent on lobes.—Rare; naturalized from Europe.

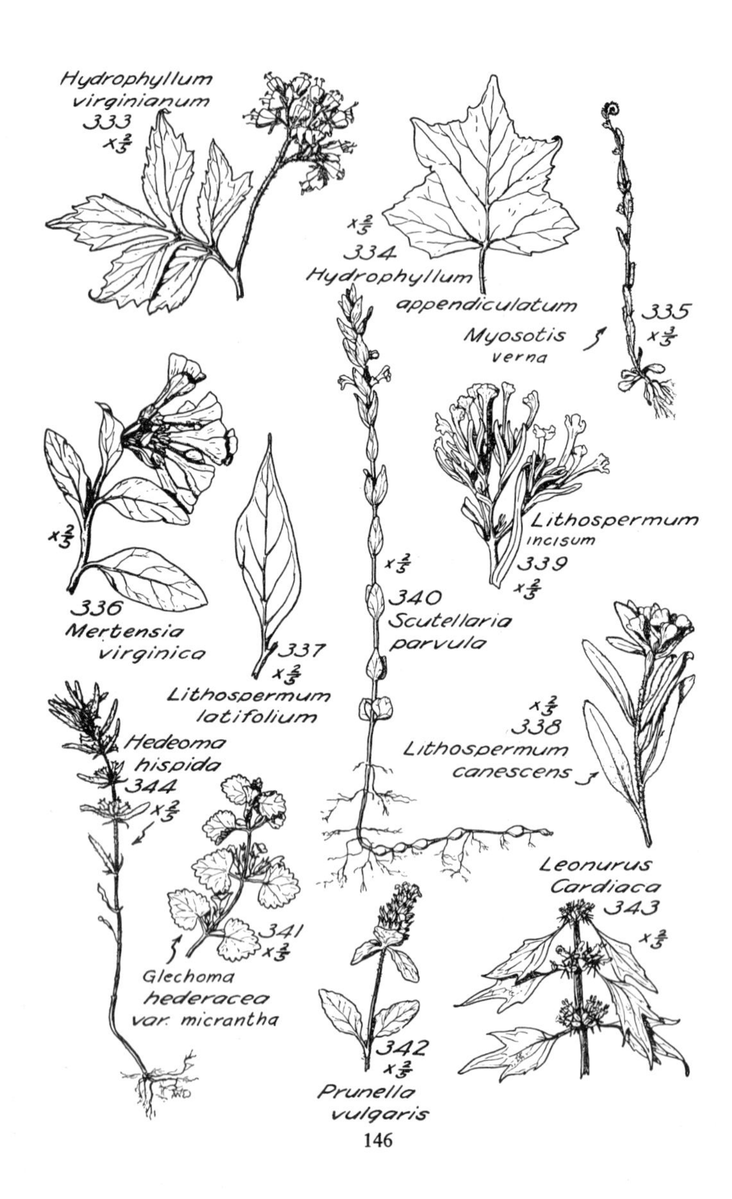
Hydrophyllum virginianum
333
x 2/5
x 2/5
334
Hydrophyllum appendiculatum
335
x 3/5
Myosotis verna
Lithospermum incisum
339
x 2/5
x 2/5
340
Scutellaria parvula
x 2/5
336
Mertensia virginica
337
x 2/5
Lithospermum latifolium
x 2/5
338
Lithospermum canescens
Hedeoma hispida
344
x 2/5
341
x 2/5
Glechoma hederacea var. micrantha
Leonurus Cardiaca
343
x 2/5
342
x 2/5
Prunella vulgaris

3. **L. latifòlium** Michx. (Fig. 337) Corolla yellow, 4.5–4.8 mm. long, pubescent on lobes.—Woods and open ground, north to Brown and Pierce Counties.

4. **L. incìsum** Lehm. PUCCOON. (Fig. 339) Leaves ribbon-like, whitened with fine hairs; corolla yellow.—Dry sand, north to Barron, Portage, and Sheboygan Counties.

5. **L. canéscens** (Michx.) Lehm. HOARY PUCCOON. (Fig. 338) Corolla orange-yellow, the tube naked at base within.—Prairies and sandy woods, mostly southward.

6. **L. cròceum** Fernald. Corolla light yellow or orange, the tube hairy at base within.—Dry soil, mostly southern.

LABIÀTAE MINT FAMILY

Herbs; stems usually square; foliage often with a volatile aromatic oil; fruit formed of 4 nutlets, each 1–seeded.

a. Leaves without petioles *b*.	
b. Leaves not more than 3 times as long as broad *c*.	
c. Leaves 2–4 cm. long	1. *Ajuga*.
c. Leaves about 1 cm. long.	2. *Scutellaria*.
b. Leaves about 10 times as long as broad (Fig. 344)	9. *Hedeoma*.
a. At least the lower leaves petioled *d*.	
d. Leaf-blades not over 1.5 cm. long, and about as broad (Fig. 341)	3. *Glechoma*.
d. Leaf-blades larger, mostly longer than broad *e*.	
e. Leaf-blades palmately veined (Fig. 343) . .	7. *Leonurus*.
e. Leaf-blades pinnately veined *f*.	
f. Flowers in dense elongate heads *g*.	
g. Leaf-blades sharply toothed.	4. *Dracocephalum*.
g. Leaf-blades wavy-margined or entire .	5. *Prunella*.
f. Flowers in distant whorls *h*.	
h. Calyx with 5 nearly equal and pointed teeth	6. *Lamium*.
h. Calyx 2–lipped	8. *Salvia*.

1. **Ájuga** BUGLE WEED

A. genevénsis L. Flowers blue, 1.5 cm. long, several in the axil of each broad 3–lobed bract.—Escaping from cultivation and locally abundant in Waukesha and Milwaukee Counties.

2. **Scutellària** SKULLCAP

S. párvula Michx. Stems finely woolly, simple or slightly branched, 0.8–3 dm. high; rootstocks long, usually *strongly constricted at frequent intervals;* leaves about 1 cm. long; flowers opposite, 5–10 mm. long.—Dry sandy soil and sandstone bluffs, mostly southward. Typical *S. parvula*, with stems and leaves covered by close short hairs, has been found only in Pierce County; our common plant is var. **Leónardi** (Epling) Fernald (Fig. 340), which is glabrous or minutely scabrous.

3. **Glechòma** GILL-OVER-THE-GROUND; CREEPING CHARLIE

G. hederàcea L. *Stems creeping;* flowers few together in the axils of foliage leaves; corolla 1.6–2.2 cm. long, blue.—Rare; the common plant is var. **micrántha** Moricand (Fig. 341), with corolla 1–1.5 cm. long.—In damp or shady places, mostly near dwellings; naturalized from Europe.

4. **Dracocéphalum** DRAGON HEAD

D. parviflòrum Nutt. Plants 1.5–8 dm. high; leaf-blades ovate-lanceolate; flowers bluish, in the axils of crowded *awn-toothed or fringed leafy bracts.*—Mostly northward; not common.

5. **Prunélla** SELF-HEAL

P. vulgàris L. (Fig. 342) Stems simple or a little branched; leaves ovate-oblong, narrowed at base, about a third as broad as long; flowers 3 in a cluster, many clusters making up a dense cylindrical head; calyx green or purple; corolla commonly bluish, sometimes pink or white.—Frequent weed in lawns and along roadsides. Naturalized from Eurasia.

6. **Làmium** DEAD NETTLE

L. maculàtum L. Plants erect; leaf-blades heart-shaped, round-toothed, frequently marked with a white spot on the upper side; corolla purplish or white, with a ring of hairs inside near the base. —Occasional; introduced from Europe.

7. **Leonùrus** MOTHERWORT

L. Cardìaca L. (Fig. 343) Tall perennial; leaves with petioles about as long as the *deeply 3-cleft and coarsely toothed blade;* flowers in whorls in the upper leaf-axils; calyx-lobes long and needle-like; *corolla densely hairy.*—Waste places and pastured woods; naturalized from Europe.

8. **Sálvia** SAGE

S. praténsis L. Stem reaching a meter in height, somewhat hairy; lower leaves petioled, the blades rounded to slightly heart-shaped at base, irregularly and somewhat doubly toothed; stem-leaves without petioles; corolla blue, the upper lip strongly arching.—Established at Rochester, where it has probably escaped from cultivation.

9. **Hedeòma** MOCK PENNYROYAL

H. híspida Pursh. (Fig. 344) Plants mostly small, *very strongly scented;* leaves ribbon-like; stem with downwardly-pointing bristles; flowers in whorls in the leaf-axils, *borne along nearly the entire length of the plant;* calyx bristly; corolla bluish.—Dry sandy soil.

SOLANÀCEAE Nightshade Family

Leaves alternate; fruit a berry in our spring-flowering species.

a. Plants herbaceous *b.*
  b. Flowers blue . . . . 1. *Solanum.*
  b. Flowers cream, yellow, or white. . . . . . . 2. *Physalis.*
a. Plants shrubby . . . . 3. *Lycium.*

1. Solànum Bittersweet; Matrimony Vine

S. Dulcamàra L. Somewhat climbing; leaf-blades heart-shaped, sometimes with small lateral leaflets (Fig. 345); flowers about 1 cm. in diameter, several in an open cluster; anthers opening by pores or chinks; berries red.—Wet thickets, shores, old fencerows, and roadsides; naturalized from Europe.

2. Phýsalis Ground Cherry

Corolla broad and open; berry yellowish in the inflated calyx.

a. Annuals; corolla white with yellow center. . . . 1. *P. grandiflora.*
a. Deep-rooted perennials; corolla yellow *b.*
  b. Plants sticky-hairy . . . . 2. *P. heterophylla.*
  b. Plants hairy but not sticky . . . . 3. *P. virginiana.*

1. **P. grandiflòra** Hook. Leaves about half as broad as long.—Clearings, etc., northern Wisconsin.

2. **P. heterophýlla** Nees. (Fig. 346) Leaf-blades rounded or heart-shaped at base, nearly as broad as long.—Sandy soil.

3. **P. virginiàna** Mill. Leaf-blades several times as long as broad; calyx sunken at the base.—Sandy soil.

3. Lýcium Matrimony Vine

L. halmifòlium Mill. Shrub with long drooping branches; leaves lanceolate, short-petioled; corolla short funnel-form, greenish-purple.—Occasional; introduced from Europe.

SCROPHULARIÀCEAE Figwort Family

Corolla mostly 2–lipped; stamens usually 4, in 2 pairs, or the flower with only 2 stamens; fruit a many-seeded capsule, formed of 2 carpels.

a. Corolla nearly regular *b.*
  b. Flowers 2 cm. or more in diameter . . . . . 1. *Verbascum.*
  b. Flowers less than 1 cm. in diameter . . . . . 7. *Veronica.*
a. Corolla 2–lipped *c.*
  c. Corolla with a spur (Figs. 347, 348) . . . . . 2. *Linaria.*
  c. Corolla without a spur *d.*
    d. Anther-bearing stamens 4 *e.*
      e. Leaves not lobed *f.*
        f. Stamens shorter than the corolla (Figs. 349, 350) *g.*

g. Leaves with petioles . . . . 4. *Scrophularia.*
g. At least the upper leaves without petioles *h.*
h. Flowers blue and white . . . . 3. *Collinsia.*
h. Flowers purple or whitish . . . 5. *Penstemon.*
f. Stamens longer than the corolla (Fig. 356) . . . . 8. *Synthyris.*
e. Leaves lobed at least halfway to the midrib *i.*
i. Lobes ribbon-like (Fig. 357) . . . . 9. *Castilleja.*
i. Lobes rounded, not over twice as long as broad (Fig. 358) . . . . 10. *Pedicularis.*
d. Stamens 2 *j.*
j. Leaves alternate . . . . 8. *Synthyris.*
j. Leaves opposite . . . . 6. *Gratiola.*

1. Verbáscum

V. Blattària L. MOTH MULLEIN. Stem tall and stout, about 1 m. high; leaves in a basal rosette and scattered on the stem, the lower with margins lobed; flowers in long simple racemes, yellow.—Occasional southeastward; adventive from Europe.

2. Linària TOADFLAX

Stems simple or branched; *leaves alternate, ribbon-like;* flowers in racemes.

a. Flowers yellow and orange . . . . 1. *L. vulgaris.*
a. Flowers blue *b.*
b. Plant with few glands or none . . . . 2. *L. canadensis.*
b. Whole plant with stalked glands . . . . 3. *L. minor.*

1. **L. vulgàris** Hill. BUTTER AND EGGS. (Fig. 347) Leaves numerous, pale green; corolla 2–3 cm. long (including the spur), the orange palate contrasting with the rest of the flower.—A common weed; naturalized from Europe.

2. **L. canadénsis** (L.) Dumont. (Fig. 348) Stems usually simple or nearly so, very slender; corolla 1 cm. or less long.—Sandy ground, often in disturbed soil; north to Eau Claire and Waupaca Counties.

3. **L. mìnor** (L.) Desf. Low and branching; corolla 5–8 mm. long.—A rather uncommon weed along railroads.

3. Collínsia BLUE-EYED MARY

C. vérna Nutt. Slender herbs; leaves clasping the stem, broadest at the base, toothed; flowers about 6 in a whorl; corolla deeply 2-lipped, blue and white.—Janesville.

4. Scrophulària FIGWORT

Coarse herbs, 1–1.7 m. high; leaf-blades heart-shaped or rounded at base, sharply toothed; petioles long; branches of the inflorescence with copious gland-tipped hairs; corolla yellowish- or purplish-green, with a scale inside the upper lip representing a fifth stamen (Fig. 349).

1. **S. marilándica** L. Inflorescence pyramidal; rudimentary stamen purplish-brown.—North to Dunn, Sauk, and Outagamie Counties. Flowers later than the next, usually in July.—Oak woods.

2. **S. lanceolàta** Pursh. (Fig. 349) Inflorescence slender; rudimentary stamen yellowish-green.—Common on roadsides and rocky banks.

5. **Penstémon** BEARD-TONGUE

Stems usually several in a clump, not branched except in the inflorescence; stem-leaves opposite, without petioles, often somewhat clasping; corolla tubular, dilated above, more or less 2–lipped, the upper lip 2–lobed, the lower 3–cleft (Fig. 350).

a. Leaves toothed *b.*
  b. Leaves 2–4 cm. wide. . . . . 2. *P. Digitalis.*
  b. Leaves not over 1 cm. wide *c.*
    c. Pubescence of middle internodes often glandular, or absent. . . . . 3. *P. gracilis.*
    c. Pubescence of middle internodes white, spreading, somewhat crinkled. . . . . 1. *P. hirsutus.*
a. Leaves not toothed . . . . 4. *P. grandiflorus.*

1. **P. hirsùtus** (L.) Willd. (Fig. 350) Stem reaching a meter in height; inflorescence with stalked glands, the lower branches about as long as their subtending leaves; stem-leaves mostly long and narrow.—Open ground, Sheboygan and Green Lake Counties, southeastward.

2. **P. Digitàlis** Nutt. Stems rather stout, about a meter or more high; lower stem-leaves sometimes reaching 16 cm. in length and 4 cm. in width; upper leaves triangular; inflorescence open, the *lower branches usually many times exceeding their subtending leaves.* —Fields, southern Wisconsin; probably adventive or escaping from cultivation.

3. **P. grácilis** Nutt. Stems 2–4 dm. high, smooth or nearly so except in the glandular inflorescence; leaves very narrow; inflorescence narrowly cylindrical, the *lower branches only occasionally exceeding their subtending leaves.*—Western Wisconsin, from Burnett and Monroe Counties to La Crosse County.—Var. **wisconsinénsis** (Pennell) Fassett has the stem densely covered with very short powder-like hairs, and the leaves usually finely hairy.—Sandy places, Eau Claire and Portage Counties to the lower Wisconsin River.

4. **P. grandiflòrus** Nutt. Plant 5–10 dm. high, stout, entirely without hairs or glands, and with a whitish bloom; leaves rounded or blunt at tip, the upper nearly as broad as long; inflorescence unbranched; *corolla 4–5 cm. long.*—Western Wisconsin.

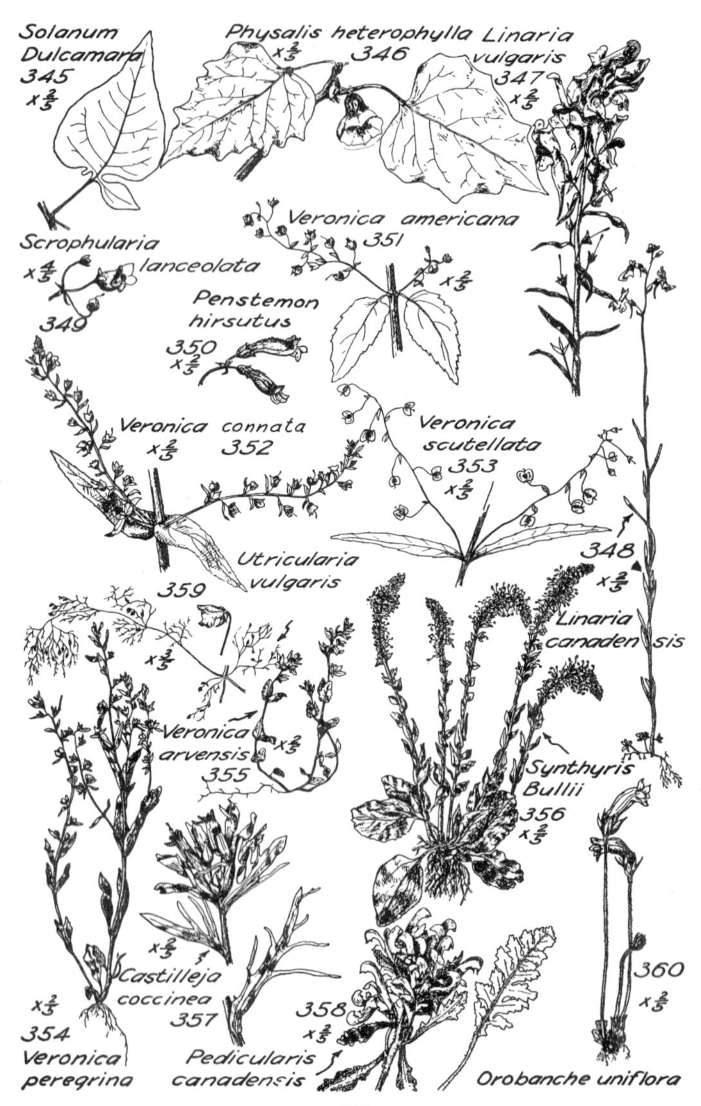
Solanum
Dulcamara
345
x2/5
Physalis heterophylla
x2/5
346
Linaria
vulgaris
347
x2/5
Veronica americana
351
x2/5
Scrophularia
x4/5
lanceolata
349
Penstemon
hirsutus
350
x2/5
Veronica connata
x2/5
352
Veronica
scutellata
353
x2/5
348
x2/5
Linaria
canadensis
Utricularia
vulgaris
359
x3/5
Veronica
arvensis
355
x2/5
Synthyris
Bullii
356
x2/5
x2/5
Castilleja
coccinea
357
358
x2/5
360
x2/5
x2/5
354
Veronica
peregrina
Pedicularis
canadensis
Orobanche uniflora

6. **Gratìola** MARSH HYSSOP

G. neglécta Torr. Stem 1–3 dm. high; leaves opposite, without petioles; flowers on peduncles 1–2.5 cm. long; corolla 0.8–1.5 cm. long, pale yellow.—Muddy places.

7. **Verónica** SPEEDWELL

Corolla-lobes spreading; stamens 2.

a. Flowers in long racemes in the axils of leaves *b*.
  b. Stems velvety . . . . 1. *V. officinalis.*
  b. Stems almost or quite without hairs *c*.
    c. Leaves all petioled (Fig. 351) . . . . 2. *V. americana.*
    c. Leaves, at least those of the flowering stems, without petioles *d*.
      d. Leaves lanceolate, clasping the stem at the broad base (Fig. 352) . . . . . 3. *V. connata.*
      d. Leaves nearly linear, narrowed to the base (Fig. 353) . . . . 4. *V. scutellata.*
a. Flowers along the stem in axils of foliage leaves *e*.
  e. Stems creeping . . . . 5. *V. serpyllifolia.*
  e. Stems erect *f*.
    f. Corolla whitish . . . . 6. *V. peregrina.*
    f. Corolla deep violet-blue . . . . 7. *V. arvensis.*

1. **V. officinàlis** L. *Stems creeping;* leaves oval, toothed, hairy, with very short petioles or none; racemes 20–30-flowered, the pedicels shorter than the flowers; flowers pale lavender, with blue lines.—Door to Kenosha Counties.

2. **V. americàna** (Raf.) Schwein. (Fig. 351) Plants creeping only at base, with erect stems; leaf-blades broadest near the base, toothed; racemes 10–25-flowered, several times as long as their subtending leaves; pedicels slender, several times as long as the pale blue purple-striped flowers.—Wet shores, mostly northward.

3. **V. connàta** Raf. (Fig. 352) Stems mostly in the water; leaves obscurely toothed, mostly 1 cm. or more wide; racemes 3–4 times as long as their subtending leaves, coarse, 15–30-flowered, the pedicels 3–6 mm. long; corolla pale blue (*V. Anagallis-aquatica,* in part).—North to Door, Adams, and Pierce Counties.—The typical form has the pedicels with minute stalked glands; var. **glabérrima** (Pennell) Fassett has pedicels without glands.

4. **V. scutellàta** L. (Fig. 353) Stems slender and weak, occasionally with some weak hairs; leaves very narrow, long-pointed, often with minute distinct teeth; racemes 5–20-flowered, seldom twice as long as their subtending leaves; pedicels very slender, 6–10 mm. long; flowers blue.—Occasional in wet places.

5. **V. serpyllifòlia** L. THYME-LEAVED SPEEDWELL. Leaves short-petioled, the blades oval, obtuse, obscurely toothed, mostly 1 cm. or less long; corolla 3–4 mm. wide, whitish or pale blue with *deeper stripes.*—Open woods and grassy places.

6. **V. peregrìna** L. PURSLANE SPEEDWELL. (Fig. 354) Lowest leaves petioled, with ovate blades, the *upper oval to linear, without petioles;* flowers very small, shorter than their bracts.—A roadside and garden weed.—Var. **xalapénsis** (HBK.) St. John & Warren is covered with gland-tipped hairs.

7. **V. arvénsis** L. CORN SPEEDWELL. (Fig. 355) Leaves mostly short-petioled, the blades oval, crenate; stem with spreading hairs. —Occasional in fields; naturalized from Europe.

8. **Synthyrís**

S. Búllii (Eaton) Heller. (Fig. 356) Root-leaves petioled, the blades rounded, covered with short, white hairs; stems unbranched, with small hairy leaves without petioles; flowers in a dense spike *(Besseya, Wulfenia)*.—Open woods and prairies; southern tier of counties; Pierce County.

9. **Castillèja**

Leaves in a small basal rosette, and scattered on the unbranched stems, narrow, hairy, *cut into ribbon-like lobes.*

1. **C. coccínea** (L.) Spreng. SCARLET PAINTED CUP. (Fig. 357) Flowers pale yellow, less conspicuous than the *scarlet-tipped or yellow-tipped leaves* in whose axils they are borne.—Locally abundant.

2. **C. sessiliflòra** Pursh. Corolla tubular, 3–4 cm. long; floral leaves green.—Limestone bluffs, high prairies, and sand, north to Pierce and Columbia Counties.

10. **Pediculàris** WOOD BETONY; LOUSEWORT

P. canadénsis L. (Fig. 358) Stems simple, clustered, hairy, 1.5–4 dm. high; *leaves pinnate or pinnatifid, the divisions with rounded teeth;* flowers in a short spike, yellow, rarely scarlet.—Dry sandy woods and fields.

LENTIBULARIÀCEAE BLADDERWORT FAMILY

Aquatics or plants of moist ground; corolla irregular, usually 2–lipped, having a short tube with a spur near its base, the throat partly closed by a palate; ovary of 2 carpels; fruit a many-seeded capsule.

Utriculària BLADDERWORT

Plants submerged, *bearing bladders which catch small insects;* leaves divided into hair-like segments; flowers on an emersed spike, yellow.

1. **U. vulgàris** L. (Fig. 359) Leaves 2–3 times pinnately parted, bearing bladders.—Common in shallow water.

2. **U. intermèdia** Hayne. Leaves 4–5 times forked; bladders on separate leafless branches.—Peat bogs, less common.

OROBANCHÀCEAE Broom-rape Family

Herbs, not green, parasitic on roots of other plants; stem stout, fleshy; leaves replaced by scales; corolla 2–lipped with 2 folds in the throat; fruit a capsule with many compartments.

a. Flowers crowded in a thick scaly spike . . . . . 1. *Conopholis.*
a. Flowers on long pedicels . . . . 2. *Orobanche.*

1. Conópholis Squaw-root

C. americàna (L.) Wallr. Parasitic on the roots of trees, mostly oaks; plant yellow or chestnut-colored throughout, not branched, 0.5–2 dm. high, looking something like a pine cone; flowers covered by thick scales.—Woods; locally abundant in southern Wisconsin.

2. Orobánche Broom-rape

Parasitic on herbs. Stems short, the above-ground portions bearing several small bracts; flowers with a curved tube, each on a long, erect, naked pedicel from the axil of a bract.

1. **O. uniflòra** L. (Fig. 360) Flowers 1–5; pedicels longer than the short stem, which is only 1–7 cm. tall; flowers lavender, fading to yellowish or white.—Sandy prairies, thickets, or moist woods, southern Wisconsin and Door County; rare.

2. **O. fasciculàta** Nutt. Flowers 6–12, purplish; pedicels not longer than the elongate stem which is 5–10 cm. high.—Sandy soil, Green, Iowa, Sheboygan, and Ozaukee Counties; rare.

PLANTAGINÀCEAE Plantain Family

Leaves all basal, simple, strongly veined; flowers in a slender spike; corolla papery, 4–lobed; stamens 4; fruit a many-seeded capsule.

Plantàgo Plantain

a. Leaf-blades more than half as broad as long *b.*
 b. Side-veins of the leaf arising along the midrib. 1. *P. cordata.*
 b. Veins of the leaf free to the base of the blade. 2. *P. major.*
a. Leaf-blades many times longer than broad *c.*
 c. Leaf-blades lanceolate (Fig. 362) or oblanceolate *d.*
  d. Leaves lanceolate, hairless, bracts and sepals hairless, spikes short, seeds brown . . . 3. *P. lanceolata.*
  d. Leaves oblanceolate, often toothed, hairy, bracts and sepals short-hairy, spikes long, seeds red . . . . 6. *P. rhodosperma.*
 c. Leaf-blades ribbon-like (Fig. 363) *e.*
  e. Bracts shorter than the flowers . . . . . . 4. *P. Purshii.*
  e. Bracts much longer than the flowers . . . . . 5. *P. aristata.*

1. **P. cordàta** Lam. Leaf-blades heart-shaped at base, on long petioles.—Along streams, Racine and Milwaukee Counties.

2. **P. màjor** L. COMMON PLANTAIN. Leaf-blades broadly oval, thick and leathery, tapered to the petiole or almost square across the base (Fig. 361). *P. Rugelii* Dcne., whose petioles are usually dark red at base (*P. major* is usually green), can be distinguished for certain only with ripe fruit. Both are common along roadsides and paths, and in lawns and fields.

3. **P. lanceolàta** L. RIB-GRASS. Leaves long and narrow, strongly ribbed (Fig. 362); spikes short, lengthening as the fruit matures, on scapes 2–7 dm. high.—A weed in grass-lands; naturalized from Europe.

4. **P. Púrshii** R. & S. (Fig. 363) *Whole plant woolly;* leaves much shorter than the spike.—Sandy prairies.

5. **P. aristàta** Michx. Similar to No. 4, but greener and less woolly, with loose hairs.—Dry places southward; rare.

6. **P. rhodospérma** Dcne. A hairy species with red seeds.—Introduced from southwest into Iowa County.

RUBIÀCEAE MADDER FAMILY

Leaves opposite and with stipules, or apparently whorled; ovary of 2–4 carpels, the calyx adherent to its wall; stamens as many as the lobes of the corolla; corolla-lobes with their edges touching when in bud.

a. Leaves whorled (Figs. 364–370) . . . . 1. *Galium.*
a. Leaves opposite *b.*
  b. Stems creeping . . . . 2. *Mitchella.*
  b. Stems erect. . . . . 3. *Houstonia.*

1. Gàlium BEDSTRAW

Slender herbs, with square stems; calyx-lobes none; stamens 4, or rarely 3; fruit dry, globular, of 2 nearly separate lobes.

a. Leaves mostly 4 in a whorl, gradually pointed or rounded, not with a short abrupt point (Figs. 365–368) *b.*
  b. Flowers without pedicels (Fig. 365) *c.*
    c. Corolla hairy . . . . 2. *G. circaezans.*
    c. Corolla not hairy. . . . . 3. *G. lanceolatum.*
  b. Flowers with pedicels *d.*
    d. Flowers in much-branched terminal clusters (Fig. 367) . . . . 4. *G. boreale.*
    d. Peduncles unbranched or with 2–4 branches, in the axils of foliage leaves *e.*
      e. Corolla with 3 lobes *f.*
        f. Flowers mostly solitary, on roughened curved pedicels . . . . 5. *G. trifidum.*
        f. Flowers in 2's or 3's, on smooth straight pedicels. . . . . 6. *G. tinctorium.*
      e. Corolla with 4 lobes *g.*
        g. Leaves ascending or spreading, lanceolate . . . . 7. *G. obtusum.*
        g. Leaves pointing downward, linear . 8. *G. labradoricum.*

a. Leaves 5–8 in a whorl, with short abrupt rigid tips *h.*
h. Flowers in a terminal inflorescence that forks several times; leaf-margins smooth or with a few bristles; fruit smooth . . . . 9. *G. concinnum.*
h. Flowers on axillary peduncles that are 3-flowered or slightly forking; leaf-margins copiously hairy or bristly; fruit bristly *i.*
i. Leaves 5–8 mm. broad, 3–4 times as long. . 10. *G. triflorum.*
i. Leaves 2–4 mm. broad, about 10 times as long . . . . 1. *G. Aparine.*

1. **G. Aparìne** L. CLEAVERS; GOOSE GRASS. (Fig. 364) Stems weak and reclining; leaves about 8 in a whorl; flowers white; fruit bristly.—Moist woods, mostly southward.

2. **G. circaézans** Michx. WILD LICORICE. Stems erect, smooth, 3 dm. high; leaves 1.5–4.5 cm. long, *a third to a half as wide, obtuse* (Fig. 365), their margins fringed with fine hairs; corolla greenish; fruit bristly.—Rich woods in southern Wisconsin; rare.

3. **G. lanceolàtum** Torr. WILD LICORICE. Similar to No. 2; leaves 3–7.5 cm. long, *about a fourth as wide, long-pointed* (Fig. 366); corolla yellowish, turning dark purple; fruit bristly.—Not common.

4. **G. boreàle** L. NORTHERN BEDSTRAW. (Fig. 367) *Stems erect*, smooth, 3–9 dm. high; leaves long and narrow, roughened on the margins; *flowers very many, white.*—Railroad embankments, bluffs, meadows, and along streams. A variable species. Common.

5. **G. trífidum** L. Stems slender, weak, reclining, roughened; leaves obtuse; fruit smooth.—Northern Wisconsin; rare southward.

6. **G. tinctòrium** L. (Fig. 368) Similar to No. 5, but stouter. —Marshlands.

7. **G. obtùsum** Bigel. Stems erect, smooth; leaves 1–2 cm. long, obtuse, slightly roughened on the margins and midrib; fruit smooth.—Moist ground.

8. **G. labradóricum** Wiegand. Similar, but weak and much more slender, generally hidden among grasses.—Swales and swamps.

9. **G. concínnum** T. & G. (Fig. 369) Stems low and slender, 1.5–3 dm. high, smooth or minutely roughened on the angles; leaves in 6's, narrow, the margins slightly roughened upwardly; fruit smooth. —Woods, north to Barron and Brown Counties.

10. **G. triflòrum** Michx. SWEET-SCENTED BEDSTRAW. (Fig. 370) Stems often reclining, 3–10 dm. long; peduncles 3-flowered; flowers greenish; fruit with hooked prickles.—Common in woods.

2. **Mitchélla** PARTRIDGE BERRY

M. rèpens L. (Fig. 371) Smooth trailing evergreen herb; *leaf-blades nearly round;* flowers in pairs in the axils of leaves; corolla

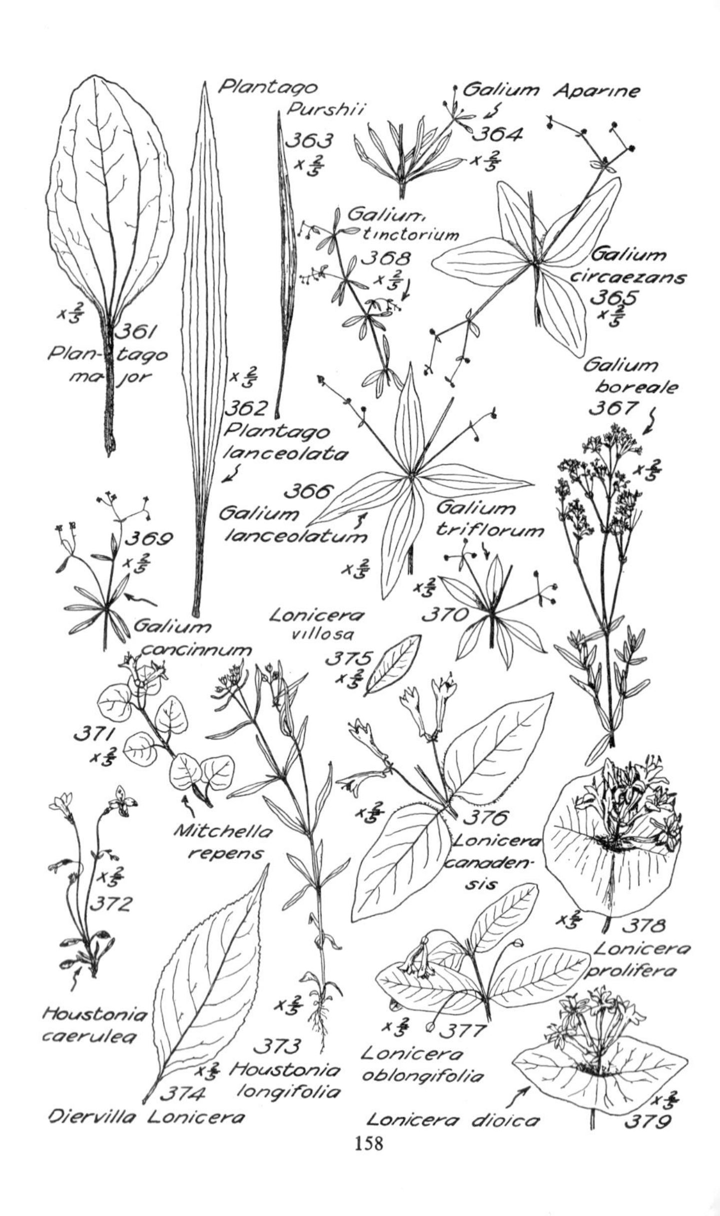
Plantago
Purshii
363
x 2/5
Galium Aparine
364
x 2/5
x 2/5
361
Plan- tago
ma jor
Galium
tinctorium
368
x 2/5
Galium
circaezans
365
x 2/5
x 2/5
362
Plantago
lanceolata
Galium
boreale
367
x 2/5
366
Galium
lanceolatum
x 2/5
Galium
triflorum
x 2/5
370
369
x 2/5
Galium
concinnum
Lonicera
villosa
375
x 2/5
371
x 2/5
Mitchella
repens
x 2/5
376
Lonicera
canaden-
sis
x 2/5
372
Houstonia
caerulea
x 2/5
378
Lonicera
prolifera
x 2/5
x 2/5
377
Lonicera
oblongifolia
373
x 2/5
Houstonia
longifolia
374
Diervilla Lonicera
Lonicera dioica
x 2/5
379

white, bearded within, tinged with purple; berry red, formed of 2 coherent ovaries and their calyces.—Shady woods, south to Kenosha and Sauk Counties, rarely to Dane County.

3. Houstònia

Small herbs, with basal rosettes of leaves; stem leaves with their bases connected by stipules; calyx and corolla 4–lobed.

1. **H. caerùlea** L. BLUETS; INNOCENCE. (Fig. 372) *Plants slender, delicate,* 0.5–2 dm. high; leaves 6–9 mm. long; flowers few on each stem, bluish or white.—Moist grassy places, north to Dane County.

2. **H. longifòlia** Gaertn. (Fig. 373) Plants stouter and coarser, 1–2.5 dm. high; leaves 1.5–2.5 cm. long; flowers several in a branched inflorescence, pale purple or nearly white.—Gravelly and sandy ground, mostly northward.

CAPRIFOLIÀCEAE HONEYSUCKLE FAMILY

Closely resembling the preceding family in technical characters, but usually without stipules (sometimes with appendages at the base of the petiole representing stipules in *Viburnum*); corolla-lobes successively overlapping when in bud.

a. Corolla tubular or bell-shaped; leaves simple *b.*
  b. Shrubs *c.*
    c. Leaves taper-pointed (Fig. 374) . . . . . . 1. *Diervilla.*
    c. Leaves not taper-pointed *d.*
      d. Corolla long-tubular, somewhat irregular 2. *Lonicera.*
      d. Corolla short-bell-shaped, nearly regular 3. *Symphoricarpos.*
  b. Herbs *e.*
    e. Plants delicate, creeping (Fig. 380) . . . . 4. *Linnaea.*
    e. Plants coarse, erect (Fig. 381) . . . . 5. *Triosteum.*
a. Corolla spreading, open *f.*
  f. Leaves simple . . . . 6. *Viburnum.*
  f. Leaves pinnately compound . . . . 7. *Sambucus.*

1. Diervílla BUSH HONEYSUCKLE

D. Lonícera Mill. Low shrubs; leaves petioled, toothed (Fig. 374); flowers 3 or more in the upper leaf-axils or in a terminal cluster; corolla yellowish, sometimes marked with reddish, somewhat irregular.—Woods, more common northward.—Var. **hypomálaca** Fernald. Leaves velvety beneath.—Door County.

2. Lonícera HONEYSUCKLE

Shrubs with entire leaves and terminal or axillary clusters of flowers.

a. Erect shrubs; flowers 1–2 in the axil of each leaf *b.*
  b. Leaves broadest near the base (Fig. 376) *c.*
    c. Lobes of the corolla nearly as long as the tube *d.*

d. Peduncles smooth, mostly longer than flowers; flowers fading to pink . . 2. *L. tatarica.*
d. Peduncles densely hairy, mostly shorter than flowers; flowers fading to yellow 3. *L. Morrowi.*
c. Lobes of the corolla much shorter than the tube. . . . . 4. *L. canadensis.*
b. Leaves broadest near the middle (Figs. 375, 377) *e.*
e. Peduncle shorter than the flower . . . . . 1. *L. villosa.*
e. Peduncle longer than the flower . . . . . 5. *L. oblongifolia.*
a. Climbing vines; flowers mostly numerous in terminal clusters (Figs. 378, 379) *f.*
f. Leaves without hairs on the margins *g.*
g. Corolla-tube 1–1.5 cm. long; anthers 4–5 mm. long . . . . 6. *L. prolifera.*
g. Corolla scarcely 1 cm. long; anthers 2.5–3 mm. long . . . . 7. *L. dioica.*
f. Leaves with a fringe of hairs along the margin 8. *L. hirsuta.*

1. **L. villòsa** (Michx.) R. & S. MOUNTAIN FLY HONEYSUCKLE. Stems 3–9 dm. high, with ascending branches; *young twigs finely woolly* and sometimes with sparse spreading hairs; leaf-blades oval (Fig. 375), somewhat hairy beneath; bracts longer than the ovaries; corolla yellowish; berries blue.—Rare in deep bogs.

2. **L. tatárica** L. TARTARIAN HONEYSUCKLE. Shrub 1.5–3 m. high; leaves 2–4 cm. long, rounded or obtuse at tip, with short petioles; *corolla white or rose-color, 1.5 cm. long.*—An aggressive weedy shrub, often escaping from cultivation in southern Wisconsin.

3. **L. Mórrowi** Gray. Shrub similar to No. 2, but leaves hairy below and corolla white turning yellow after flowering. Eurasian shrub often escaped in southern Wisconsin.

4. **L. canadénsis** Marsh. AMERICAN FLY HONEYSUCKLE. (Fig. 376) Similar; corolla greenish-yellow, 1.5–2 cm. long; *leaf-blades fringed with hairs* below the middle.—Northern, and rarely in bogs southeastward.

5. **L. oblongifòlia** (Goldie) Hook. SWAMP FLY HONEYSUCKLE. (Fig. 377) Corolla deeply 2-lipped, 1–1.5 cm. long, yellowish-white.—Rare in swamps, northward and eastward.

6. **L. prolífera** (Kirchner) Rehder. Extensively climbing over shrubs; *leaves strongly bluish-whitened beneath, the uppermost pair joined into a nearly round disk* (Fig. 378) which is also strongly whitened above; corolla yellow; stamens conspicuous, the *filaments without hairs.*—Common in fields and woods.

7. **L. dioìca** L. Usually climbing; leaves without hairs, somewhat whitened beneath, *the uppermost pair joined into a 4-sided disk* (Fig. 379) which is strongly angled at the ends and longer than broad; corolla yellow or reddish, without hairs; *filaments hairy.* —Oak woods.—Var. **glaucéscens** (Rydb.) Butters has the leaves

and corolla with spreading hairs, and is found occasionally *(L. glaucescens)*.

8. **L. hirsùta** Eat. HAIRY HONEYSUCKLE. Climbing vine; *leaves copiously fine-hairy*, somewhat whitened beneath, the uppermost forming a broad disk; corolla yellow, filaments hairy.—South to Barron, Wood, and Ozaukee Counties.

3. **Symphoricárpos** SNOWBERRY

S. occidentàlis Hook. WOLFBERRY. Often producing stout unbranched canes; flowers 4–10 per leaf-axil, crowded in short racemes.—Bluffs and dry prairies near the Mississippi River, and spreading eastward along railroads.

4. **Linnaèa** TWINFLOWER

L. boreàlis L., var. **americàna** (Forbes) Rehder. (Fig. 380) Slender creeping evergreen, somewhat woody, plant; leaves short-petioled, with rounded blades; *peduncles upright, with 2* (rarely 4 or 6) *delicate pinkish, very fragrant flowers.*—Shady woods northward; rarely southward as far as Dane and Milwaukee Counties.

5. **Trióstеum** HORSE GENTIAN

Coarse, usually dark green herbs, 0.5 to 1.2 m. high. Middle leaves with their bases uniting around the stem or only narrowing at the base; velvety beneath (or smooth in some forms). Flowers clustered in the axils of the leaves; corolla greenish yellow to purple; fruits orange or red, with three large seeds.*

a. Principal leaves broadly clasping the stem; stem hairs of a short, glandular type; flowers 3–4 in the leaf-axils; style exserted 1.5–3 mm. beyond the corolla-lobes; fruit light orange, densely covered with short glandular hairs . . . . 1. *T. perfoliatum.*

a. Principal leaves narrowed to the base (Fig. 381); stem hairs of a long, nonglandular type, or of both long and short types; flowers 1–5 in each leaf-axil; style included within the corolla-lobes (exserted in No. 3); fruit bright orange or red *b.*

  b. Style included; flowers 3–5 in each leaf-axil; fruit bright orange; stem hairs of both long and short types . . . . 2. *T. aurantiacum.*

  b. Style exserted 1.5–2.5 mm.; flowers 1–2 in each leaf-axil; fruit red (sometimes purplish); stem hairs mostly of a long, nonglandular type . . 3. *T. illinoense.*

1. **T. perfoliatum** L. Leaves thick, of a rugose texture, dark green above, light green below; corolla reddish-purple with cream-colored spots near the base.—On sandy, thin or rocky soil in open woods and thickets. Collected in the southern one-third of the state and in Dunn County.

* Adapted from F. C. Lane, *Triosteum* MS, 1955.

2. **T. auranthacum** Bickn. (Fig. 381) Leaves as above, except thinner and tapering to the base. Corolla dull purplish-red.—Found throughout the state in rich hilly or rocky woods and thickets.

3. **T. illinoénse** (Wieg.) Rydb. Leaves pale green, shortened and more oval than the two species above; corolla dull reddish-purple with cream-colored spots.—In rich, open woods, wooded ravines and rocky wooded slopes near streams, usually in a limestone area. Specimens have been collected in the southwest corner of the state, from Vernon to Rock Counties; rare, and not previously reported from Wisconsin.

6. **Vibúrnum**

Simple-leaved shrubs; leaf-buds naked or with a pair of scales; calyx-lobes, corolla-lobes, and stamens 5; fruit a 1–seeded drupe.

a. Leaves palmately veined and sometimes lobed (Figs. 382, 385) *b.*	
b. Leaves slightly hairy or glabrous beneath *c.*	
c. Petioles with stipules at base and 2 glands at summit	1. *V. trilobum.*
c. Petioles without stipules or glands	2. *V. edule.*
b. Leaves velvety beneath.	3. *V. acerifolium.*
a. Leaves pinnately veined, not lobed (Figs. 383, 384) *d.*	
d. Stipules present	4. *V. Rafinesquianum.*
d. Stipules absent *e.*	
e. Inflorescence stalked	5. *V. cassinoides.*
e. Inflorescence not stalked, the branches arising directly from a clump of leaves . .	6. *V. Lentago.*

1. **V. trílobum** Marsh. HIGH-BUSH CRANBERRY. Shrub 1–4 m. high; leaves 3–lobed, the lobes somewhat toothed (Fig. 385); flowers in a flat-topped inflorescence, the *marginal flowers with large white corolla and no stamens or pistils*, the inner fertile and with small corolla; fruit bright red.—Moist thickets. Similar to *V. Opulus* L., a European plant, cultivated and often escaping.

2. **V. edùle** (Michx.) Raf. Blades shallowly lobed or not lobed; flowers uniform.—Barron Hills.

3. **V. acerifòlium** L. ARROW-WOOD. Shrub 1–1.5 m. high; leaves maple-like (Fig. 382); flowers all alike and fertile; fruit crimson, turning black.—Woods; south to Sauk and Kenosha Counties.

4. **V. Rafinesquiànum** Schultes. DOWNY ARROW-WOOD. Shrub 6–14 dm. high; *leaves with 6–11 teeth on each side*,velvety beneath, and petioles 3–7 mm. long (Fig. 383). Var. **affìne** (Bush) House has the leaves not downy beneath, with petioles 5–12 mm. long, and is much less common. Between these two varieties occur occasional intermediates, with short petioles and smooth leaves, or with long petioles and leaves downy beneath.

5. **V. cassinoìdes** L. *Leaf-margins with obscure and irregular shallow teeth or none;* petioles scarcely winged.—Marinette and Oconto Counties.

6. **V. Lentàgo** L. NANNYBERRY. Shrub or tree reaching 9 m. in height; leaf-blades ovate, with *25–40 knobbed teeth on each side* (Fig. 384); petioles winged; *midrib red-dotted beneath;* fruit 1–1.5 cm. long, blue-black.—Woods and thickets.

7. Sambùcus ELDER

1. **S. canadénsis** L. COMMON ELDER. (Fig. 386) Shrubs 1–4 m. high; *pith white;* lower leaflets often 2–3-parted; flowers white, in *a broad flat-topped panicle;* blossoming in June and July; fruit purple-black.—Moist ground, common.

2. **S. pùbens** Michx. RED-BERRIED ELDER. (Fig. 387) Plant 0.5–3.5 m. high; *pith brown;* flowers yellowish-white, or tinged with purple, in *a narrow ovoid panicle;* blossoming in May; fruit red, ripening in July.—Mostly northward, but occasionally found southward, especially in the Driftless Area.

ADOXÀCEAE MOSCHATEL FAMILY

Adóxa MOSCHATEL

A. Moschatéllina L. Delicate herbs; basal leaves 3–parted, the leaflets again 3–parted, the ultimate divisions stalked and deeply 3–cleft; stem-leaves 2, 2–3 cm. long, 3–parted or deeply 3–cleft; flowers greenish or yellowish.—Rare on moist sandstone cliffs in southwestern Wisconsin.

VALERIANÀCEAE VALERIAN FAMILY

Valeriàna VALERIAN

Dioecious; leaves in a rosette at the base of the stem, and opposite on the stem, without stipules, closely fringed with short hairs; sepals and petals borne at the summit of the ovary; calyx with plumed bristles which are closely coiled in flower but expand as the fruit matures.

1. **V. ciliàta** T. & G. Root large and deep; leaves thickish, the upper usually pinnate with 3–7 *ribbon-like divisions* (*V. edulis* of Ed. 7, not Nutt.).—Moist meadows and prairies, north to Dane and Waupaca Counties.

2. **V. uliginòsa** (T. & G.) Rydb. Roots fibrous; leaves thin, the upper with *7–15 lanceolate divisions.*—Northeastward.

CAMPANULÀCEAE BLUEBELL FAMILY

Herbs; corolla blue, regularly 5–lobed; stamens 5, usually free from the corolla; style one; stigmas 2 or more; fruit a capsule.

a. Leaves as broad as long . . . . 1. *Specularia.*
a. Leaves mostly longer than broad . . . . 2. *Campanula.*

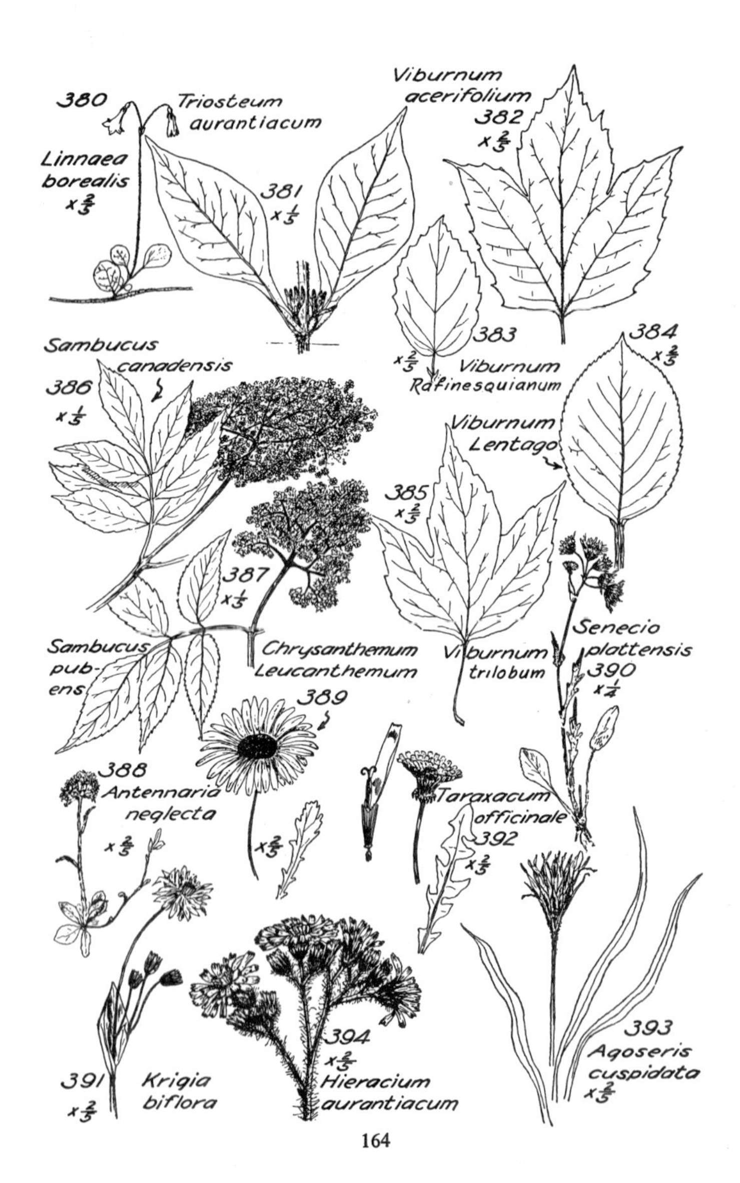
380
Linnaea
borealis
x 2/5
Triosteum
aurantiacum
381
x 1/5
Viburnum
acerifolium
382
x 2/5
383
x 2/5
Viburnum
Rafinesquianum
384
x 2/5
Viburnum
Lentago
Sambucus
canadensis
386
x 1/5
385
x 2/5
387
x 1/5
Sambucus
pub-
ens
Chrysanthemum
Leucanthemum
Viburnum
trilobum
Senecio
plattensis
390
x 1/4
389
388
Antennaria
neglecta
x 2/5
x 2/5
Taraxacum
officinale
392
x 2/5
393
Agoseris
cuspidata
x 2/5
394
x 2/5
Hieracium
aurantiacum
391
x 2/5
Krigia
biflora

1. **Speculària** Venus's Looking-glass

S. perfoliàta (L.) A.DC. Stems usually unbranched, 1–9 dm. high; leaves roundish, less than 1 cm. long, heart-shaped at base; flowers not pediceled, in the upper leaf-axils; corolla rather flat, circular in outline.—Sterile open ground and dry sandstone bluffs, north to Jackson and Waushara Counties.

2. **Campánula** Bellflower; Bluebell

C. rotundifòlia L. Bluebell; Harebell. Stem 1–5 dm. high; basal leaves (rarely present on flowering stems) long-petioled, with roundish blades; stem leaves narrowly ribbon-like; flowers several, long-peduncled; corolla bell-shaped.—Sandy and rocky places.

COMPÓSITAE Composite Family

Flowers many in a dense head simulating a single flower, surrounded by an involucre of several close, often overlapping bracts.

Series I. *Tubuliflorae*

Flowers of two sorts, the inner with a tubular corolla, the outer (rarely absent) strap-shaped, simulating petals; juice not milky.

a. Outer strap-shaped flowers whitish or bluish, or absent *b.*
  b. Stem-leaves simple, sometimes toothed or lobed; bruised leaves not aromatic *c.*
    c. Involucral bracts white and papery . . . . 2. *Antennaria.*
    c. Involucral bracts green, not papery *d.*
      d. Tube-flowers yellow *e.*
        e. Stem-leaves pinnately lobed. . . . . 5. *Chrysanthemum.*
        e. Stem-leaves not lobed . . . . 1. *Erigeron.*
      d. Tube-flowers white. . . . . 6. *Petasites.*
  b. Leaves cut into many ribbon-like divisions; bruised leaves aromatic *f.*
    f. Heads many in a flat-topped inflorescence; rays present . . . . 4. ***Achillea.***
    f. Heads few, terminating short leafy branches; rays absent. . . . . 3. ***Matricaria.***
a. Outer strap-shaped flowers yellow . . . . 7. ***Senecio.***

Series II. *Liguliflorae*

Flowers all strap-shaped; juice milky.

a. Plant smooth or woolly, without long hairs *b.*
  b. Leaves rather broad, the sides not parallel *c.*
    c. Heads 1-several on each scape; leaves entire or shallowly toothed *d.*
      d. Involucral bracts smooth . . . . 8. *Krigia.*
      d. Involucral bracts woolly . . . . 12. *Crepis.*
    c. Heads solitary on each scape; leaves pinnately lobed nearly to the midrib . . . 10. *Taraxacum.*
  b. Leaves ribbon-like, with parallel sides *e.*
    e. Leaves borne on the stem . . . . 9. *Tragopogon.*
    e. Leaves all basal . . . . 11. *Agoseris.*
a. Plants with spreading hairs 3 mm. long. . . . . 13. *Hieracium.*

1. **Erígeron** FLEABANE

Plants with the aspect of *Aster* but with the bracts of the involucre subequal instead of overlapping as in that genus; tube-flowers yellow.

a. Rays 100–150 . . . . 2. *E. philadelphicus.*
a. Rays 40–80 *b.*
  b. Well-developed heads 2–3 cm. broad . . . . 1. *E. pulchellus.*
  b. Heads 1–1.5 cm. broad . . . . 3. *E. strigosus.*

1. **E. pulchéllus** Michx. ROBIN'S PLANTAIN. Plants with soft white hairs; stems producing offshoots from the base, simple or slightly branched above; stem-leaves few and rather small; rays light bluish-purple.—Dry soil in open woods, north to Jackson, Sauk, and Milwaukee Counties.

2. **E. philadélphicus** L. Plants hairy; stem somewhat branched; stem-leaves larger than in the preceding; rays rose-purple or flesh-color.—Fields and woods.

3. **E. strigòsus** Muhl. DAISY-FLEABANE. Stems roughened with close short hairs; rays white.—Fields.

2. **Antennària** LADIES' TOBACCO; PUSSY'S TOES

Stem, and often the leaves, covered with cobwebby hairs; plants with stolons from the base; staminate and pistillate flowers on different plants, a single patch often consisting entirely of one sex; involucral bracts thin, papery.

a. Rosette-leaves, at base of plant, 0.2–2.1 cm. wide, with only the midrib prominent all the way to the tip on the lower side *b.*
  b. Middle and upper leaves with a flat paper-like tip *c.*
    c. Stolons creeping, with scattered leaves much smaller than those at the tip (Fig. 388) *d.*
      d. Leaves tapering to a petiole, dull and cobwebby above . . . . 1. *A. neglecta.*
      d. Leaves with bases abruptly narrowed to a petiole, bright green and not hairy above . . . . 2. *A. campestris.*
    c. Stolons ascending, with nearly uniform large leaves, forming dense mats . . . . . . 3. *A. canadensis.*
  b. Middle and upper leaves with a short firm awl-like tip, or without specialized tip *e.*
    e. Stolons prostrate, not leafy except at tip; rosette leaves not abruptly narrowed to a tip. . . . . 4. *A. petaloidea.*
    e. Stolons ascending, leafy; rosette leaves with a short abrupt tip . . . . 5. *A. neodioica.*
a. Rosette leaves 0.7–5.5 cm. wide, with 3–7 long prominent ribs beneath *f.*
  f. Rosette leaves with a minute short tip; pistillate involucre 5–8 mm. high . . . . 6. *A. plantaginifolia.*
  f. Rosette leaves with a prominent small tip; pistillate involucre 8–11 mm. high *g.*

g. Rosette leaves somewhat 4–sided, blunt or somewhat acute *h*.
h. Leaves cobwebby above; plants without glands . . . . 7. *A. fallax.*
h. Leaves green above or with cobwebby hairs which are soon lost; stem or leaves with minute purple glandular hairs . . . . 8. *A. Parlinii.*
g. Rosette leaves rather tongue-shaped, tapered to a rounded tip . . . . 9. *A. munda.*

1. **A. neglécta** Greene. (Fig. 388) Basal leaves with cobwebby hairs on upper surface; heads remaining in a close bunch when fruiting; both pistillate and staminate plants abundant.—North to Washburn, Jackson, and Waupaca Counties.

2. **A. campéstris** Rydb. Basal leaves with cobwebby hairs on upper surface; stem elongating so that heads are separated when fruiting; both pistillate and staminate plants present.—Rare in northwestern Wisconsin.

3. **A. canadénsis** Greene. Basal leaves bright green and glabrous on upper surface, or soon becoming so; pistillate plants abundant, staminate rare.—Practically throughout Wisconsin.

4. **A. petaloìdea** Fernald. Pistillate plants not common, but widely distributed; staminate plants very rare.

5. **A. neodioìca** Greene. Staminate plants very rare. The typical *A. neodioica*, with cobwebby stem-leaves 1 mm. or less wide and bracts with linear-oblong obtuse tips, is widespread but not common, as are also var. **attenuàta** Fernald, which is similar but has acute tapering tips, and var. **grándis** Fernald, with stem-leaves 5–8 mm. wide; var. **chlorophýlla**, with the leaves green and smooth above, has been found, to date, only in Bayfield, Vilas, and Door Counties.

6. **A. plantaginifòlia** (L.) Hook. Both pistillate and staminate plants widespread and abundant.

7. **A. fállax** Greene. Both pistillate and staminate plants widespread and abundant, but the staminate rare in some other regions.

8. **A. Parlínii** Fernald. Both pistillate and staminate plants present in Wisconsin, but the staminate rare in some other regions. The common form has the upper leaf-surfaces quite without cobwebby hairs, and minute purple gland-tipped hairs fairly numerous on stem and leaves; it is found from Vernon, Juneau, and Outagamie Counties southward. Var. **arnoglóssa** (Greene) Fernald, which has the upper leaves slightly cobwebby when young, and the glandular hairs less numerous, is at present known in Wisconsin only from Necedah Mound and Devil's Lake.

9. **A. múnda** Fernald. Pistillate plant widespread, staminate rare.

3. **Matricària** PINEAPPLE-WEED

M. matricarioìdes (Less.) Porter. Low much-branched plants; leaves with a pineapple odor when bruised; disk domed, 5–8 mm. in diameter, yellowish.—A weed along roadsides, city streets, and in gardens; naturalized, probably from the Pacific slope.

4. **Achillèa** YARROW; MILFOIL

A. Millefòlium L. Plants 3–10 dm. high; stems simple, forked in the inflorescence; *leaves aromatic when bruised, pinnate, the leaflets deeply divided;* heads small, whitish, many together in a flat-topped inflorescence. Forma **ròsea** Rand & Redf. is in shades of pink.—Common in open ground; naturalized from Europe.

5. **Chrysánthemum** DAISY

C. Leucánthemum L., var. **pinnatífidum** Lecoq & Lamotte. (Fig. 389) Stems simple or forked above; basal leaves long-petioled, the blades coarsely toothed or deeply cleft; stem leaves deeply toothed; rays white, tube-flowers yellow.—Locally abundant in fields, more frequent northward and eastward; naturalized from Europe.

6. **Petasìtes** SWEET COLTSFOOT

Perennial; stems stout, bearing 10 or more purplish or greenish bracts, the lower somewhat inflated and clasping; heads in a raceme; flowers white, fragrant.

1. **P. palmàtus** (Ait.) Gray. Stems with short, crinkly, somewhat glandular hairs; leaves with rounded and deeply 5–7-lobed blades, coming from the rootstock only as the fruit matures.—Swamps, from Douglas County to Manitowoc County.

2. **P. sagittàtus** (Pursh) Gray. Stems densely white-woolly; leaf-blades evenly toothed, broadly triangular to arrow-shaped.—Less common; Manitowoc and southern Douglas Counties.

7. **Senécio** RAGWORT

Leaves alternate, toothed, only the basal with petioles; heads usually several.

a. Stems leafy to the inflorescence *b*.
  b. Heads without ray-flowers . . . . 1. *S. vulgaris.*
  b. Heads with ray-flowers . . . . 2. *S. congestus*, vars.
a. Stems leafy below, above nearly naked or with much reduced leaves *c*.
  c. Blades of basal leaves heart-shaped at base . . 3. *S. aureus.*
  c. Blades of basal leaves narrowed to the petiole *d*.
    d. Internodes smooth . . . . 4. *S. pauperculus.*
    d. Internodes woolly . . . . 5. *S. plattensis.*

1. **S. vulgàris** L. *Plant usually much branched near the base;* leaves pinnately deeply cut, the divisions oblong, sharply toothed; short lowest bracts of the involucre black-tipped.—An infrequent weed; introduced from Europe.

2. **S. congéstus** (R. Br.) DC., var. **intónsus** Fern. *Stem stout,* not branched below; leaves lanceolate, without petioles, variously toothed, clasping the stem at base. The inflorescence in var. **palústris** is *long hairy* (*S. palustris*); var. **tónsus** is *smoother*, with *few or no long hairs.*—Northwestern Wisconsin.

3. **S. aùreus** L. GOLDEN RAGWORT. Basal leaves long-petioled, the blades rounded, toothed; stem leaves pinnate or pinnately deeply cleft, the uppermost bract-like.—Wet meadows, moist cliffs, and low, wet woods.

4. **S. paupérculus** Michx. Basal leaves petioled, grading into mere bracts on the upper part of the stem; blades toothed in the lower leaves, pinnately lobed in the upper; stem with tufts of wool at the leaf-bases, otherwise smooth.—Damp ground.

5. **S. platténsis** Nutt. (Fig. 390) Similar to the preceding, but stem and blades of the basal leaves woolly.—Dry places.

8. **Krígia**

Leaves all in a basal rosette; heads on long naked or nearly naked scapes; corollas yellow.

1. **K. virgínica** (L.) Willd. Scapes naked, terminated by a single head.—Sandy soil along the Wisconsin River, from Spring Green to Mazomanie.

2. **K. biflòra** (Walt.) Blake. (Fig. 391) Plant very smooth and somewhat bluish-powdery; scapes with two bracts near the summit, enclosing the bases of several peduncles.—Common in open sandy ground.

9. **Tragopògon** GOAT'S BEARD

Stem tall, smooth; leaves grass-like, smooth, somewhat clasping at base; heads large, solitary, yellow.

1. **T. praténsis** L. Stem scarcely enlarged below the head; bracts of involucre shorter than the flowers.—Fields and roadsides, probably less common than the next; naturalized from Europe.

2. **T. màjor** Jacq. Stems conspicuously enlarged upward below the head; bracts of involucre longer than the flowers.—Fields and roadsides; naturalized from Europe.

10. **Taráxacum** DANDELION

T. officinàle Weber. (Fig. 392) Plants varying in size; leaves all basal; scape hollow; flowers bright yellow.—Common and abundant; naturalized from Europe.

11. Agóseris

A. cuspidàta (Pursh) Raf. (Fig. 393) Leaves all basal; scape 3 dm. high, woolly below the head; flowers yellow.—Prairies, from Columbia and Sauk Counties southward and westward; not common.

12. Crèpis HAWK'S-BEARD

C. tectòrum L. Basal rosette of coarsely pinnately toothed leaves; stem furrowed, somewhat whitened with a fine wool, branched; flowers yellow.—Sandy ground, locally abundant; adventive from Europe.

13. Hieràcium ORANGE HAWKWEED

H. aurantìacum L. Leaves mostly basal, with rough brown hairs; scapes 2–6 dm. high, usually with 1 or 2 small leaves; heads several (Fig. 394); flowers orange-red.—Fields; rare in southern Wisconsin, but a noxious weed farther north; naturalized from Europe.

Glossary

ACHENE. A small, dry, one-seeded fruit.
ACUMINATE. With a long tapering point (Fig. 408).
ACUTE. With a sharp point (Fig. 411).
ADVENTIVE. Imperfectly naturalized.
ALTERNATE (of leaves). Borne along a stem, with only one at each level.
ANTHER. The upper, usually enlarged part of a stamen, bearing the pollen (Figs. 395, 396).
APEX. The end farthest from the central stem.
AURICLE. An ear-like lobe.
AXIL. The angle formed by a leaf with the stem.
AXILLARY. Arising from a node in the axil of leaf (see flowers in Figs. 402 and 403, or the inflorescences in Figs. 233 and 352).

BERRY. A juicy fruit, with several compartments (carpels).
BIPINNATE. Pinnate, with the leaflets themselves pinnate.
BLADE. The expanded flattened part of a leaf (Figs. 406, 414).
BLOOM. A white or bluish powdery or waxy covering.
BRACT. A more or less modified, usually small and scale-like leaf, subtending a flower or on a stem.
BRANCHLET. A twig or small branch.
BULB. An underground bud with scaly or fleshy layers.

CALYX. The outer, usually green, whorl of a flower, made up of sepals (Figs. 395, 396, 397). Plural: calyces.
CALYX-LOBE. The free part of a sepal which is united below with other sepals (Fig. 397).
CALYX-TEETH. Bristle-like or very short calyx-lobes.
CALYX-TUBE. The lower tubular portion of a calyx formed of united sepals (Fig. 397).
CAPSULE. A dry fruit, with two or more united carpels, opening at maturity.

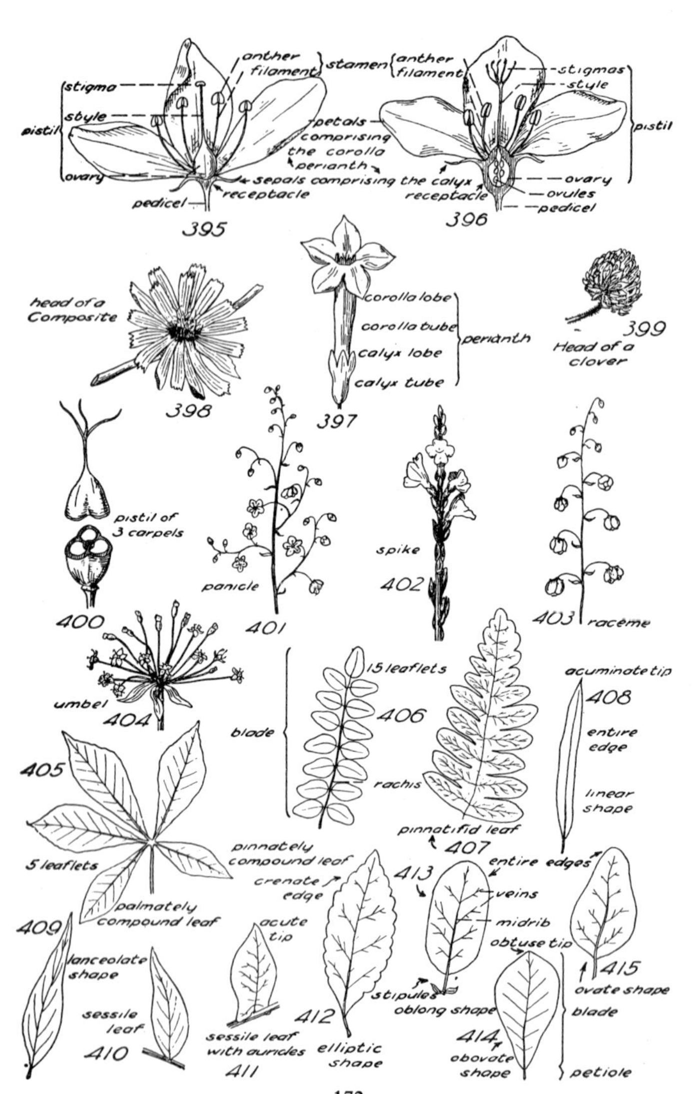
stigma
style
pistil
ovary
pedicel
anther
filament
stamen
anther
filament
petals
comprising
the corolla
perianth
sepals comprising the calyx
receptacle
receptacle
stigmas
style
pistil
ovary
ovules
pedicel
395
396
head of a
Composite
398
corolla lobe
corolla tube
calyx lobe
calyx tube
perianth
397
399
Head of a
clover
pistil of
3 carpels
400
panicle
401
spike
402
403
raceme
umbel
404
15 leaflets
406
blade
rachis
pinnatifid leaf
407
acuminate tip
408
entire
edge
linear
shape
405
5 leaflets
palmately
compound leaf
pinnately
compound leaf
crenate
edge
413
entire edges
veins
midrib
obtuse tip
415
409
lanceolate
shape
sessile
leaf
410
acute
tip
sessile leaf
with auricles
411
412
elliptic
shape
stipules
oblong shape
414
obovate
shape
blade
petiole
ovate shape

CARPEL. A macrosporophyll; a modified, seed-bearing leaf, of which from one to several make up a pistil, the number often determined by observing the number of stigmas, or of compartments in the ovary (see Fig. 400).

CATKIN. A spike of flowers, closely aggregated without pedicels but with conspicuous scales, the whole flexible and drooping at maturity.

CELL (when used of a fruit). A compartment, or carpel.

CLEFT. Cut halfway or more to the base.

CM. A centimeter, 1/100 of a meter (about 2/5 of an inch; see scale).

COMPOUND. Divided into several leaflets, each of which is distinct and not joined to the other leaflets by any leaf-like tissue (Figs. 405, 406).

CORM. Enlarged, fleshy, solid base of a stem.

COROLLA. The whorl of a flower just within the calyx, usually of white or colored, separate or united petals (Figs. 395, 396, 397).

COROLLA-LOBE. The free part of a petal which is united below with other petals (Fig. 397).

COROLLA-TUBE. The lower tubular portion of a corolla, formed of united petals (Fig. 397).

COTYLEDON. The leaf of an embryo plant as found in the seed.

CRENATE. Scalloped; with rounded teeth (Fig. 412).

CULM. The stem of a grass or grass-like plant.

CYME. See p. 177 for definition.

DEFLEXED. Bent downward.

DIOECIOUS. With the staminate (male) and pistillate (female) flowers on different plants.

DISSECTED. Cut into numerous segments.

DIVIDED. Lobed or segmented to the base.

DM. A decimeter, 1/10 of a meter (about 4 inches).

DOWNY. Covered with short, fine hairs.

ELLIPTIC. Narrowed equally at each end (Fig. 412).

EMBRYO. The little dormant plant in a seed.

ENTIRE. Without teeth or lobes (Figs. 408, 413, 415).

EXSERTED. Extending beyond the corolla–lobes.

FILAMENT. The usually thread-like stalk of a stamen (Figs. 395, 396).

FLEXUOUS. Bent alternately in opposite directions. Zigzag.
FOLIOLATE. With leaflets.

HEAD. A dense cluster of flowers without pedicels, sometimes with (Figs. 392, 393), and sometimes without (Fig. 399) an involucre.
HERB. A plant with nonwoody stems, which die back to the ground level each winter.
HERBACEOUS. Not woody, of soft texture and usually green.

IMPRESSED. Furrowed.
INCLUDED. Within the corolla–lobes.
INFLORESCENCE. The flowering portion of a plant.
INTERNODE. The portion of a stem between two nodes.
INTRODUCED. Brought intentionally from another region.
INVOLUCRE. A collection of bracts around a flower or cluster of flowers (Fig. 404), especially in *Compositae* (Figs. 388–394).

KEEL. A ridge like the keel of a boat.

LANCEOLATE. Long and tapering, and broadest near the base (Fig. 409).
LAX. Of loose arrangement; weak and reclining.
LEAF-AXIL. *See* AXIL.
LEAFLET. A single division of a compound leaf (Figs. 405, 406).
LINEAR. Long and narrow, and with parallel margins (Fig. 408)
LIP. One of the petals in the *Orchidaceae*, enlarged and often cleft or inflated; one of the two divisions into which the corolla is sometimes cut when it is composed of united petals (Fig. 350).
LOBED. With divisions (Figs. 145, 264, 345, 407).

M. A meter (39.37 inches).
MIDRIB. The main vein of a leaf (Fig. 413).
MM. A millimeter, 1/10 of a cm. (about 1/25 of an inch; see scale).

NATURALIZED. Thoroughly established.
NERVE. A small vein.
NETTED-VEINED. With the veins branching, and sometimes re-uniting toward the edge of the leaf. Or netted veins on a seed.
NODE. The level on a stem where one or more leaves are borne.

OBLONG. Longer than broad, with nearly parallel sides (Fig. 413).
OBOVATE. Egg-shaped, with the broadest part toward the apex (Fig. 414).

OBTUSE. Blunt or rounded at the end (Fig. 414).
OPPOSITE (of leaves). Arranged in pairs on the stem, two at each node.
OVAL. Broadly elliptic.
OVARY. The lower, usually swollen, part of a pistil, where the seeds develop (Figs. 395, 396).
OVATE. Egg-shaped, with the broadest part toward the base (Fig. 415).

PALMATE. Radially lobed or divided (Fig. 405).
PANICLE. A loose, several times branched inflorescence, with stalked flowers (Fig. 401).
PARALLEL (of veins). All running from the base to tip of leaf without branching (Figs. 24, 29).
PARASITE. A plant growing on and deriving nourishment from another living animal or plant.
PEDICEL. The stalk of a single flower (Figs. 395, 396).
PEDUNCLE. A primary flower-stalk, bearing a cluster or a solitary flower.
PERENNIAL. Living for several years.
PERIANTH. Calyx, or calyx and corolla (Figs. 395, 396, 397).
PERIANTH-TUBE. A tube formed of united sepals and petals.
PETAL. A division of the corolla (Figs. 395, 396).
PETIOLE. The stalk of a leaf (Fig. 414).
PINNATE. Compound, with the leaflets on the opposite sides of a common axis (Fig. 406).
PINNATIFID. Pinnately deeply cleft, but not into distinct leaflets (Fig. 407).
PISTIL. The seed-bearing (female) part of a flower, having typically style, stigma, and ovary (Figs. 395, 396), formed of one to several carpels (Fig. 400).
PLUMOSE. With fine spreading hairs.
POD. A dry fruit which splits open.
PRICKLE. A small sharp outgrowth.

RACEME. An inflorescence with stalked flowers borne on a common axis (Fig. 403).
RACHIS. The axis of a spike or compound leaf (Fig. 406).
RECEPTACLE. The often somewhat enlarged tip of a stem, bearing the sepals, petals, stamens, and pistils (Figs. 395, 396, where the receptacle is indicated by vertical shading).
REFLEXED. Bent back or downward.

REGULAR. Symmetrical on several radii.
ROOTSTOCK. A horizontal underground stem.
ROSETTE. A close cluster of leaves in a circular form, as in the dandelion and in *Antennaria* (Fig. 388).

SAPROPHYTE. A plant growing on and deriving nourishment from dead plant or animal matter.
SCALE. A thin brownish body, usually a degenerate leaf.
SCAPE. A leafless flowering stem arising from the ground, as in a dandelion.
SEPAL. A division of a calyx (Figs. 395, 396).
SESSILE. Arising directly from the stem, without any stalk (Figs. 410, 411).
SHEATH. A tubular envelope, usually about a stem and formed by the base of a leaf.
SIMPLE. Not compound; of one piece (Figs. 407–415).
SINUS. The cleft between two lobes.
SPATHE. A large bract or pair of bracts enclosing an inflorescence.
SPADIX. A spike with a fleshy axis.
SPIKE. An inflorescence of flowers without pedicels on an elongated common axis (Fig. 402).
SPIKELET. A small spike, especially that of the *Gramineae*.
SPINE. A sharp rigid woody outgrowth from a stem.
SPUR. A hollow tubular or sac-like extension from some part of a flower.
STAMEN. The pollen-bearing (male) organ of a flower (Figs. 395, 396).
STELLATE. Star-like.
STERILE. Unproductive; without stamens or pistils.
STIGMA. The usually sticky tip of the style, on which the pollen lodges; it may be single (Fig. 395), or there may be as many stigmas as there are carpels in the pistil (Figs. 396, 400).
STIPITATE. With a short stalk.
STIPULE. An appendage at the base of a petiole (Fig. 413).
STOLON. A basal branch disposed to root.
STOLONIFEROUS. Bearing stolons.
STYLE. The slender upper part of a pistil (Figs. 395, 496).
SUB. Somewhat, or slightly less than.

TAPROOT. The main, vertical root of a plant.
TENDRIL. A stem, leaf, etc., modified to twist about a support.
TERMINAL. Borne at the tip of the stem (as the flower in Fig. 267, and the inflorescence in Figs. 244, 246).

THORN. A short, stiff, sharp, modified branch.

TOOTHED. Notched or jagged on the edge. Singly toothed: with all teeth alike (Figs. 56, 384); doubly toothed: with small teeth on the larger ones (Figs. 65, 69).

TUBER. A short, underground swelling of a stem.

TUBERCLE. A warty outgrowth.

UMBEL. An inflorescence in which the flower-stalks all arise from one point (Fig. 404).

VASCULAR BUNDLE. A strand of conductive tissue.

VEIN. A thread of vascular tissue in a leaf.

WHORL. The arrangement of organs in a circle about a common axis.

WHORLED (of leaves). With several borne at one node.

CYME. A type of inflorescence in which a central flower terminates the stem and opens first, a pair of branches below this continues the growth and these in turn are terminated by flowers. At the base of each flower-stalk the branching is again repeated by dichotomies, etc., resulting in a more or less flat-topped cluster.

Index